T3-BGM-548

To Merwin Schofield
            Christmas 1928.
    From Grandma & Grandpa Schofield

HOW COLOR PRINTING IS DONE

A plate is made for each of the three printing colors, yellow, red and blue, as explained on page 382. First, yellow is printed, then red on the yellow, and last, blue on the yellow and red combination. Combinations of these three colors in various proportions produce all the other tints which appear in the original subject. Above are shown the separate plates and also the combined result of all three. Extreme care is necessary to make all the plates register exactly together.

THE WONDER BOOK OF KNOWLEDGE

THE MARVELS OF MODERN INDUSTRY AND INVENTION
THE INTERESTING STORIES OF COMMON THINGS
THE MYSTERIOUS PROCESSES OF NATURE
SIMPLY EXPLAINED

COMPILED AND EDITED

BY

HENRY CHASE HILL

WITH THE CO-OPERATION OF EXPERTS
REPRESENTING EACH INDUSTRY

Illustrated with
780 Photographs and Drawings

PHILADELPHIA
THE JOHN C. WINSTON COMPANY
PUBLISHERS

Copyright, 1927, by

L. T. MYERS

———

Copyright, 1917–19–23–26

———

PRINTED IN U. S. A.

Wonder Book

Preface

This book is presented to those, both young and old, who wish to have a non-technical account of the history, evolution and production of some of the every-day wonders of the modern industrial age; coupled with occasional glimpses of the wonderful object-lessons afforded by nature in her constructive activities in the animal, vegetable, and mineral kingdoms; and simple, understandable answers to the myriad puzzling questions arising daily in the minds of those for whom the fascination of the "Why" and "How" is always engrossing.

Although not intended primarily as a child's book, the interest-compelling pictures and clear, illuminating answers to the constant avalanche of questions suggested by the growing mind, unite in making far happier children in the home and brighter children at school. Parents and teachers will also recognize the opportunity to watch for subjects by which the child's interest appears to be more than ordinarily attracted, and, in so doing, will be enabled to guide the newly-formed tendencies into the proper channels. With the greatest thinkers of the age advocating vocational training, and leading educators everywhere pointing out that the foundation of a practical education for life must be laid in the home, thoughtful parents will not overlook the fact that a book which both entertains and instructs is of supreme importance in the equipment of their children.

In the preparation of this book its function has been considered as that of gathering up some of the multitudinous bits of information of interest, both to the inquiring child and the older reader, and putting them in shape to be digested by the ordinary searcher after knowledge. The book is intended, not for a few technical specialists, but for the larger number of men, women, and children who are not interested in exhaustive treatises, but who are seeking to gain some fair idea about the numberless everyday subjects that arise in ordinary conversation, or that they meet with in reading and about which they desire some definite and satisfactory information.

Most of us realize that we live in a world of wonders and we recognize progress in industries with which we come in personal contact, but the daily routine of our lives is ordinarily so restricted by circumstances that many of us fail to follow works which do not come within our own experience or see beyond the horizon of our own specific paths.

The workman who tends the vulcanizer in the rubber factory has come to take his work as a matter of course; the man who assembles a watch, or a camera, is not apt to appreciate the fact that there have been marvelous developments in his line of manufacturing; the operator of a shoe machine, or of an elevator, does not see anything startling or absorbing in the work—and so we find it almost throughout the entire list of industries.

The tendency of the seemingly almost imperceptible movement marking onward development in the work that is familiar is to dull the mind toward opportunities for improvement in the accustomed task. With the exception of the man who is at times impressed with the remarkable advances made in some strikingly spectacular industry, because such knowledge comes to him suddenly, the average workman is often too much inclined to regard himself as a machine, and performs his duties more or less automatically, without attempting to exercise imagination or those powers of adaptation upon which all progress has been builded.

A single volume is of necessity too limited a space for anything approximating a complete record of the vast progress which has been made in American Industry. Consequently it has only been possible to select the more characteristic features of the twentieth century and point out the strides by which some of the prominent industries have advanced to their present proportions. If the hitherto undisputed maxim that "the more the individual knows the more he is worth to himself and his associates" still prevails, the chronicling of the developments in some fields should stimulate thought and experiment toward the adaptation of similar methods in others. It is to that end that authorities in each of the industries presented have co-operated in the compilation of this interesting and instructive volume.

THE EDITOR.

Table of Contents

TABLE OF CONTENTS

The Story of the Submarine*

Origin of Submarine Navigation.

The history of invention has no chapter more interesting than that of sailing under the ocean's waves. The navigation of the air approaches it in character, but does not present the vital problems of undersea travel. Both these new fields of navigation have been notably developed within recent years, largely as a result of the great World War. It is the story of sailing in the depths beneath the ocean's surface with which we here propose to deal. The problem was settled easily enough

A Submarine About to Submerge

for his purpose by Jules Verne, in his "Twenty Thousand Leagues Under the Sea." But that was pure fiction without scientific value. It is with fact, not fiction, that we are here concerned.

The story takes us back three hundred years, to the reign of James I, of England, when a crude submarine boat was built, to be moved by oars, but one of no value other than as a curiosity. At a later date a man named Day built a similar boat, wagering that he would go down one hundred yards and remain there twenty-four hours. So far as is known, he still remains there, winning the wager which he has not come up to claim.

Other such boats were constructed at intervals, but the first undersea boat of any historical importance was the "American Turtle," built by a Yankee named David Bushnell during the time that the British held New York in the Revolutionary War. He sought to blow up the British frigate "Eagle" with the aid of a torpedo

* Illustrations by courtesy of the Lake Torpedo Boat Co., unless otherwise indicated.

and nearly succeeded in doing so, seriously scaring the British shippers by the explosion of his torpedo.

The next to become active in this line of discovery was Robert Fulton, the inventor of the first practical steamboat. He, like Bushnell, was an American, but his early experiments were in France, where Napoleon patronized him. With his boat, the "Nautilus," he made numerous descents, going down twenty-five feet in the harbor of Brest and remaining there an hour. He said that he could build a submarine that could swim under the water and destroy any war vessel afloat. But the French Admiralty refused to sustain him, one old admiral saying, "Thank God, France still fights her battles on the surface, not beneath it."

Fulton finally went to England and there built a boat with which he attached a torpedo to a condemned brig, set aside for that purpose. The brig was blown up in the presence of an immense throng, and Fulton finally sold his invention to the British government for $75,000. Nothing further came of it.

The submarine next came into practical view during the American Civil War, when the Confederate government built several such vessels, known usually as "Davids" from their inventor. Now, for the first time, did such a craft demonstrate its powers. On the night of February 17, 1864, one of the "Davids," the "Hunley," blew up the steamship "Housatonic" in Charleston harbor. The wave caused by the explosion swamped the submarine and it and its crew found a watery grave.

Other submarines were built and experimented with, not only in the United States but in European countries. One of the later inventors was an Irish-American named John P. Holland, who, in 1876, built a submarine called the "Fenian Ram." The "Ram" collapsed with the collapse of the Fenian movement. Other boats were built and tried, but the successful period of the submarine was deferred until after 1893, when the United States Congress appropriated $200,000 to encourage such an enterprise and invited inventors to submit designs. This, and a similar movement in France, formed the first official recognition of the value of vessels of this class.

The prize offered by Congress brought out three designs, one by Mr. Holland, the "Ram" inventor, one by George C. Barker, and a third by Simon Lake. The names of Holland and Lake have since been closely associated with the history of the submarine. Mr. Holland's device secured approval and in 1894 he received a contract to build a submarine vessel. This, named the "Plunger," was begun in 1895, but was finally abandoned and a vessel of different type, the "Holland," was built in its place. It was accepted by the government in 1900. A number of others similar to the "Holland" were subsequently built.

The American Types.

The type of these vessels was what became known as the "diving." They were controlled by a rudder placed at the stern of the vessel and acting in both a horizontal and a vertical direction, the force of the screw propeller driving the boat forward in the direction desired. In 1904 the navy of the United States possessed eight Holland boats and there were also a number of them in the British navy.

Mr. Lake's design, offered in 1893 but not accepted, had as its novel feature a plan by which a door could be opened in the bottom of the ship and the crew leave and enter it in diving suits, the water being kept out by the force of compressed air. To maintain the vessel on an even keel he introduced four vanes, called "hydroplanes," for regulating the depth of descent. By aid of these and the horizontal rudder it was found that the vessel would run for hours at a constant depth and on a level keel. There were other devices for diving or rising to the surface.

In 1901 Mr. Lake built a large vessel of this type which was sold to the Russian government and was in commission at Vladivostock during the Russian-Japanese

War. He afterwards received orders from this and other governments for a number of vessels of the even-keel type, and his principles of control have since been generally adopted as the safest and most reliable controlling agency for under-water craft.

We have not in the above brief statement described all the efforts to invent a satisfactory under-water boat. In several of the nations of Europe experiments, more or less available, had been tried, but the most practical results were achieved by the American inventors, Bushnell, Fulton, Davy, Holland and Lake. It will suffice here to say that the most successful of submarines were those constructed by Holland and Lake. An important addition was made in 1901 in a French boat, the "Morse," built at Cherbourg. The difficulty of navigators telling where they were when under water, and of changing their course safely without coming to the surface to reconnoitre, was in a large measure overcome by the addition of a "peri-

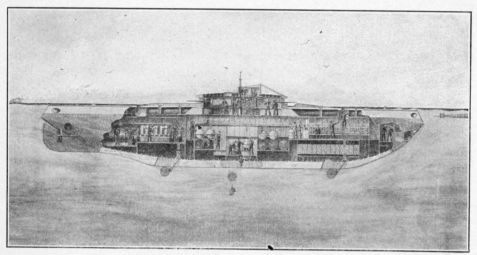

A MINE-PLANTING SUBMARINE DESIGNED IN BERLIN BY SIMON LAKE IN 1895 FOR THE RUSSIAN GOVERNMENT

scope." This, rising above the water, and provided with reflecting lenses, enabled the steersman to discover the surface conditions and see any near vessel or other object. The "Morse" was able to sink in seventy seconds and her crew could remain under water for sixteen hours without strain.

Twentieth Century Submarines.

We have given an epitome of the development of the submarine vessel up to the opening of the twentieth century. It had now reached a successful status of achievement and during the early years of that century was to display a remarkable progress. Holland and Lake may be looked upon as the parents of the modern development of the submergible boat, their designs being at the base of the great European progress.

France took up the work actively, its most successful early vessel being the "Narval," built in 1899. This was 118 feet long by 8 feet 3 inches beam, 106 tons surface and 168 submerged displacement. She was a double-deck vessel controlled by Lake hydroplanes, and had installed steam power for surface travel and electric power for undersea work. The French at this time kept their methods secret, and no useful type had been developed in England, the result being that a plant was provided for the building of Holland boats in that country. Germany used the Lake devices, which had not been patented in that country and were made use of by the Krupps. Thus it appears that the modern submarines, as now built and used in the navies of the world, owe their success to principles of construction and devices for control originated and developed by American inventors.

Engine Power.

The internal-combustion engine is the heart of the submarine. Steam, with its heavy engine, has been long set aside, and electricity, derived from the storage battery, yet awaits sufficient development. Gasoline succeeded them. The internal-

A PROTECTOR FITTED FOR EXPERIMENTAL WORK UNDER ICE

combustion engine became essential from its light weight and the fact that it could be started and shut down instantly. This is of prime importance, as permitting quick submergence or emergence, either to escape from a high-speed destroyer or to capture a merchantman. It weighs less per horse power, takes up less room and requires less fuel per hour than any other reliable motor. It was early used in both the Holland and Lake boats and is still the chief prime motor.

The difficulty with the early boats was that they were slow in speed, making only from eight to nine knots per hour. Increased speed was demanded by governments and more powerful engines, within a fixed limit of weight, were demanded. In doing this engines were built of such flimsy construction that they soon went to pieces. The gasoline used also gave off a gas of highly explosive character and one very likely to escape from leaky tanks or joints. Several explosions took place in consequence, in one of which twenty-three men were killed. As a result all the nations demanded that a non-explosive fuel should be used, and builders turned to the Diesel engine as offering a solution to the difficulty.

This heavy oil engine, weighing about five hundred pounds per horse-power, was not adapted to the submarine, and efforts have been made to decrease the weight. These have not as yet had a satisfactory result and experiments are still going on.

The Periscope.

As the engine is the heart of the submarine, the periscope is its eye. This is, in its simpler forms, a stiff, detachable tube from fifteen to twenty feet long and about four inches in diameter. On its top is an object glass which takes in all objects within its range and transmits an image of them through a right-angled prism and down the tube. By means of other lenses and prisms an image of the external object is thus made visible to those within the submarine. In this process of transmission

A Submarine Under Ice

there is a certain loss of light, and to allow for that the image is magnified to about one-quarter above natural size.

To obtain in this manner a correct idea of the distance of the object seen proved difficult, but by continued experiment this difficulty has been overcome. Mr. Lake developed an instrument suited to this purpose and one which gave a simultaneous view of the entire horizon. There is one fault in the periscope not easy to obviate. It is an instrument for day use only. When dark comes on it becomes useless, and this does away with the possibility of a successful submarine attack by night.

The periscope is the one part of the submarine scout equipment that is open to vision from the surface. But while the outlook of the undersea captain, aided by his telescopic sights, has a radius of several miles, the periscope tube, of only four or five-inch diameter and painted of a neutral tint, is not easily seen. If the sea is a little choppy it is difficult to discover it with the naked eye at about 300 or 400 yards away, or in a smooth sea at over 500 yards.

The idea that a submarine may be located by an aeroplane is looked upon by Mr. Lake as a fallacy, except in water of crystal-like clearness, like that of the Mediterranean or the Caribbean, and periscopes are now being made to scour the heavens as well as the horizon, so that the presence of an enemy aeroplane can easily be seen. An attack by an aeroplane bomb, therefore, can readily be avoided, in view of the difficulty of hitting such an object from the upper air.

The submarine is the guerrilla of the sea. Its tactics are like those of the Indian who fights under cover or lies in ambush for his enemy. It is the weaker party and can hope for success only through strategy. The old adage that "all is fair in love and war" applies to this new weapon of destruction as to every warlike instrument. It is its invisibility that makes the submarine the terror of the seas. This has been well proved during the World War. The North Sea and the English Channel were invaded by German submarines which made great havoc among merchant ships. And it is well to draw attention to the fact that submarines are safe from each other. In no case has a battle taken place between two of these armed sharks except in the one instance reported of an Austrian sinking an Italian submarine. But in this case the Italian boat was on the surface and was at the time practically a surface ship.

During the war the Germans were especially active in the use of the submarine, and did much in making them an effective terror of the seas. With no mercantile

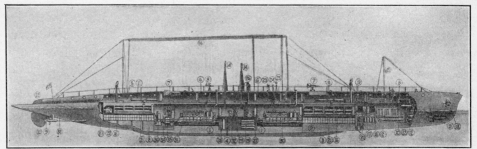

TYPE OF HIGH SPEED OCEAN-GOING SUBMARINE

marine of their own to guard, they had a free field for attack in the abundant shipping of their foes. The loss of ships was so numerous and become such a common occurrence that little attention was finally paid to them except when great loss of life took place, as in the signal instance of the "Lusitania."

The Voyage of the "Deutschland."

The great mission of the submarine during the World War was as a commerce destroyer. Many ships were sunk and many lives, with cargoes of great value, were lost, and it was not until the summer of 1916 that the submarine appeared in a new rôle, that of a commerce carrier. On July 9th of that year the people of Baltimore were astounded by the appearance in their port of a submarine vessel of unusual size and novel errand. Instead of being a destroyer of merchandise, this new craft was an unarmed carrier of merchandise. It had crossed the Atlantic on a voyage of 4,000 miles in extent, laden with dyestuffs to supply the needs of American weavers.

This new type of vessel, the "Deutschland," was an undersea craft of 315 feet length and a gross tonnage of 701 tons, its cargo capacity being more than 1,000 tons. It had crossed the ocean in defiance of the wide cordon of enemy warships which swarmed over part of its route, and reached port in safety after a memorable voyage, to the surprise and interest of the world. Leaving the port of Bremenhaven on June 18th, and halting at Heligoland for four days to train its crew, it made its way across the Atlantic in sixteen days. During the voyage it lay for two hours on the ocean bottom in the English Channel and was submerged in all not over ninety hours, the remainder of the voyage being made on the surface.

Its crew, composed of twenty-six men and three officers, found their novel voyage rather agreeable than otherwise. Supplied with plenty of good food, a well-selected library, a graphophone with an abundance of music records, and other means of convenience and enjoyment, their voyage was more of a holiday than a hardship, and they reached their transatlantic port none the worse for their hazardous trip. It was not the longest that had been made. Other submarines had voyaged from German ports to the eastern limit of the Mediterranean, but it was the most notable and attracted the widest attention.

The return voyage promised to be more perilous than the outgoing one. A fleet of British and French ships gathered around the outlet of Chesapeake Bay, alert to capture the daring mariners and their ship, if possible. Ready to leave

THE GERMAN MERCHANT SUBMARINE "DEUTSCHLAND" WHICH CROSSED THE ATLANTIC IN 1916, AFTER ELUDING THE BRITISH BLOCKADE

Courtesy of Baltimore American and C. & P. Telephone Co.

Baltimore on July 20th, with a return cargo of gold, nickel and rubber, the captain of the "Deutschland" shrewdly awaited a favorable opportunity and on August 1st began his voyage, plunging under sea as he left the American coast-line and easily evading the line of floating foemen. The return to its home port a success, a second round-trip voyage was made and completed on December 11th, in the course of which a convoying tug-boat was rammed and sunk with the loss of several lives, shortly after leaving New London, Conn. The "Deutschland" was sent out by private parties, for purely commercial purposes, not as a military enterprise.

Such is the story of a pioneer enterprise, that of the use of submarine vessels as commerce carriers. It is one not likely to be supplemented in times of peace, since surface boats would be cheaper and more available. But in future wars—if such there are to be—it may point to a future of advantageous trade.

Submarine Dredging.

Commerce is not the only peaceful mission of the submarine. In 1895 was organized an association known as the Lake Submarine Company, its purpose being to use the Lake type of submarine boat for the recovery of lost treasures from the sea bottom and for other possibilities of undersea work. This company is still in existence, its various purposes being to recover sunken ships and their cargoes, to build breakwaters and other submerged constructions, to aid in submarine tunnel building, to dredge for gold, to fish for pearls and sponges, and for similar operations.

The first vessel adapted to these purposes was the "Argonaut," built by Simon Lake in 1894. The important feature of this boat was a diver's compartment, enabling divers to leave the vessel when submerged, for the purpose of operating on wrecks or performing other undersea duties. This vessel and its successors have bottom doors for the use of divers, as previously stated. They are now used for numerous purposes for which they are much better adapted then the old system of surface diving, the sea bottom being under direct observation and within immediate reach.

A SEMI-SUBMERSIBLE WRECKING APPARATUS

This sea bottom, in localities near land, is abundantly sown with wrecks, old and new, and in many cases bearing permanently valuable cargoes, such as gold and coal. The Lake system greatly simplifies the work of search for sunken ships, the vessels being able in a few hours' time to search over regions which would have taken months in the old method. Many wrecks have been found by these bottom-prowling scouts and valuable material recovered. Thus vessels laden with coal have been traced that had been many years under the water and deeply covered with sand and silt, and their cargoes brought to the surface.

The gold-dredging spoken of refers to the working of gold-bearing sands found at the mouth of certain rivers in Alaska and South America. Places on the Alaskan coast, laid bare at high tide, are said to have yielded as much as $12,000 per cubic yard. With the Lake system it is possible to gather material from such localities to a depth of 150 or more feet, the material being drawn up by suction pumps into the vessel and its gold recovered.

Another important application is that of fishing for pearl shells, sponges and coral. This is blind work when done by divers from the surface, the returns being largely matters of chance. By aid of submerged boats, with their powerful electric lights, the work becomes one of certainty rather than of chance. The recovery of the oyster, clam and other edible shell-fish is also a feature of the work which the Lake Company has in view. The present method of dredging is of the "hit or miss" character, while the submarine method is capable of thorough work. Vessels have been designed for this purpose with a capacity of gathering oysters from good ground at the rate of 5,000 bushels per hour. In regard to submarine engineering, of its many varieties, the Lake system is likely to be a highly useful aid and assistance.

These particulars are given to show that the submarine vessel is not wholly an instrument of "frightfulness," as indicated by its use in war, but is capable of being made useful for many purposes in peace. Some of these have here been very briefly stated. With continued practice its utility will grow, and by its aid the sea bottom up to a certain depth may become as open to varied operations as is the land surface.

The Story of the Panama Canal

America has captured the forces of Nature, harnessed the floods and made the desert bloom, builded gigantic bridges and arrogant skyscrapers and bored roadways through solid rock and beneath water, but the most spectacular of all spectacular accomplishments is the Panama Canal.

Some four centuries ago, Balboa, the intrepid, the persevering, led his little band of adventurers across the Isthmus of Darien, as it was then called, and, leaving their protection, gave rein to his impatience by going on ahead and climbing alone, slowly and painfully, the continental divide, from which vantage point he discovered the world's largest ocean.

We are told that, later, gathering his followers, he walked out into the surf and with his sword in his right hand and the banner of Castile in his left gave the vast expanse of water its present name and claimed all the land washed by its waves the lawful property of the proud country to which he owed allegiance.

The narrowness of the Isthmus naturally suggested the cutting of a waterway through it. It interposed between Atlantic and Pacific a barrier in places less than fifty miles wide. To sail from Colon to Panama—forty-five miles as the bird flies—required a voyage around Cape Horn—some ten thousand miles. Yet it was nearly four centuries before any actual effort was made to construct such a canal.

In 1876 an organization was perfected in France for making surveys and collecting data on which to base the construction of a canal across the Isthmus of Panama, and in 1878, a concession for prosecuting the work was secured from the Colombian Government. In May, 1879, an international congress was convened, under the auspices of Ferdinand de Lesseps, to consider the question of the best location and plan for the canal.

The Panama Canal Company was organized, with Ferdinand de Lesseps as its president, and the stock of this company was successfully floated in December, 1880. The two years following were devoted largely to surveys, examinations and preliminary work. In 1889 the company went into bankruptcy and operations were suspended until the new Panama Canal Company was organized in 1894.

The United States to the Rescue.

The United States, not unmindful of the advantages of an Isthmian Canal, had, from time to time, made surveys of the various routes. With a view to government ownership and control, Congress directed an investigation, with the result that the Commission reported, on November 16, 1901, in favor of Panama and recommended the lock type of canal, appraising the value of the rights, franchises, concessions, lands, unfinished work, plans and other property, including the railroad of the new Panama Canal Company, at $40,000,000. An act of Congress, approved June 28, 1902, authorized the President of the United States to acquire this property at this figure, and also to secure from the Republic of Colombia perpetual control of a strip of land not less than six miles wide across the Isthmus and the right to excavate, construct and operate and protect thereon a canal of such depth and capacity as would afford convenient passage to the largest ships now in use or which might be reasonably anticipated.

Later on a treaty was made with the Republic of Panama whereby the United States was granted control of a ten-mile strip constituting the Canal Zone. This was ratified by the Republic of Panama on December 2, 1903, and by the United

UNCLE SAM'S BIG WORK AT PANAMA

A bird's-eye view of the great canal, showing how the Atlantic and Pacific
Oceans are here joined.

Courtesy of The Ingersoll Rand Company.

DRILLING ROCK, PANAMA CANAL.

These powerful steam drills are capable of sinking holes in the solid rock at the rate of seven feet per hour.

States on February 23, 1904.   On May 4, 1904, work was begun under United States control.

The Canal and the Navy.

The opening of the canal has greatly increased the effectiveness of the Navy of the United States.   It has reduced the distance between the central points of the Atlantic and Pacific coasts from 13,000 to 5,000 miles and greatly reduced the problem of coaling on a cruise from coast to coast.   It has made possible the concentration of a fleet at either entrance of the canal which, with a cruising speed of fifteen knots, could reach the center of the Pacific coast in nine days and the center of the Atlantic coast in five days.

Where, formerly, the fleets stationed opposite the middle of each coast were, from a cruising point of view, as far apart as opposite sides of the world, they are now as near as if one were off New York and the other off Buenos Aires.

With regard to the monetary saving to the United States resulting from the availability of the canal for naval use, it is apparent that the distance and time between the coasts have been reduced to less than two-fifths of the former figures.   The cost of coast-to-coast movements is reduced accordingly, for though vessels of the Navy pay tolls, such payment is in effect a transfer of money from one branch of the government to another.

The strategic importance of the canal is inestimable from a monetary standpoint.

The Great Canal.

The Isthmus of Panama runs east and west and the canal traverses it from Colon on the north to Panama on the south in a general direction from northwest to southeast, the Pacific terminus being twenty-two miles east of the Atlantic entrance.   The principal features of the canal are a sea-level entrance channel from the east through Limon Bay to Gatun, about seven miles long, five-hundred-foot bottom width and forty-one-foot depth at mean tide.   At Gatun the eighty-five-foot lake level is obtained by a dam across the valley.   The lake is confined on the Pacific side by a dam between the hills at Pedro Miguel, thirty-two miles away. The lake thus formed has an area of 164 square miles and a channel depth of not less than forty-five feet at normal stage.

At Gatun ships pass from the sea to the lake level, and *vice versa*, by three locks in flight.   On the Pacific side there is one lowering of thirty feet at Pedro Miguel to a small lake fifty-five feet above sea level, held by a dam at Miraflores, where two lowerings overcome the difference of level to the sea.   The channel between the locks on the Pacific side is five hundred feet wide at the bottom and forty-five feet deep, and below the Miraflores locks the sea-level section, about eight miles in length, is five hundred feet wide at the bottom and forty-five feet deep at mean tide. Through the lake the bottom widths are not less than one thousand feet for about sixteen miles, eight hundred feet for about four miles, five hundred feet for about three miles and through the continental divide from Bas Obispo to Pedro Miguel, a distance of about nine miles, the bottom width is three hundred feet.   The total length of the canal from deep water in the Caribbean, forty-one-foot depth at mean tide to deep water in the Pacific, forty-five-foot depth at mean tide, is practically fifty miles, fifteen miles of which are at sea level.

The Hydroelectric Station.

The hydroelectric station uses water from Gatun Lake for driving three turbo-generators of 2,000-kilowatt capacity each, which supply electricity for the operation of the lock and spillway machinery, the terminal shops and adjacent facilities, and

SUBMARINES USED IN DEFENDING THE PANAMA CANAL

The vessels here shown are used in defense of the Pacific side of the canal. They appear as anchored in the new concrete docks at Colon, preparatory to their passage through the canal, after having made the longest sea voyage then on record for submarines.

Copyright by Underwood & Underwood, N. Y.

Copyright by the International News Service.   THROUGH THE PANAMA CANAL
The U. S. battleship "Ohio" in the east chamber of the Pedro Miguel Locks.   On the left is seen the electric locomotive used in drawing vessels through.

LADDER DREDGE, PANAMA CANAL

SUCTION DREDGE, PANAMA CANAL

The upper view shows a ladder dredge, which operates by means of buckets on a continuous chain, dumping the contents of the buckets into the scow which lies alongside. The lower view shows a suction dredge, which operates on soft mud or sands, pumping the discharge through the pipe seen at the left of the illustration. The pipe may be carried to any desired point and used for filling.

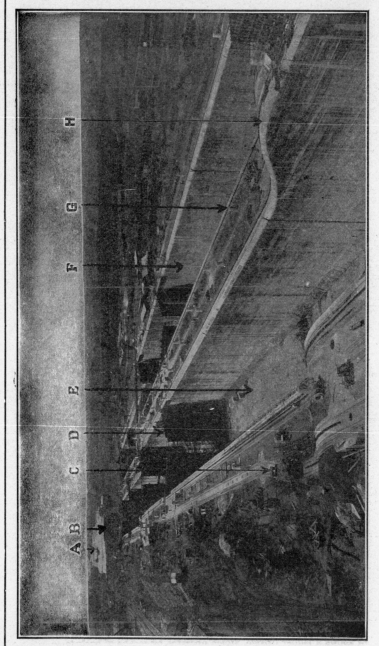

Copyright, C. H. Graves Co.

GATUN LOCKS

A. Sea-level section of canal, seven miles long, from Atlantic Ocean to Gatun Locks, where by a series of three locks vessels are raised to Gatun Lake, eighty-five feet above sea level. B. Small area of land dredged away as soon as Gatun Locks were completed. C. Electric towing motor, four of which tow each vessel entirely through the locks. They run on cog rail along the lock walls. D. Lock gate under construction. E. Floor of first lock from Atlantic side. Note holes in floor for admitting the water. F. Lock for vessels coming from Pacific side. G. Base on which concrete posts were erected for electric lights. A row of lights on all sides of the locks making operation at night as safe as day. H. Incline from locks of different levels up and down which the towing motors run on cog rails.

GAILLARD CUT LOOKING SOUTH FROM BEND IN EAST BANK NEAR GAMBOA

The train and shovel are standing on the bottom of the cut. The water in the drainage canal is about ten feet below the bottom of the canal, or at elevation +30.

A CYLINDRICAL VALVE MACHINE, MOTOR AND LIMIT SWITCH.

This machine is one of many which are used to regulate the flow of water to the locks. All valves are controlled from a central operating station on each of the three sets of locks. The limit switch automatically shuts off the power and stops the motor when the valve is entirely open or shut.

CUCARACHA SLIDE ATTACKED BY A FLEET OF DREDGES

This great slide was the source of much trouble to the engineers. At one time it entirely blocked the canal at the narrow point shown in this photograph, but the seven dredges of the ladder, suction and dipper type, made short work of cutting the 150-foot channel shown here, and then proceeded with the work of entirely clearing the cut. The view looks north from the slide past Gold and Contractor's Hills.

Copyright by Underwood & Underwood, N. Y.

Steam Shovel Buried Under Fall of Rock

THE GREAT GAILLARD CUT

At this point the canal is cut through what is practically a mountain range. The material excavated consisted largely of rock and formed one of the highest engineering problems in the world's history. The cut is nine miles long, 300 feet wide, 272 feet greatest depth and required the excavation of 100,000,000 cubic yards of material.

for the lighting of the locks and the canal villages and fortifications. Transmission over the Zone is effected through four substations and a connecting high voltage transmission line which follows the main line of the Panama Railroad.

Gatun Lake, impounded by Gatun Dam, has an area of 164 square miles when its surface is at the normal elevation of eighty-five feet above sea level, and is the largest artificially-formed lake in the world. The area of the water-shed tributary to the lake is 1,320 square miles. During the rainy season, from April to the latter part of December, the run-off from this basin exceeds considerably the consumption of water, and the surplus is discharged through the spillway of Gatun Dam. Toward the end of the rainy season the surface of the lake is raised to about eighty-seven feet above sea level, in order to afford a surplus or reserve supply to keep the channel

STEAM SHOVEL LOADING ROCK

These great machines, which are able to dig out and load several tons of material at each operation, made the rapid progress in digging the canal possible.

full to operating depth during the dry season, in part of which the consumption and evaporation are in excess of the supply. It is calculated that when this level has been attained at the beginning of the dry season the reserve is sufficient to assure a surface elevation of at least seventy-nine feet at the end of the dry season in spite of the consumption at the hydroelectric station, and allowing forty-one passages of vessels through the locks each day with the use of the full length of the chambers, or fifty-eight lockages a day when the shorter sections of the chambers are used and cross filling is employed, which would usually be the case. This is a greater number of lockages than can be made in one day.

Gigantic Obstacles.

The greatest difficulty encountered in the excavation of the canal was due to slides and breaks which caused large masses of material to slide or move into the

One of the Guard Gates, Gatun Locks, Panama Canal. Each lock is provided with four gates. This shows the method of construction, the gate being only partially finished.

GATUN UPPER LOCKS, EAST CHAMBER

The view is looking north from the forebay showing the upper guard gates and emergency dam.

excavated area, closing off the drainage, upsetting steam shovels and tearing up the tracks. The greatest slide was at Cucaracha, and gave trouble when the French first began cutting in 1884. Though at first confined to a length of 800 feet, the slide extended to include the entire basin south of Gold Hill, or a length of about 3,000 feet. Some idea of the magnitude of these slides can be obtained from the fact that during the fiscal year 1910 of 14,921,750 cubic yards that were removed, 2,649,000 yards, or eighteen per cent, were from slides or breaks that had previously existed or that had developed during the year.

The one greatest undertaking of the whole excavation was the Gaillard Cut. Work had been in progress on this since 1880, and during the French control over 20,000,000 cubic yards were removed. On May 4, 1904, when the United States took charge, it was estimated that there was left to excavate 150,000,000 cubic yards. Some idea of the size of this big cut may be formed from the fact that this division has within its jurisdiction over 200 miles of five-foot-gage track laid, about fifty-five miles of which is within the side slopes of the Gaillard Cut alone.

Gatun Dam.

The great dam at Gatun is a veritable hill—7,500 feet over all, 2,100 feet wide at the base, 398 feet through at the water surface, and 100 feet wide at the top, which is 115 feet above sea level. The dimensions of the dam are such as to assure that ample provision is made against every force which may affect its safety, and while it is made of dirt, a thing before unheard of, it is of such vast proportions that it is as strong and firm as the everlasting hills themselves.

Fluctuations in the lake due to floods are controlled by an immense spillway dam built of concrete. The front of the dam is the arc of a circle 740 feet long with fourteen openings which, when the gates are raised to the full height, permit a discharge of 140,000 cubic feet per second. The water thus discharged passes through a diversion channel in the old bed of the Chagres River, generating, by an enormous electric plant, the power necessary for operating the locks.

The locks of the canal are in pairs, so that if any lock is out of service navigation will not be interrupted, also, when all the locks are in use the passage of shipping is expedited by using one set of locks for the ascent and the other for descent. These locks are 110 feet wide and have usable lengths of 1,000 feet. The system of filling adopted consists of a culvert in each side wall feeding laterals from which are openings upward into the lock chamber. The entire lock can be filled or emptied in fifteen minutes and forty-two seconds when one culvert is used and seven minutes and fifty-one seconds, using both culverts. It requires about ten hours for a large ship to make the entire trip through the canal.

Meeting all Emergencies.

Many extraordinary feats of engineering were accomplished to overcome the difficulties presented. Special contrivances, wonderful in their operation, were invented to meet exigencies and emergencies.

The first and greatest problem attempted by the United States was to make the Canal Zone healthful. This strip of land from ocean to ocean abounded in disease-breeding swamps and filthy habitations unfit for human beings. The death-rate was appalling and the labor conditions terrible. During the first two and a half years, therefore, all energies were devoted to ridding the Isthmus of disease by sanitation, to recruiting and organizing a working force and providing for it suitable houses, hotels, messes, kitchens and an adequate food supply. This work included clearing lands, draining and filling pools and swamps for the extermination of the mosquito, the establishment of hospitals for the care of the sick and injured and

Photograph, Underwood & Underwood, N. Y.   LOCK GATE OPERATING MACHINERY

The great gear wheel, known as a "bull wheel," is connected with one leaf of the gate on the right by means of a strut so that revolving the bull wheel by means of an electric motor through a train of gears results in opening or closing the gate.

PANAMA, PAST AND PRESENT

Scene showing the repaving of one of Panama's old muddy streets with vitrified brick. Sewers and water pipes were laid throughout the city, resulting in a great reduction of disease.

the building of suitable quarantine quarters. Municipal improvements were undertaken in Panama and Colon and the various settlements in the Canal Zone, such as the construction of reservoirs, pavements and a system of modern roads. Over 2,000 buildings were constructed besides the remodeling of 1,500 buildings turned over by the French company.

It was only after all this preliminary sanitation was accomplished that the real work of digging the canal could go forward with any hope of success. These hygienic conditions had the result of making the Canal Zone one of the most healthful spots in the world, and work on the canal became so popular that it was no longer necessary to enlist recruits from the West Indies, the good pay, fair treatment and excellent living conditions bringing thousands of laborers from Spain and Italy. The greatest number employed at any one time was 45,000, of which 5,000 were American.

A Battle Won.

The completion of this herculean task marked an epoch in the history of the world. A gigantic battle against floods and torrents, pestilence and swamps, tropical rivers, jungles and rock-ribbed mountains had been fought—and won! Well worthy a place in the halls of immortal fame are the names of the thousands of sturdy sons who, with ingenuity, pluck and perseverance never before equaled, succeeded in making a pathway for the nations of the world from ocean to ocean.

This great and daring undertaking, which had for its object the opening up of new trade routes and lines of commerce, annihilating distance and wiping out the width of two continents between New York and Yokohama and making the Atlantic seaboard and the Pacific coast close neighbors, is the climax of man's achievement and the greatest gift to civilization. It will help in the consummation of man's loftiest dreams of world friendship and world peace.

*So far, in the use of the canal, over forty per cent of the vessels which have passed through it have been engaged in the coastwise trade of the United States— each of them saving about 7,800 miles on each trip. If their average speed be taken at ten knots, they have averaged a saving of over a month at sea on each voyage from coast to coast. Where formerly the round trip of a ten-knot vessel required about fifty-five days' actual steaming, the time at sea for the same trip for the same vessel is now reduced to about twenty-two days.

The canal makes San Francisco nearer to Liverpool by 5,666 miles, a saving of two-fifths of the old journey by Magellan. The distance between San Francisco and Gibraltar has been reduced from 12,571 miles to 7,621 miles, a saving of 4,950 miles, or thirty-nine per cent of the former distance.

From San Francisco to Buenos Aires, via Valparaiso and Magellan, is approximately 7,610 miles, which is shorter than the route through the canal, by which the distance is 8,941 miles. To Rio de Janeiro, the distance via Magellan is 8,609 miles; by the canal 7,885 miles. To Pernambuco, on the eastern promontory of South America, the distance via Magellan is 9,748 miles; via the canal 6,746 miles. To Para the distances via Magellan and via the canal are 10,852 and 5,642 miles, respectively.

From San Francisco to Freetown, on the west coast of middle Africa, the distance by the most practicable route, using the Strait of Magellan, is 11,380 miles. Through the canal and by way of the island of Barbados, the distance is 7,277 miles. The new route is less than two-thirds of the former.

With reference to the trade between the Atlantic coast of the United States and the west coast of South America, New York is nearer to Valparaiso by 3,717 miles by virtue of the canal; to Iquique, one of the great nitrate ports, by 4,139 miles; and to Guayaquil by 7,405 miles. From New York to Guayaquil the present

*The following information and statistics by courtesy of The Panama Canal, Washington office,

FORTY TONS OF DYNAMITE DESTROY THE LAST BARRIER BETWEEN THE OCEANS

The blowing up of Gamboa Dike, the last of the dikes in the Panama Canal. This dike separated the water in the Gatun locks from Gaillard Cut. The removal of the dike by a discharge of forty tons of dynamite, set off by President Wilson, from Washington, was the last stage in the completion of the great waterway. Dredges were put to work immediately widening the channel at Cucaracha slide in Gaillard Cut, so that within a short time the canal was ready for use throughout its entire length.

Copyright by Underwood & Underwood.

STEAM SHOVEL AT WORK IN GAILLARD CUT, WITH LARGE ROCK IN MOUTH OF SHOVEL

The great progress made in digging the Panama Canal was largely due to the steam shovels.

distance of 2,765 miles is approximately twenty-seven per cent of the former distance —10,270 miles.

As to the Far East, New York is nearer to Yokohama by 3,768 miles than formerly by way of the Suez Canal, but the latter route is eighteen miles shorter than the Panama route for vessels plying between New York and Hongkong. New York is forty-one miles nearer Manila by Panama than by Suez, and 3,932 miles nearer Sydney by Panama. New York is now, by virtue of the Panama Canal, nearer than Liverpool to Yokohama by 1,880 miles, and nearer than Liverpool to Sydney by 2,424 miles.

When the ship enters the harbor of either of the terminal ports it is boarded by officers of the canal who examine its bill of health and clearance, see that its certificate of canal measurement is properly made out, and ascertain any of the vessel's needs in the matters of fuel, supplies, extra men to handle the lines during the passage of the locks, etc. These matters are immediately reported to the Captain of the Port, who gives the necessary orders to insure proper attendance on the vessel's needs and directs its start through the canal whenever it is ready.

In all stages of its transit of the canal the vessel must have on board a government pilot. There is no charge for pilotage on vessels going directly through the canal without stopping to discharge cargo or passengers at the terminal ports. The pilot is on board in an advisory capacity and is required to confer with the master of the vessel, giving him the benefit of his knowledge and advice as to the handling of the vessel in the various reaches, but the master, who is best acquainted with the peculiarities of his vessel and her ways of answering the helm, is responsible for the navigation of the vessel, except when she is passing through the locks.

The handling of a vessel during its transit of the canal is like the handling of a railway train on its "run." The course is equipped with all requisite signals, facilities for mooring, like sidings, and a system of communication between points along the line, which includes a special telephone system connecting all the important points of control in series.

As soon as the vessel starts on its transit of the canal, the Captain of the Port at the point of entrance telephones its starting to the other stations along the course. As the vessel arrives and departs from each of these points, the fact is telephoned along the line, so that there is exact knowledge at each station all the time of the status of traffic, and complete co-operation from the several points of control.

The transit of the canal requires about ten hours, of which approximately three hours are spent in the locks. In the sea-level channels and Gaillard (formerly "Culebra") Cut the speed of vessels is limited to six knots; through Gatun Lake they may make ten, twelve and fifteen knots, according to the width of the channel. A vessel may clear from the canal port at which it enters and, after passing through the last of the locks, put direct to sea without further stop.

The handling of a vessel all through the canal, except in the locks, is essentially the same as its handling through any charted channel where observance of signals, ranges and turns is necessary. The canal channel throughout is very accurately charted, fully equipped with aids to navigation, and governed by explicit rules with which the pilots, of course, are thoroughly familiar.

In the locks, the vessel is under the control of the lock-operating force. As the vessel approaches the locks, the operator in charge at the control house indicates by an electrically operated signal at the outer end of the approach wall if the vessel shall enter the locks and, if so, on which side; or if it shall keep back or moor alongside the approach wall. If everything is ready for the transit of the locks, the vessel approaches the center approach wall, which is a pier extending about a thousand feet from the locks proper, lines are thrown out, and connections are made with the electric towing locomotives on the approach wall.

The vessel then moves forward slowly until it is in the entrance chamber, when lines are thrown out on the other side and connections are made with towing locomotives on the side wall. Six locomotives are used for the larger vessels, three on each wall of the lock chamber. Two keep forward of the vessel, pulling and holding her head to the center of the chamber; two aft, holding the vessel in check; and two slightly forward of amidships, which do most of the towing of the vessel through the chamber. The locomotives are powerful affairs, secured against slipping by the engagement of cogs with a rack running along the center of the track, and equipped with a slip drum and towing windlass, which allow the prompt paying out and taking in of hawser as required. No trouble has been experienced in maintaining absolute control over the vessels.

The water within the lock chamber proper, beyond the entrance chamber, is brought to the level of that in the approach, the gates toward the vessel are opened, the fender chain is lowered, and the locomotives maneuver the vessel into the chamber and bring it to rest. The gates are then closed, the water raised or lowered, as the case may be, to the level of that in the next chamber, the gates at the other end are opened, and the vessel moved forward. Three such steps are made at Gatun, two at Miraflores, and one at Pedro Miguel.

When the vessel has passed into the approach chamber at the end of the locks, the lines from the towing locomotives on the side wall are first cast off, then those from the locomotives on the approach wall, and the vessel clears under its own power.

Towing is not ordinarily required in any part of the canal, except in the locks, for steam or motor vessels. Tug service for sailing ships or vessels without motive power is at the rate of $15 per hour. If the channel in the cut has been disturbed by a slide, tugs may be used to handle vessels past the narrow places, but in such cases there is no charge for the service to vessels of less than 15,000 gross tonnage.

What is a Geyser?

The famous geyser shown in the illustration is called "Old Faithful" because of the clock-like regularity of its eruptions. For over twenty years it has been spouting at average intervals of sixty-five minutes.

Geysers were first observed in Iceland and the name, therefore, comes from that language, being derived from the word "geysa," meaning "to gush" or "rush forth." That is just what they do.

There are really three different kinds of geysers; one which throws up hot water, either continually or, like "Old Faithful," at intervals; one which simply emits steam and no water and one which is a sort of a hot-water cistern.

The "Grand Geyser" at Firehole Basin in Yellowstone Park is the most magnificent natural fountain in the whole world. The "Great Geyser" and the "New Geyser" are the most remarkable ones in Iceland, where there about a hundred altogether. The basin of the former is about seventy feet in diameter, and at times it throws up a column of hot water to the height of from eighty to two hundred feet in the air.

The hot-lake district of Auckland, New Zealand, is also famous in possessing some of the most remarkable geyser scenery in the world. It was formerly noted for the number of natural terraces containing hot water pools, and its lakes all filled at intervals by boiling geysers and hot springs, but the formation of the country was considerably altered by a disastrous volcanic outbreak in 1886, its beautiful pink and white terraces being destroyed. It still has, however, a circular rocky basin, forty feet in diameter, in which a violent geyser is constantly boiling up to the height of ten to twelve feet, emitting dense clouds of steam. This is one of the natural wonders of the southern hemisphere and is much visited by tourists traveling through New Zealand.

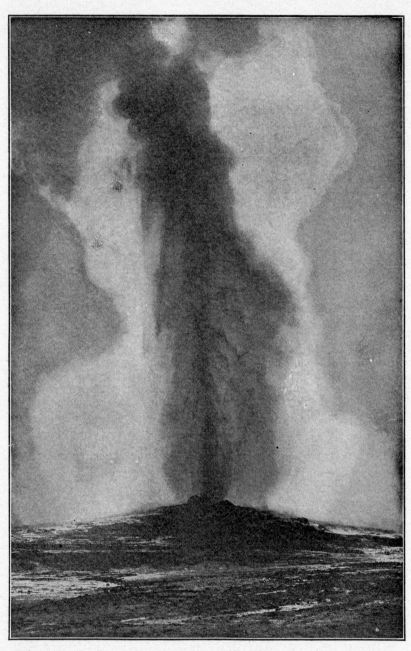

Photo by Brown Bros. "OLD FAITHFUL" IN ERUPTION

What Kind of Dogs are Prairie-Dogs?

Prairie-dogs are not really dogs at all, but a kind of a squirrel called a marmot. As the visitors to city Zoological Parks already know, these animals make little mounds of earth, and a great many of these are found in one locality, which is known as a "dog-town." It is possible to travel for days at a time through country which is dotted over with mounds, every one of which is the home of a pair or more of prairie-dogs. These mounds are usually about eighteen feet apart, and consist of about as much earth as would fill a very large wheelbarrow. This is thrown up by the prairie-dog when he digs out his subterranean home. His dwelling sometimes has one entrance and sometimes two, and there are many much-traveled paths between the different hillocks, showing that they are very neighborly and sociable with one another.

In choosing a town site, they select one which is covered with short, coarse grass, such as is found especially in fields on high ground and mountain sides, for it is on this grass and certain roots that the prairie-dogs feed. On the plains of New Mexico, where for miles you will not find a drop of water unless you dig down into the earth for a hundred feet or so, with no rain for several months at a time, there are many very large "dog-towns," and it is, therefore, clear that they are able to live without drinking, obtaining enough moisture for their needs from a heavy fall of dew.

At about the end of October, when the grass dries up and the ground becomes frozen hard, so that digging is out of the question, the prairie-dog creeps into his burrow, blocking up the opening in order to keep out the cold and make everything snug, and goes to sleep until the following spring, without having had to lay up a store of food, as some animals do, to last him through the long, hard winter months. If he opens up his house again before the end of cold weather, the Indians say it is a sure sign that warmer days are near at hand.

If one approaches very cautiously so as not to be observed, a large "dog-town" presents a very curious sight. A happy, animated scene stretches away as far as the eye can see. Little prairie-dogs are found everywhere, on the top of their mounds, sitting up like squirrels, waving their tails from side to side and yelping to each other, until a most cheerful-sounding concert is produced. If you listen carefully, as you draw nearer, however, you will notice a different tone in the calls of the older and more experienced animals, and that is the warning signal for the whole population to disappear from view into their burrows. Then, if one hides quietly in the background and waits patiently for some time, sentinels will mount up to their posts of observation on top of the mounds and announce that it is safe to come out of their burrows and play about again, as the danger is past.

What is Spontaneous Combustion?

Spontaneous combustion is the burning of a substance or body by the internal development of heat without the application of fire.

It not infrequently takes place among heaps of rags, wool and cotton when sodden with oil; hay and straw when damp or moistened with water; and coal in the bunkers of vessels.

In the first case, the oil rapidly combines with the oxygen of the air, this being accompanied by great heat. In the second case, the heat is produced by a kind of fermentation; and in the third, by the pyrites of the coal rapidly absorbing and combining with the oxygen of the air.

The term is also applied to the extraordinary phenomenon of the human body, which has been told of some people, whereby it is reduced to ashes without the application of fire. It is said to have occurred in the aged and persons that were fat and hard drinkers, but most chemists reject the theory and altogether discredit it.

The Story of the Talking Machine*

The leaders in the creation of talking machines were Thomas A. Edison, Emile Berliner, and Eldredge R. Johnson, each of whom owns many patents in this field. While Edison holds the honor of inventing the talking machine as a reproducing

A Large Cabinet Model of the Orthophonic Victrola

instrument, to Johnson belongs much of the credit for bringing it to its present high state of development. The company which he founded and now heads is the largest talking machine manufacturing organization in the world.

---

* Illustrations by courtesy of the Victor Talking Machine Company.

John McCormack, famous tenor, listening to a reproduction of his own voice.

The talking machine is to music and sound what books are to writing—a means of making a permanent record. It reproduces the human voice in song or speech, the various musical instruments, the cries of animals, or in fact any sound vibration which can be heard by the human ear, just as they were originally.

This is accomplished, first by capturing these original sounds and recording them upon a talking machine record, and second by providing a mechanism which is so affected by the record as to give forth duplicates of the sounds imprinted upon it.

When sounds are engraved upon a record they are represented by a small wavy line traced upon its surface, these waves corresponding to the air vibrations which constitute sound. Let us say that a singer's voice is being recorded for the talking machine. The air vibrations set up in his throat travel through space and strike against a delicate recording mechanism which vibrates in sympathy and sets in motion a needle or stylus which traces the wavy groove on the soft surface of the record. For the sake of conserving space, this line is arranged in closely spiral form on a flat circular disc which requires little storage room.

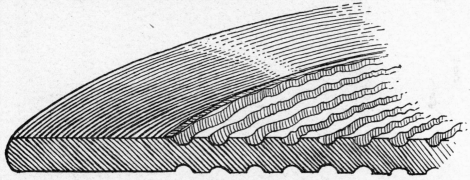

An enlarged cross-sectional view of a talking machine record, showing the wavy grooves in which the needle runs, and by means of which vibrations are imparted to the diaphragm of the reproducing apparatus. Each wave in the groove represents a change of pitch in the sound given out.

This master record, made direct from the singer's voice, serves as a model for duplicate records which can be produced in any number by a simple process. Every such disc is a permanent record of that singer's voice and needs only a talking machine to produce sounds exactly similar to the original.

The talking machine reverses the process of recording by beginning with the wavy line and working back to the air vibrations, which we call sounds. The record is laid upon a turn-table, revolved by a spring motor. A needle is made to follow the wavy groove cut in the record, with the result that the needle vibrates exactly as the needle of the recording instrument did when it cut the groove. This vibrating talking machine needle moves a sensitive diaphragm which sets up air vibrations, and these air vibrations are collected and concentrated by a horn, which sends them out into the world in faithful reproduction of the singer's voice.

This simple process, which is hardly more complex in its essential principle than turning water into ice and back into water again, has not been perfected without a great deal of labor and scientific study. The correct principles and methods of doing it have been worked out by a large number of investigators, all of whom in greater or less degree contributed something to the knowledge of the subject. As early as 1807 experiments were made with the idea of making a permanent record of sound, but these early studies made no attempt to solve the problem of making that record yield up the sounds it had absorbed. This was not accomplished until 1877, when Thomas A. Edison evolved the first crude talking machine.

View of the orthophonic talking machine, with screen removed showing the unusual external
appearance of the six-foot folded horn.

This first model was very imperfect, being turned by hand and giving forth only a ghostly echo of the sounds it was intended to reproduce. The early records were tinfoil cylinders, which later experimenters replaced with cylinders of a wax-like composition, which in turn were supplanted by flat discs. The first machines, being hand-driven, were very jerky and uneven in performance, a difficulty which was later removed by installing an electric motor. This was found too costly and undependable, however, and in the end a compact spring motor was adopted. Other and minor refinements, both as to methods of recording and reproduction, were introduced continually in the fifty years following the appearance of the first machine.

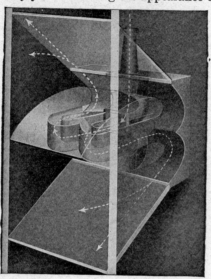

THE FOLDED HORN OF THE ORTHOPHONIC VICTROLA

Despite the large number of minor improvements incorporated in the talking machine for the first half century following its invention, no fundamental change occurred until 1925, when a notable series of experiments resulted in a striking advance in the science of talking machine acoustics. This change involved a new angle of approach to talking machine design, a substitution of the principle of mathematical exactness for the old trial-and-error method of arriving at conclusions. And oddly enough this new principle was introduced from an agency outside the field of the talking machine.

In the development of the long-distance telephone, electrical engineers discovered a principle which they called Matched Impedance, by means of which many of the obstructions encountered in talking over long-distance wires were eliminated. Put briefly, this principle is founded on the fact that such obstructions are caused less by the number and power of disturbing influences than by their inequality to each other—that if they are equal and well matched, the resistance is reduced. They discovered, moreover, that it was possible to translate this electrical principle into mechanical terms and apply it to acoustical mechanisms, like the talking machine, which have nothing to do with electricity.

This they did, and the mathematical formula which they evolved was used to design an entirely new type of talking machine, the first radical improvement in fifty years. To distinguish it from the old type it was given the descriptive appellation of "orthophonic," meaning "true sound," because acoustical engineers demonstrated in laboratory tests that its efficiency was 100 per cent greater than any previous type.

A Smaller Talking Machine

The adoption of this principle necessitated the re-designing of the talking machine from needle to horn opening. All measurements and proportions were governed by the mathematical formula. The appearance, as regards the actual mechanism, underwent no marked change. The needle and diaphragm remained, and the swinging tone arm which leads into the horn. In these, the changes were too subtle to be at once apparent to the eye. But the horn itself was radically altered. Its length was increased to seventy inches—almost six feet—and in addition it was ingeniously folded up and enclosed within the cabinet of the machine, so that when the opening was screened it was entirely invisible.

As a result of this striking advance, and certain recent improvements in methods of recording, it is now possible to record and reproduce any sound which the human ear can distinguish. Where before the high and low notes of any musical selection were lost or muffled on the talking machine, they are now heard with all the force and clarity of the middle registers. Moreover it is possible to record larger musical ensembles than ever before, and certain instruments such as the harp, clavichord, and harpsichord, which before successfully resisted all attempts, no longer present any problem. These instruments, besides all others, are now so well reproduced that there is no difficulty in distinguishing one from another. Another advantage is that all the small echoes and overtones which characterize the original are now caught and reproduced, so that the effect is exactly as though the hearer were present at the original recording.

The significance of all this is profound. In future it will be possible to record whole symphonies, whole operas and plays, debates, meetings, and congresses, a thing which was heretofore prevented by the limitations still existing in methods of recording and reproduction. A new day has dawned in acoustics, for it is now possible to save and preserve the virtuosity of the artist, the pronunciation of obscure and dying dialects, and every sound of value, for the instruction or amusement of generations yet unborn. It is even possible that language in the future may cease to change from age to age as in the past, because the pure idiom and pronunciation of the best forms can be preserved and handed down to our descendants by means of talking machine records in the schools, undefiled by time or the ignorance and carelessness of man.

What are Petrified Forests?

In the first place, petrification is the name we give to the animal and vegetable bodies which have, by slow process, been converted into stone. We mean very much the same thing when we refer to "Fossil Forests."

Although in most instances there are comparatively few traces of its vegetable origin left, coal owes its existence primarily to the vast masses of vegetable matter deposited through the luxuriant growth of plants in former epochs of the earth's history, and since slowly converted into a petrified state.

Coal fields today present abundant indications of the existence of huge ancient forests, usually in the form of coal formed from the roots of the trees. Several such forests have been uncovered, of which one in Nova Scotia is a good example, remains of trees having been found there, six to eight feet high, one tree even measuring twenty-five feet in height and four feet in diameter.

The remains of a fossil forest have been found in an upright position in France, and in a colliery in England, in a space of about one-quarter of an acre, there have been found the fossilized stumps of seventy-three trees, with roots attached, and broken-off trunks lying about, one of them thirty feet long and all of them turned into coal.

A remarkable group of petrified trees, some of them twelve feet in diameter, exists in California, and another in Yellowstone Park, in which the trees are still erect, though converted into stone. An extraordinary forest of such trees has been found in Arizona, lying over a wide space of ground, some of them six feet in diameter and perfectly preserved.

These trees are rather mineralized than fossilized. They are found in volcanic regions and are supposed to be due to the action of hot water, which carried off the organic material and deposited dissolved silica in its place. In some instances the wood has been converted into solid jasper or has been changed into opal or agate, or filled with chalcedony or crystallized quartz, with beautifully variegated colors.

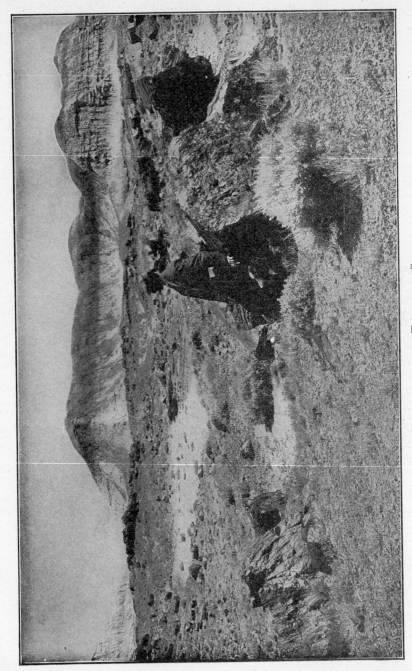

TREES THAT HAVE TURNED TO STONE

A scene in one of the Petrified Forests of Arizona.   Broken trunks of trees are lying all about.

What Animals are the Best Architects?

Animals of a great many different kinds have helped show man the way, in taking advantage of the opportunities which nature affords him to feed, clothe and protect himself, but one of the smallest of the animal kingdom is probably the cleverest of all—the spider. Spiders have many different kinds of enemies, ranging from man down to the very smallest, but dangerous, insects, and most of their enemies possess enormous advantages over them in either strength or agility, or both combined; enemies with wings, swift in movement and able to retreat where the spider cannot follow them; enemies clad in an impenetrable coat of armor, against which the spider's weapons are powerless, while the spider's own body is soft and vulnerable. These handicaps have been met by the spider with a multitude of clever contrivances, and if invention and skill are to be regarded as an index to intellectual development, it should be very significant to realize how far spiders are ahead of our near relatives, the almost human members of the monkey family.

One of the most interesting of the spider race is the "trap-door" spider which inhabits warm countries all over the earth. The "trap-door" spider not only builds a home for herself by digging a deep hole in the ground and lining it with silk to prevent the sides from falling in, but she also adds a neat little door to keep out the rain and other troublesome things. She usually chooses sloping ground for her homestead so that the door, which she fastens at the edge of its highest point by a strong silk-elastic hinge, swings shut of its own weight after being opened. She disguises the entrance to her home in a manner superior to the famous art of concealment practiced by the Indians, by planting moss on the outside of the door—living moss taken from the immediate neighborhood—so that the entrance to her house harmonizes perfectly with its surroundings, its discovery being made more difficult by the fact that in her careful selection of a site for her dwelling she also appears to be influenced by the presence of patches of white lichen which distract the eye.

The male spider does not seem to take any part in designing, constructing or decorating the home and does not even share its occupancy, leaving it to the mother and her family—often forty or more children at a time—and living a vagrant life, camping out in holes and ditches when he is not tramping around over the whole countryside. The mother spider, however, like many other animals, takes excellent charge of her children, and guards them carefully from all harm. At the first sign of a commotion going on outside her front door she is known to invariably assemble her family behind her, out of harm's way, and then place her back against the swinging door, holding it shut with some of her feet and clinging tightly to the inner walls of her home with the others.

There is one kind of spider which has developed an even more elaborate style of architecture, digging another room and adding an upper side gallery to her main residence, and placing a second door at the junction of the two tunnels. The doors are made to swing back and forth in both directions, and she constructs a handle on the outer one, by which she fastens it open with a few threads attached to any convenient grass stems or little stones, when she expects to come home from a hunting expedition with her arms full. If a dangerous enemy threatens her home she usually retreats to the second room, in the hope that he will decide she is out and depart in search of another victim elsewhere, but if he discovers her secret, she slams the second swinging door in his face. Should she be beaten in the pushing match at that point, she slips into the upper side gallery opening above the door, and her enemy's presence within the inner room automatically blocks the entrance to her hiding place by holding up the swinging door across its only opening.

The Story of the Motorcycle*

Interest in the development of mechanically propelled two-wheel vehicles began soon after the introduction of the bicycle in its first practicable form. Man's natural dislike for manual labor quickly found objection to the physical effort of bicycle travel, and accordingly sought to devise mechanical means of overcoming it.

The earliest known attempt to construct a two-wheel vehicle which would proceed under its own power was made by W. W. Austin, of Winthrop, Mass., in the year 1868. This crude affair consisted of a small velocipede upon which was mounted a crude coal-burning steam engine. The piston rods of the engine were connected directly with cranks on the rear wheel. The boiler was hung between the two wheels and directly back of the saddle, while the engine cylinders were placed slightly above horizontal just behind the boiler. Despite the crudity of this outfit, Austin claimed that he had traveled some 2,200 miles on this, the "granddaddy" of all motorcycles.

COPELAND MODEL, 1884

L. D. and W. E. Copeland, two Californian experimenters, are credited with the next known effort to produce a two-wheeler which would travel by its own power. Their first model appeared in 1884. The bicycle to which this miniature steam-

AUSTIN STEAM VELOCIPEDE, 1868

ROPER'S MACHINE, 1886

power plant of the Copeland brothers' invention was attached was one of the old high-wheel models with the small steering wheel forward. The steam engine of this truly ingenious contrivance, together with the boiler and the driving pulley, weighed

*Illustrations by courtesy of the Hendee Manufacturing Co.

only sixteen ounces. The Copeland model was probably the first motorcycle to use belt drive. It should be understood that propulsion of this first Copeland model was not intended to depend solely upon mechanical power, but to be operated in connection with the foot pedals.

The Copeland brothers are to be credited with the first attempt to produce the motorcycle upon a commercial basis, but their efforts were unsuccessful. Their invention seemed to be far ahead of the times, but their project passed by unappreciated.

In 1886, S. H. Roper, of Roxbury, Mass., appeared with a steam-propelled bicycle which consisted of a specially designed engine placed in a bicycle frame of the type with which we are familiar today. This invention was awkward, and its weight of 150 pounds made it difficult to handle, but in spite of that its inventor is said to have obtained considerable use from it.

THE PENNINGTON MOTORCYCLE, 1895

The year 1895 saw the first public exhibition of mechanically operated two-wheel vehicles held at Madison Square Garden, New York City. The sensation of the show was a motorcycle which was presented by E. J. Pennington of Cleveland. This was the first public appearance of a cycle propelled by a combustion engine, and in that regard it may be called the first appearance of the motorcycle in the form that is known today. The Pennington machine was the first-known vehicle to attempt the use of gasoline.

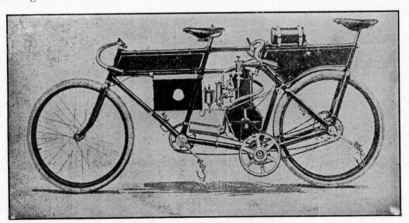

HEDSTROM MOTOR TANDEM, 1898

History fails to relate a great deal about the mechanical detail of the Pennington model, but it is said to have made a very creditable performance in exhibition. It appeared at the Madison Square Garden in two forms, as a single motorcycle and as a motor tandem.

There was little or no interest in motor vehicles of any description in that period of the early nineties, consequently the Pennington efforts were fruitless. Shortly,

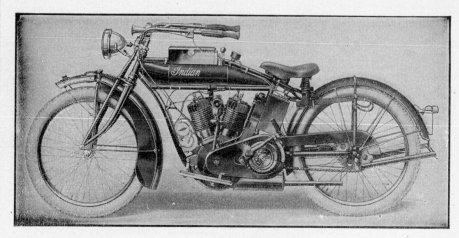

A BIG TWIN MODEL

AN UP-TO-DATE "FEATHERWEIGHT" MODEL

after the public exhibition of his models, financial difficulties are said to have over-taken Pennington and he is reported to have departed suddenly for foreign climes, bringing his experiments to an abrupt end.

Along in the late nineties a keen interest in bicycle racing led to the introduction of what is known as the motor-paced tandem. This consisted of a regulation tandem bicycle on which was mounted a gasoline motor geared up to the rear wheel with a chain drive. The tandem rider on the forward seat did the steering and the foot pedaling, and the rear rider operated the motor. It is believed that the first of these tandems came over here from France.

By 1898 the popularity of the motor-paced racing bicycle became so great that attention was soon directed toward their manufacture. Chief among the bicycle manufacturers who took up the making of the motor-paced tandem was Oscar Hedstrom, a racer with many notable victories to his credit. He believed that he could make a motor tandem which would prove far superior to any other American machine made, if not better even than any foreign machine.

CRADLE SPRING FRAME CONSTRUCTION

The machine which he produced with a motor of his own design was entered in some big races at the Pan-American Exposition in Buffalo in 1901 where nearly every record was broken. Mr. Hedstrom's partner on this tandem outfit was Henshaw, a bicycle racer of some repute. Following their début on the motor tandem at Buffalo, this pair proceeded to make records throughout the country, several of which still stand today.

In 1901 a bicycle manufacturer of Springfield, Mass., foresaw a future for a motorcycle designed for pleasure purposes instead of exclusively for racing. Hitherto, all motor-propelled cycles had used the power of the engine of whatever form it was merely as an aid to locomotion. None had been successful in producing a machine that could proceed anywhere solely under its own power. Convinced that such a machine could be produced, and certain that it would find a ready market, this manufacturer set about to put his ideas into execution.

FIRST HEDSTROM MOTORCYCLE WITH TRI-CAR, 1902

He recognized in Oscar Hedstrom, as the leader of the motor tandem racing field, the man who knew more about combustion engines than any other man in America, and accordingly enlisted his services. Oscar Hedstrom retired to a little mechanical laboratory in Middletown, Conn., and in a short four months emerged with a completed motorcycle which he had not only designed himself, but had constructed entirely by his own labor. Its performance on its first trial trip was absolutely astounding to every observer. In road tests under every conceivable condition, this first motorcycle of Oscar Hedstrom's displayed a perfection of mechanical operation which had to that time never been approached. It moved entirely under its own power, could climb hills and could travel on the level road at speeds which had never before been exhibited by vehicles of that type.

By reason of the successful performance of his first motorcycle, Oscar Hedstrom is given the credit, in many quarters, for producing the first motorcycle of practicable construction. All successful machines of this type since then are said to have been modeled more or less on the fundamental principles of that first Hedstrom machine. Part of Hedstrom's success was due to his mastery of the important problem of carburetion, and a carburetor expressly designed for that first machine constituted a marked step in motorcycle development. The leading carburetors of today are said to be based upon the principles of the first Hedstrom carburetor. The date of the appearance of the first Hedstrom motorcycle was 1901.

Manufacture of the motorcycle upon a commercial scale forthwith commenced in the bicycle manufactory at Springfield, Mass. Such is said to have been the humble beginning of the motorcycle.

Their first motorcycle was offered to the public in 1902. Its mechanical detail

MODERN "SIDE-CAR" MODEL

is worthy of note for the sake of comparison with the models of the current year. Its motor was the Hedstrom single-cylinder motor of 1¾ horse-power; frame, 22 inches; tires, 1¾ inches, single tube; chain drive; weight, 93 pounds. From the year 1902 to 1909, the style of their motorcycle remained substantially the same in appearance. The models of that period are referred to as "camel backs" by reason of the location and shape of the gasoline tank on the rear mud guard. In 1909, the loop frame was introduced to provide additional strength to the machine, being required by the increased weight of the motor; 1906 saw the introduction of twin cylinders for racing models, and the following year they appeared in the regular models.

Motorcycle design has made wonderful progress. The powerful, easy-riding machines of today with their many refinements are truly marvelous pieces of mechanism. Mechanical perfection is as nearly approached as it is possible for the best brains and the most approved methods of manufacture to attain. There are numerous modern refinements which have contributed materially to the present-day popularity of the motorcycle that are worthy of special note. Chief of these is the kick-starter, which enables the rider to start the engine of his machine without mounting it upon a stand or pedaling on the road. Improved clutches, gear ratios which permit varying speeds, double-braking systems and electric lights are present-day refinements which add zest to the sport of motorcycling.

One of the greatest of all motorcycling comfort creations is a device known as the cradle spring frame which consists of pairs of cushion-leaf springs of the semi-elliptical type, which are located at the rear of the frame just beneath the saddle. This affords the maximum of riding comfort by the elimination of all jar and jolt occasioned by an uneven roadway.

Magneto ignition first appeared in 1908; previous to that date all ignition had been dependent upon batteries of the ordinary dry-cell variety.

The last two years has seen the introduction of what is known as the light-weight model. This style of motorcycle has a smaller motor, which is usually of the two-stroke type, single cylinder. The frame is of lighter construction, the mechanism

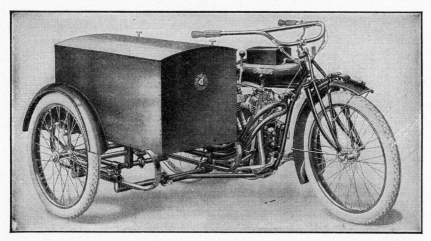

MODERN DELIVERY VAN FOR GROCERS, DRUGGISTS, ETC.

is simpler, and of course the speed is reduced. This type of two-wheeler, however, finds favor among those who like power and speed but in modified form. Lower initial cost and lower operation expense are factors which especially recommend the light-weight models.

There has been considerable difference of opinion as regards the comparative efficiency of chain drive and belt drive. The consensus of opinion, however, seems to favor the chain drive, as evidenced by its use on most of the leading makes of present-day machines. Some of the light-weight models are using belt drive, but chain drive is generally conceded to be superior. In the early days of motorcycling, belt drive was rather generally used, but the heavy duty required soon brought about the change to present usage.

Motorcycle manufacture is today carried on in some of the largest and most up-to-date manufactories that can be found in the United States. The oldest and the largest factory devoted to motorcycle manufacture is said to be that which has been built up under the direction of the Springfield manufacturer, the man who first saw the great commercial possibilities in the development of the motorcycle for pleasure and business purposes. His company had a capitalization of $12,500,000 in 1916. Some 2,400 skilled workmen were employed in its two big Springfield plants. Its output, said to be the largest in the industry, is over 25,000 machines per year. Numerous models meeting varying requirements are produced.

Soon after the first practicable motorcycle appeared in 1902 there arose a demand for a contrivance that would accommodate an additional passenger. Consequently, there was produced an attachment called a tri-car. This was mounted on two pneumatic-tired wheels which were fitted to the front fork together with necessary steering devices. Later it was found that the passenger conveyance could better be carried at the side mounted upon a springed chassis which was supported by a third wheel. That form was thereupon generally adopted, and remains today the general practice in the manufacture of motorcycle side-cars, as they are called.

Naturally enough, interest in motorcycles was quickly directed toward their application to commercial uses, and to that end there were produced numerous styles of side vans and parcel carriers intended for parcel delivery.

The use of the motorcycle for commercial purposes was for a time overshadowed by the abnormally rapid development of the automobile, but the factor of upkeep and operation costs of an automobile is bringing the motorcycle into prominence now. In this respect the motorcycle is said to have the advantage overwhelmingly. The tendency, however, among business houses is to investigate their individual requirements for delivery service and determine to what purposes either form of motor vehicle is best adapted. For light parcel system there is said to be no form of delivery that excels the motorcycle in speed and efficiency and nothing with operation costs so low. The commercial motorcycle is said to be gaining widespread favor, and therein lies its greatest future.

Foreign countries have contributed little or nothing to the development of the motorcycle. To be sure, efforts were made to produce two-wheel motor vehicles, but little success is recorded. Record of the earliest known effort was found in an English newspaper of 1876. This report, however, was very meager and lacking in any profusion of mechanical detail. Moreover, beyond the newspaper reports there is little verification that any steps were really taken at that time. The French contribute the only known features that are credited to foreign inventors. The DeDion motor was used in some of the racing motor tandems which appeared in this country in the late nineties. Other French racing bicycles were no doubt in existence, but there is no history which can ascribe any truly constructive innovations in motorcycle making to any foreign country. The motorcycle in its form of today was designed and built by America.

How is the Weather Man Able to Predict Tomorrow's Weather?

The Weather Bureau was founded in 1870 by the United States Government, its purpose being to make daily observations of the state of the weather in all parts of the country, and to calculate from the results a forecast for each section of the country, based on the information thus obtained, these predictions being published so that the people of each district may know in advance the kind of weather likely to occur.

While these forecasts are of great convenience to practically everyone, and of importance to the agriculturist, they are frequently of still more importance to ship masters, storm warnings being given that may keep them in port when storms are expected and thus save their ships from the danger of injury or shipwreck. This system has made great progress since its institution, and reports are now received daily from more than 3,500 land stations and about fifty foreign stations, while by means of wireless telegraphy, under normal conditions, some 2,000 ships send reports of the weather conditions at sea.

WEATHER BUREAU BOX KITE

The Government Weather Bureau uses large box kites carrying recording barometers, thermometers and other apparatus to ascertain weather conditions high in the air. This view shows a kite about to be sent up from an observatory.

Study of results has led to the belief that more than eighty per cent of winds and storms follow beaten paths, their movements being governed by physical conditions, a knowledge of which enables the Weather Bureau officials to estimate very closely their probable speed and direction and send warning of their coming in advance. Within two hours after the regular morning observation at eight o'clock, the forecasts are telegraphed to more than 2,300 principal distributing points, from which they are further sent out by mail, telegraph and telephone, being mailed daily to 135,000 addresses and received by nearly 4,000,000 telephone subscribers.

One of the most valuable services rendered is that of the warnings of cyclonic storms for the benefit of marine interests. These are displayed at nearly three hundred points on the ocean and lake coasts, including all important ports and harbors, warnings of coming storms being received from twelve to twenty-four hours in advance. The result has been the saving of vast amounts of maritime property, estimated at many millions of dollars yearly.

Agriculturists also derive great advantage from these warnings, especially those engaged in the production of fruits, vegetables and other market garden products. Warnings of frosts and of freezing weather have enabled the growers of such products to protect and save large quantities of valuable plants. It is said that on a single night in a small district in Florida, fruits and vegetables were thus saved to the amount of more than $100,000. In addition, live stock of great value has been saved by warnings a week in advance of the coming of a flood in the Mississippi; railroad companies take advantage of the forecast for the preservation, in their shipping business, of products likely to be injured by extremes of heat or cold, and in various other ways the forecasts are of commercial or other value.

One of the chief stations for observations is that at Mount Weather, in the Blue Ridge Mountains of Virginia. This is equipped with delicate instruments in considerable variety for the study of varying conditions of the upper air. Kites and captive balloons are sent up every favorable day, ascending to heights of two or three miles, and equipped with self-registering instruments to record the temperature and other conditions of the atmosphere. At other times, free balloons are liberated, carrying sets of automatic registering instruments. Some of these travel hundreds of miles, but nearly all are eventually found and returned.

How does a Siren Fog Horn Blow?

There are a great many different kinds of signals for the guidance of vessels during fogs, when lights or other visible signals cannot be perceived.

One of the most powerful signals is the siren fog horn, the sound of which is produced by means of a disk perforated by radial slits made to rotate in front of a fixed disk exactly similar, a long iron trumpet forming part of the apparatus. The disks may each contain say twelve slits, and the moving disk may revolve 2,800 times a minute; in each revolution there are of course twelve coincidences between the slits in the two disks; through the openings thus made steam or air at a high pressure is caused to pass, so that there are actually 33,600 puffs of steam or compressed air every minute. This causes a sound of very great power, which the trumpet collects and compresses, and the blast goes out as a sort of sound beam in the direction required. Under favorable circumstances this instrument can be heard from twenty to thirty miles out at sea.

Fog signals are also used on railways during foggy weather; they consist of cases filled with detonating powder, which are laid on the rails and exploded by the engine when it runs over them.

The Story in a Watch*

Clocks and watches are often called "timekeepers," but they do not keep time. Nothing can keep it. It is constantly flying along, and carrying us with it, and we cannot stop it. What we call "time keepers" are really time measures, and are made to tell us how rapidly time moves, so that we may regulate our movements and occupations to conform to its flight.

Of course, you understand that measurement of anything is the comparing of it with some established standard. So that if you want to measure the length of anything you use a rule or a yard stick, or some other scale which is graduated into fractions of the whole standard measure. Do you know that the United States government has in a secure, fireproof vault, in one of the government buildings in Washington, a metal bar which is the authorized standard "yard" of this nation? It is a very carefully made copy of the standard yard of Great Britain. I believe that each one of the United States has also a standard which must agree in length with the government, or national standard. The same thing is true concerning standards of capacity, and standards of weight. But no vault can contain the authorized standard of time. Yet there is such a standard. And it is as accessible to one country as to another, and it is a standard which does not change. But, because all other time measures are more or less imperfect, our government tries to compare its standard clock with the ultimate standard every day.

The first mention of time which we have is found in the Book of Genesis, where it is written "and the evening and the morning were the first day." That statement gives a "measure" which was sufficient for the purpose intended, but there is nothing very accurate in it. If it had said "the darkness and the light" were the first day, it would have been just as accurate. The people who lived in those far-off days had no special occasion to know or to care what time it was. We may suppose that they were hungry when they waked at sunrise, and if they had no food "left over" from the previous day's supply they would have to hustle and find some, and if possible secure a little surplus beyond that day's needs, and so they would work, or hunt, until the "evening" came and the sun disappeared. When a man was tired, and the sun was hot, he sat down under a tree for shelter and rest. As he sat under the tree and looked about him he could not fail to notice that upon the ground was a shadow of the tree under which he sat. And as he was tired and warm he lay down and fell asleep, and when he woke, he again saw the shadow, but in another place. He noticed that the same thing occurred every day. He saw also that in the morning the shadow was stretched out in one direction, and that in the evening it lay in exactly the opposite direction, and that every day it moved very nearly the same, so he put a mark on the ground about where the shadow first appeared, and another mark at the place where it disappeared. Then one day he stuck his staff in the ground about half-way between the places of the morning and the evening shadows, which served as a noon mark. As the staff cast a shadow as readily as did the tree, the man found that it was really a better index of time than was the tree shadow, for it was much smaller and more clearly defined, and so he put up a straight stick in the ground near the hut in which he lived, and as the ground was level and smooth he drove a lot of little stakes along the daily path of the shadow, and in that way divided the day into a number of small parts. That was a crude "sun dial." (The Bible tells of the sun dial in the thirty-eighth chapter of Isaiah.) But there was nothing very accurate in the sun dial. Several hundred years later

*Courtesy of the Waltham Watch Company, and "The American Boy."

Assembling Department in a Famous American Watch Factory

the days were divided into sections which were called "hours," such as the "sixth hour" (noon), the "ninth hour" (three o'clock), the "eleventh hour" (five o'clock), etc. There was, however, nothing very accurate in those expressions, which simply indicate that there were recognized divisions of time, but with no suggestions as to the means used to determine their limits or boundaries. It is recorded of Alfred the Great, who lived in the ninth century, A. D., that he was very methodical in his employment of time, and in order to insure a careful attention to his religious duties as well as his kingly duties, he divided the day into three parts, giving one part to religious duties, one to the affairs of his kingdom, and the remainder to bodily rest. To secure an equal division of the day he procured a definite quantity of wax which he had made into six candles, of twelve inches in length, and all of uniform weight, for he found that each inch in length of candle would burn for twenty minutes —one candle for each four hours. This was an approach toward accuracy and it was effective for night use as well as for the daytime.

Perhaps the earliest mechanical time measure was the clepsydra, or water clock. It is quite probable that, in its earliest form it consisted of a vessel containing water, which was allowed to escape through a small orifice. Suitable marks, or graduations, on the sides of the vessel served to indicate the lapse of time as the water gradually receded. This device was constructed in a variety of forms, some of which employed some simple mechanism also; but from their nature they could not give very accurate indications concerning the passage of time. The "hour glass" was another form of time indicator, which was capable of uniform, though extremely limited, action. It is said that its original use was to limit the length of sermons.

It is interesting to note that discoveries and inventions, which may seem slight in themselves, sometimes form the basis of, or contribute to, other important inventions. In the year 1584 a bright young Italian was sitting in the gallery of the cathedral, in the City of Pisa, and as the lofty doors of the building opened to admit the incoming worshipers, a strong draft of air caused the heavy chandelier, which was suspended from the lofty ceiling, to swing quite a distance from its position of rest. This unusual movement attracted the attention of the young man, and as he continued to watch its deliberate movements, he did more than watch. He thought—for he noticed that the time occupied by the movement of the chandelier from one extreme position to the opposite point, seemed to be exactly uniform. He wondered why. It is the careful observation of things, and the trying to learn why they are as they are, and why they act as they do, that enables studious people to discover the laws which govern their actions. This young man, Galileo, was a thinker, and while some of his conclusions and theories have since been found erroneous, his thinking has formed the basis of much of the scientific thought and theory of later years. Galileo's swinging chandelier was really a sort of a pendulum, and we have made mention of it because it has been found that no mechanical means for obtaining and maintaining a constant and accurate movement will equal the free movement of a vibrating pendulum. This fact has led to its adoption as a means of regulating the mechanism of clocks. For, when operated under the most favorable conditions, such a clock constitutes the most accurate "time measure" yet made.

Watches are made to measure time. If anything is to be measured there must be some standard with which to compare it, for we have seen that measuring is a process of comparing a thing with an appropriate or acknowledged and fixed standard. The only known standard for the measurement of time is the movement of the earth in relation to the stars. It has taken thousands of years for mankind to learn what is now known concerning time. It has also taken hundreds of years to secure the wonderful accuracy in the measuring of time which has now been attained. We have said that nothing has been devised which will equal the accuracy of a "pendu-

VIEW OF ESCAPEMENT MAKING DEPARTMENT

lum clock." A story was told of a professor of a theological seminary who was one day on his way to a jeweler's store, carrying in his arms the family clock, which was in need of repairs. He was accosted by one of his students with the question, "Look here, Professor, don't you think it would be much more convenient to carry a watch?" A pendulum clock must of necessity be stationary, but it is now needful that people should be able to have a timepiece whenever and wherever wanted. This need is supplied by the pocket watch.

If Galileo watched the swinging of the big chandelier long enough he found that the distance through which it swung was gradually diminishing, till, at last, it ceased to move; what stopped it? It was one of the great forces of nature, which we call gravitation, and the force which kept it in motion we call momentum. But gravitation overcame momentum.

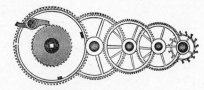

TIME TRAIN OF A WATCH

In order to maintain the constant vibration of a pendulum it is needful to impart to it a slight force, in a manner similar to that given by a boy who gives another boy a slight "push," to maintain his movement in a swing. A suspended pendulum being impossible of application to a pocket watch, a splendid substitute has been devised—in the form of the balance wheel of the watch, commonly called the "balance." The balance is, in its action and adaption, the equivalent of the vibrating, or oscillating, pendulum; and the balance spring (commonly called the hairspring), which accompanies it, is in its action equivalent to the force of gravity in its effect upon a pendulum. For the tendency and (if not neutralized by some other force) the effects of the

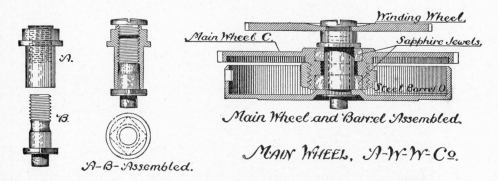

A.

B.

A-B-Assembled.

Main Wheel C.

Winding Wheel.

Sapphire Jewels.

Steel Barrel D.

Main Wheel and Barrel Assembled.

MAIN WHEEL, A-W-W-Co.

hairspring upon the watch balance, and of gravitation on the pendulum, are to hold each at a position of rest, and consequent inaction.

But we have in a pocket watch a "mainspring" to actuate the train of gear wheels which by their ultimate action give the delicate "push" to the balance wheel at distinct intervals, and so keep the balance in continued motion. In the same manner, the "weight" of a clock, acting through the force of gravity, carries the various wheels of the clock train, and gives the slight impulse to the swinging clock pendulum.

Both clocks and watches are "machines" for the measurement of time, and, therefore, it is absolutely imperative that their action must be constant, and, if accurate time is to be indicated, the action must be uniform.

The illustration shows the "time train" of an ordinary pocket watch. The various wheels are here shown in a straight line, so that their successive order

Interior of Astronomical Observatory, showing Transit Instrument. Used to Obtain Correct Local Time, by Observing the Passage of Stars Across the Meridian

may be seen, but for economy and convenience they are arranged in such way as is most convenient when constructing a pocket watch. The large wheel at the left is the "main wheel," called by watchmakers the "barrel." In it is coiled the mainspring—a strip of steel about twenty-three inches long, which is carefully tempered to insure elasticity and "pull." The outer end of the mainspring is attached to the rim of the barrel, and the inner end to the barrel arbor. Bear in mind the fact that the power which is sufficient to run the watch for thirty-six hours or more, is not in the watch itself. It is in yourself, and by the exertion of your thumb and finger, in the act of winding, you transfer that power to the spring, and thereby store the power in the barrel, to be given out at the rate which the governing mechanism of the watch will permit. The group of wheels here shown are known as the "time train," and the second wheel is called the "center," because that, in ordinarily constructed watches, is located in the center of the group, and upon its axis are put the "hour hand" and the "minute hand." On the circumference of the barrel are gear teeth, and those teeth engage corresponding teeth on the arbor of the center. These arbor teeth are in all cases called, not "wheels" but "pinions," and in watch trains the wheels always drive the pinions. Next to the center comes the third pinion and wheel, and then the fourth, which is the last wheel in the train which has regular gear teeth. Now let us look back a little and see that the wheel teeth of the barrel drive the center pinion, and the center wheel drives the third pinion and the third wheel drives the fourth pinion, etc. The speed of revolution of the successive wheels increases

BALANCE COCK AND PATENT MICROMETRIC REGULATOR; ALSO BALANCE WHEEL AND HAIR SPRING, SHOWING PATENT HAIR SPRING STUD

rapidly. The center wheel must revolve once in each hour, which is 6½ times faster than the barrel. The third wheel turns eight times faster than the center, and the fourth wheel turns 7½ times faster than the third, or 60 times faster than the center, so that the fourth pinion, which carries the "second hand," will revolve 60 times while the "center," which carries the minute hand, revolves once. If we should put all the wheels and pinions in place, and wind up the main spring, the wheels would begin to turn, each at its relative rate of speed, and we should find that, instead of running thirty-six hours, it would have run less than two minutes. What was needed was some device to serve as an accurate speed governor—and the attainment of this essential device is the one thing on which accurate time measuring depends. Without any mention of the various attempts to produce such a device, let us, as briefly as possible, describe the means used in most watches of American manufacture. While there are several distinct parts of this device, each having its individual function, they may be considered as a whole under the general term of "the escapement." Returning now to the fourth pinion, we see that it also carries a wheel, which engages another little pinion, called the escape pinion. This escape pinion also carries a wheel, but it is radically different in appearance, as well

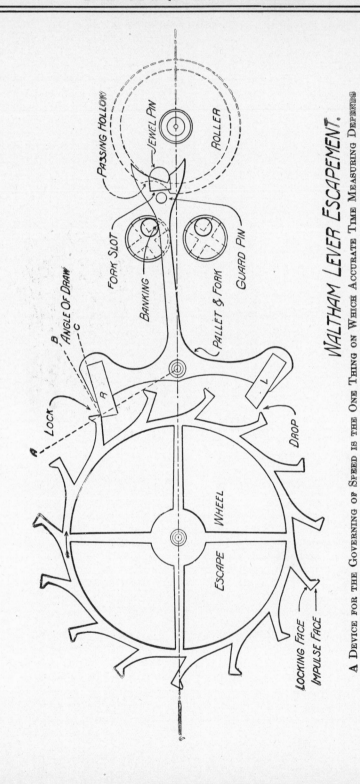

WALTHAM LEVER ESCAPEMENT.

A DEVICE FOR THE GOVERNING OF SPEED IS THE ONE THING ON WHICH ACCURATE TIME MEASURING DEPENDS

as in action, from any of the previously mentioned wheels. An examination of the "escape wheel" would show that it has a peculiarly shaped piece, which is called the "pallet," the extended arm of which is called the "fork." The fork encloses a sort of half-round stud or pin. This stud projects from the face and near the edge of a small steel disc. The stud is formed from some hard precious stone and is called the "jewel pin," or "roller pin," and the little steel disc which carries it is called the "roller." In the center or axial hole of the roller fits the "balance staff," which staff also carries the "balance wheel," and the balance spring, commonly called the "hair spring." The ends of the balance staff are made very small so as to form very delicate pivots which turn in jewel bearings. The balance wheel moves very rapidly, and, therefore, its movement must be as free as possible from retarding friction, so its bearing pivots are made very small.

Now that we have given the names of each of the different parts which compose the escapement, let us see how they perform their important work of governing

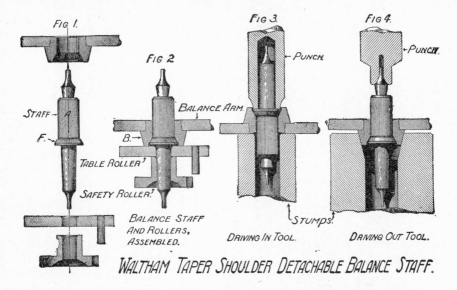

WALTHAM TAPER SHOULDER DETACHABLE BALANCE STAFF.

the speed of the little machine for measuring time. In the escape wheel, the left arm of the pallet rests on the inclined top of one of the wheel teeth. This is the position of rest. If we wind up the mainspring of the watch it will immediately cause the main wheel to turn, and, of course, that will turn the next wheel, and so on to the escape wheel. When that wheel turns to the right, as it must, it will force back the arm of the pallet which swings on its arbor. In swinging out in this way it must also swing in the other pallet arm, and that movement will bring it directly in front of another wheel tooth, so that the wheel can turn no further. It is locked and will remain so until something withdraws it. When the pallet was swung so as to cause this locking, the fork was also moved, and as it enclosed the roller pin, that too was moved and carried with it the roller and the balance wheel, and in so doing it deflected the hair spring from its condition of rest. And as the spring tried to get back to its place of rest it carried back the balance also. In going back, the balance acquired a little momentum, and so could not stop when it reached its former position, but went a little farther, and, of course, the roller and its pin also went along in company, the pin carrying the fork and the pallet swinging in the other direction, which unlocked the escape wheel tooth. Its inclined top gave the pallet a little "push" so that the first pallet was locked, forcing the fork and roller, and the balance and hair spring, to move in the opposite direction. And so the alternate actions proceed, and the balance wheel travels farther each time, until it reaches the greatest amount which the force of the mainspring can give. But before this extreme is reached, the momentum of the revolving balance carries the roller pin entirely out of the fork. As the fork is allowed to move only just far enough to allow the pin to pass out, it simply waits until the fork returns and enters its place, only to escape

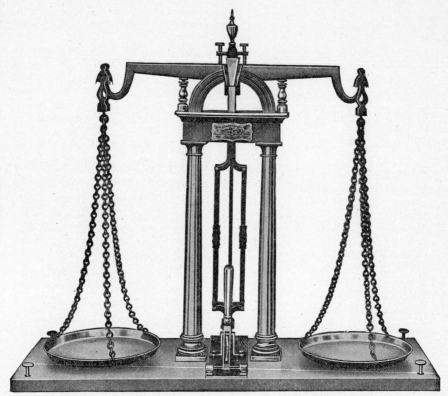

ACCURATE MEASUREMENTS ARE ESSENTIAL TO CORRECT TIME KEEPING

again on the other side. And so the motions continue to the number of 18,000 times per hour. If that number can be exactly maintained, the watch will measure time perfectly. But if it should fall short of that exact number only once each hour, it would result in a loss of 4.8 seconds each day, or 2.4 minutes in one month. A watch as bad as that would not be allowed on a railroad.

Isn't it wonderful that such a delicate piece of mechanism can be made to run so accurately? And the wonder is increased by the fact that the little machine is, to a great extent, continually moved about, and liable to extreme changes in position and in temperature. Watches of the highest grades are adjusted to five positions as well as to temperature. Some are adjusted to temperature and three positions, and still others to temperature only. The way in which a watch is made to automatically compensate for temperature changes is interesting. Varying degrees of heat and cold always affect a watch. It is a law of nature that all simple metals expand under the influence of heat and therefore contract when affected by cold. Alloys, or mixtures of different metals, act in a similar manner, but in varying degrees. Some combinations of metals possess the quality of relatively great expansibility. Another natural law is that the force required to move a body depends upon its size and weight. So it follows that with only a certain amount of available force a large body cannot be moved as rapidly as a small one. The force of 200 pounds of steam in a locomotive boiler might be sufficient to haul a train of six cars at a speed of thirty miles per hour, but if more cars be added it will result in a slower speed. The same principle applies to a watch as to a railway train. Therefore if the balance wheel becomes larger as it grows warmer, and the force

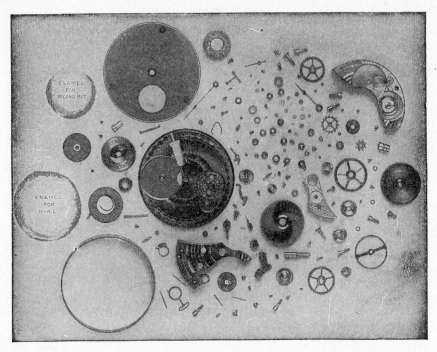

170 Parts Compose a 16 Size Watch Movement. (A Little More than ½ Actual Size)

which turns the wheel is not changed, the speed of movement must be reduced. One other natural law which affects the running of watches is this: Variations in temperature affect the elasticity of metals. Now the balance spring of a watch is made from steel, and is carefully tempered in order to obtain its highest elasticity. Increase in temperature therefore introduces three elements of disturbance, all of which act in the same direction of reducing the speed. First, it enlarges the balance wheel; second, it increases the length of the spring; third, it reduces the elasticity of the spring. To overcome these three disturbing factors a very ingenious form of balance has been devised.

A watch balance is made with a rim of brass encircling and firmly united to the rim of steel. In order to permit heat to have the desired effect upon this balance, the rim is completely severed at points near each of the arms of the wheel. If we apply heat to this balance the greater expansion of the brass portion of its rim would cause the free ends to curl inward.

In order to obtain exactly 18,000 vibrations of the balance in an hour, it will be seen that the weight of the wheel and the strength of the hair spring must be perfectly adapted each to the other. The shorter the spring is made the more rigid it becomes, and so the regulator is made a part of the watch, but its action must be very limited or its effect on the spring will introduce other serious disturbances. The practical method of securing the proper and ready adaptation of balances to springs is to place in the rims of the balance a number of small screws having relatively heavy heads. Suppose now that we have a balance fitted with screws of the number and weight to exactly adapt it to a spring, so that at a normal temperature of, say, 70 degrees, it would vibrate exactly 18,000 times per hour. When we place the watch in an oven the heat of which is 95 degrees, we might find that it had lost seven seconds. That would show that the wheel was too large when at 95 degrees, although just right at 70 degrees. Really, that is a very serious matter—it would lose at the rate of $2\frac{4}{5}$ minutes in a day. But after all it need not be so very serious, because if we change the location of one screw on each half of the balance so as to place it nearer the free end of the rim when the heat curls the rim inward, it will carry a larger proportion of the weight than if the screws had not been moved. It may require repeated trials to determine the required position of the rim screws, and both skill and good judgment are essential. It will be readily understood that numerous manipulations of this kind constitute no small items in the cost of producing high-grade watches.

Large quantities of the cheaper class of watches are now made by machinery in the United States, Switzerland, France, Germany and England. They are generally produced on the interchangeable system, that is, if any part of a watch has become unfit for service, it can be cheaply replaced by an exact duplicate, the labor of the watch repairer thus becoming easy and expeditious.

How Does the Gyro-Stabilizer Prevent Seasickness?

What the French call "mal de mer" and other people call "seasickness" threatens to be thrown into the limbo of the forgotten, if the gyro-stabilizer fulfils its mission on ocean steamers. A gyro-stabilizer is a huge spinning top of steel, made to prevent the rolling of a 20,000-ton liner. The first Sperry gyroscope was on the U. S. S. *Widgeon* in 1914. Since that date many installations have been made in war vessels and on yachts. The first of the passenger liners to be equipped with a gyro-stabilizer was the *Hawkeye State*, a United States Shipping Board vessel plying between Baltimore and Honolulu. The big stabilizer weighed 120 tons, but was so delicately balanced that it could swing into action in less than a second and a half. Within that period a roll of less than one degree in either direction sets the tremendous balancing force of the gigantic top in motion, and prevents a roll of more than two degrees, which is virtually imperceptible to passengers.

This stabilizer was designed by the engineers of the Westinghouse Electric and Manufacturing Company and the representatives of Elmer A. Sperry, American scientist and inventor of the gyro-stabilizer. The rotor, or gyroscope, is 13 feet in diameter and 44 inches thick. At full speed it revolves 800 times a minute. That means that the outer edge of the big solid wheel of steel is traveling at the rate of 6 miles a minute and exerting extraordinary balancing force. A smaller gyroscope controls the larger one. The smaller gyroscope weighs less than 150 pounds but is one of the fastest things in the world, making 5000 revolutions a minute. This great gyro-stabilizer was installed in the *Hawkeye State* in 1922.

BALANCING A BIG LINER AT SEA

To prevent the rolling of a ship and banish the fear of seasickness, the principle of the gyroscope has been successfully applied. This picture shows the huge gyro-stabilizer installed on the U. S. S. *Hawkeye State*. Although weighing 120 tons, the huge spinning top is so delicately balanced that a roll of one degree will bring into effect the great stabilizing power of the machine and prevent a roll of two degrees, which is virtually imperceptible to passengers

Seven minutes before noon

A 1100-pound bomb explodes alongside

Seven minutes after noon

THE EFFECT OF A 1100-POUND BOMB ON A BATTLESHIP

The Story in a Rifle*

How It Began.

A naked savage found himself in the greatest danger. A wild beast, hungry and fierce, was about to attack him. Escape was impossible. Retreat was cut off. He must fight for his life—but how?

Should he bite, scratch or kick? Should he strike with his fist? These were the natural defenses of his body, but what were they against the teeth, the claws and the tremendous muscles of his enemy? Should he wrench a dead branch from a tree and use it for a club? That would bring him within striking distance to be torn to p ece before he could deal a second blow.

There was but a moment in which to act. Swiftly he seized a jagged fragment of rock from the ground and hurled it with all his force at the blazing eyes before him; then another, and another, until the beast, dazed and bleeding from the unexpected blows, fell back and gave him a chance to escape. He knew that he had saved his life, but there was something else which his dull brain failed to realize.

He had invented arms and ammunition!

In other words, he had needed to strike a harder blow than the blow of his fist, at a greater distance than the length of his arm, and his brain showed him how to do it. After all, what is a modern rifle but a device which man has made with his brain permitting him to strike an enormously hard blow at a wonderful distance? Firearms are really but a more perfect form of stone-throwing, and this early Cave Man took the first step that has led down the ages to the present-day arms and ammunition.

This strange story of a development that has been taking place slowly through thousands and thousands of years, so that today you are able to take a swift shot at distant game instead of merely throwing stones.

The Earliest Hunters.

The Cave Man and his descendants learned the valuable lesson of stone-throwing, and it made hunters of them, not big-game hunters—that was far too risky; but once in a while a lucky throw might bring down a bird or a rabbit for food. And so it went on for centuries, perhaps. Early mankind was rather slow of thought.

At last, however, there appeared a great inventor—the Edison of his day.

He took the second step.

A Nameless Edison.

We do not know his name. Possibly he did not even have a name, but in some way he hit upon a scheme for throwing stones farther, harder and straighter than any of his ancestors.

The men and women in the Cave Colony suddenly found that one bright-eyed young fellow, with a little straighter forehead than the others, was beating them all at hunting. During weeks he had been going away mysteriously, for hours each day. Now, whenever he left the camp he was sure to bring home game, while the other men would straggle back for the most part empty-handed.

Was it witchcraft? They decided to investigate.

* Illustrations by courtesy of the Remington Arms-Union Metallic Cartridge Company, unless otherwise indicated

THE FIRST MISSILE
The Cave Man of prehistoric times unconsciously invented arms and ammunition.

What They Saw.

Accordingly, one morning several of them followed at a careful distance as he sought the shore of a stream where water-fowl might be found. Parting the leaves, they saw him pick up a pebble from the bank and then, to their surprise, take off his girdle of skin and place the stone in its center, holding both ends with his right hand.

Stranger still, he whirled the girdle twice around his head, then released one end so that the leather strip flew out and the stone shot straight at a bird in the water.

The mystery was solved. They had seen the first slingman in action.

The Use of Slings.

The new plan worked with great success, and a little practice made expert marksmen. We know that most of the early races used it for hunting and in war. We find it shown in pictures made many thousands of years ago in ancient Egypt and Assyria. We find it in the Roman army where the slingman was called a "funditor."

We find it in the Bible where it is written of the tribe of Benjamin: "Among all these people there were seven hundred chosen men left-handed; *every one could sling a stone at an hair breadth and not miss.*" Surely, too, you remember the story of David and Goliath when the young shepherd "prevailed over the Philistine *with a sling and with a stone.*"

Today shepherds tending their flocks upon these same hills of Syria may be seen practicing with slings like those of David. Yes, and slings were used in European armies until nearly a hundred years after America was discovered.

Something Better.

Yet they had their drawbacks. A stone slung might kill a bird or even a man, but it was not very effective against big game.

What was wanted was a missile to pierce a thick hide.

Man had begun to make spears for use in a pinch, but would you like to tackle a husky bear or a well-horned stag with only a spear for a weapon?

No more did our undressed ancestors. The invention of the greatly desired arm probably came about in a most curious way.

Long ages ago man had learned to make fire by patiently rubbing two sticks together, or by twirling a round one between his hands with its point resting upon a flat piece of wood.

In this way it could be made to smoke, and finally set fire to a tuft of dried moss, from which he might get a flame for cooking. This was such hard work that he bethought him to twist a string of sinew about the upright spindle and cause it to twirl by pulling alternately at the two string ends, as some savage races still do. From this it was a simple step to fasten the ends of the two strings to a bent piece of wood, another great advantage, since now but one hand was needed to twirl the spindle, and the other could hold it in place. This was the "bow-drill" which also is used to this day.

A Fortunate Accident.

But bent wood is apt to be springy. Suppose that while one were bearing on pretty hard with a well-tightened string, in order to bring fire quickly, the point of the spindle should slip from its block. Naturally, it would fly away with some force if the position were just right.

This must have happened many times, and each time *but once* the fire-maker may have muttered something under his breath, gone after his spindle, and then

THE SLING MAN IN ACTION

Practice developed some wonderful marksmen among the users of this primitive weapon.

settled down stupidly to his work.   He had had a golden chance to make a great discovery, but didn't realize it.

But, so it has been suggested, there was one man who stopped short when he lost his spindle, for a red-hot idea shot suddenly through his brain.

He forgot all about his fire-blocks while he sat stock still and thought.

Once or twice he chuckled to himself softly.   Thereupon he arose and began to experiment.

He chose a longer, springier piece of wood, bent it into a bow, and strung it with a longer thong.   He placed the end of a straight stick against the thong, drew it strongly back and released it.

The shaft whizzed away with force enough to delight him, and, lo, there was the first bow-and-arrow!

What Came of It.

After that it was merely a matter of improvement.   The arrow-end was apt to slip from the string until some one thought to notch it.   Its head struck with such

FEATHERING THE ARROW

WINDING THE SHAFT

force that the early hunter decided to give it a sharp point, shaped from a flake of flint, in order that it might drive deep into the body of a deer or bear.

But, most of all, it must fly true and straight to its mark. Who of all these simple people first learned to feather its shaft?   Was it some one who had watched the swift, sure-footed spring of a bushy-tailed squirrel from branch to branch?   Possibly, for the principle is the same.   At all events with its feathers and its piercing point the arrow became the most deadly of all missiles, and continued to be until long after the invention of firearms.

A Great Variety.

It is interesting to see how many different forms of bow were used.   The English had a six-foot "long bow" made of yew or ash, in a single straight piece, that shot arrows the length of a man's arm.   The Indians had bows only forty inches on the average, since a short bow was easier to handle in thick forests.   They used various kinds of wood, horn or even bone, such as the ribs of large animals.   These they generally backed with sinew.

Sometimes they cut spiral strips from the curving horns of a mountain sheep, and steamed them straight.   Then they glued these strips together into a wonderfully

THE "LONG BOW" IN SHERWOOD FOREST
One of Robin Hood's famous band encounters a savage tusker at close range.

tough and springy bow. Once in a while they even took the whole horns of some young sheep, that had not curved too much, and used the pair just as they grew. In this case each horn made one-half of the bow, and the piece of skull between was shaped down into a handle. This gave the shape of a "Cupid's Bow," but it could shoot to kill.

As to Arrows.

The arrows were quite as important, and their making became a great industry with every race. This was because so many must be carried for each hunt or battle.

Who is not familiar with the chipped flint arrow-heads that the farmer so often turns up with his plow as a relic of the period when Americans were red-skinned instead of white? These arrow-heads have generally a shoulder where the arrow was set into the shaft, there to be bound tightly with sinew or fiber. Many of them are also barbed to hold the flesh.

A Shooting Machine.

But the age of machinery was coming on. Once in a while there were glimpses of more powerful and complicated devices to be seen among these simple arms.

A new weapon now came about through warfare. Man has been a savage fighting animal through pretty much all his history, but while he tried to kill the other fellow, he objected to being killed himself.

Therefore he took to wearing armor. During the Middle Ages he piled on more and more, until at last one of the knights could hardly walk, and it took a strong horse to carry him. When such a one fell, he went over with a crash like a tin-peddler's wagon, and had to be picked up again by some of his men. Such armor would turn most of the arrows. Hence invention got at work again and produced the cross-bow and its bolt. We have already learned how the tough skin of animals brought about the bow; now we see that man's artificial iron skin caused the invention of the cross-bow.

What It Was.

What was the cross-bow? It was the first real hand-shooting machine. It was another big step toward the day of the rifle. The idea was simple enough. Wooden bows had already been made as strong as the strongest man could pull, and they wished for still stronger ones—steel ones. How could they pull them? At first they mounted them upon a wooden frame and rested one end on the shoulder for a brace. Then they took to pressing the other end against the ground, and using both hands. Next, it was a bright idea to put a stirrup on this end, in order to hold it with the foot.

Still they were not satisfied. "Stronger, stronger!" they clamored; "give us bows which will kill the enemy farther away than he can shoot at us! If we cannot set such bows with both arms let us try our backs!" So they fastened "belt-claws" to their stout girdles and tugged the bow strings into place with their back and leg muscles.

"Stronger, stronger again, for now the enemy has learned to use belt-claws and he can shoot as far as we. Let us try mechanics!"

So they attached levers, pulleys, ratchets and windlasses, until at last they reached the size of the great siege cross-bows, weighing eighteen pounds. These sometimes needed a force of twelve hundred pounds to draw back the string to its catch, but how they could shoot!

And Now for Chemistry.

Human muscle seemed to have reached its limit, mechanics seemed to have reached its limit, but still the world clamored, "Stronger, stronger! How shall we

This compact arm with its small bolt and great power was popular with many sportsmen.

kill our enemy farther away than he can kill us?" For answer, man unlocked one of the secrets of Nature and took out a terrible force. It was a force of chemistry.

Who first discovered the power of gunpowder? Probably the Chinese, although all authorities do not agree. Strange, is it not, that a race still using cross-bows in its army should have known of explosives long before the Christian Era, and perhaps as far back as the time of Moses? Here is a passage from their ancient Gentoo Code of Laws: "The magistrate shall not make war with any deceitful machine, or with poisoned weapons, or with cannons or guns, or any kind of fire-arms." But China might as well have been Mars before the age of travel. Our civilization had to work out the problem for itself.

Playing with Fire.

It all began through playing with fire. It was desired to throw fire on an enemy's buildings or his ships, and so destroy them. Burning torches were thrown by machines, made of cords and springs, over a city wall, and it became a great study to find the best burning compound with which to cover these torches. One was needed which would blaze with a great flame and was hard to put out.

Hence the early chemists made all possible mixtures of pitch, resin, naphtha, sulphur, saltpeter, etc.; "Greek fire" was one of the most famous.

What Two Monks Discovered.

Many of these were made in the monasteries. The monks were pretty much the only people in those days with time for study, and two of these shaven-headed scientists now had a chance to enter history. Roger Bacon was the first. One night he was working his diabolical mixture in the stone-walled laboratory, and watched, by the flickering lights, the progress of a certain interesting combination for which he had used pure instead of impure saltpeter.

Suddenly there was an explosion, shattering the chemical apparatus and probably alarming the whole building. "Good gracious!" we can imagine some of the startled brothers saying, "whatever is he up to now! Does he want to kill us all?" That explosion proved the new combination was not fitted for use as a thrown fire; it also showed the existence of terrible forces far beyond the power of all bow-springs, even those made of steel.

Roger Bacon thus discovered what was practically gunpowder, as far back as the thirteenth century, and left writings in which he recorded mixing 11.2 parts of the saltpeter, 29.4 of charcoal, and 29 of sulphur. This was the formula developed as the result of his investigations.

Berthold Schwartz, a monk of Freiburg, studied Bacon's works and carried on dangerous experiments of his own, so that he is ranked with Bacon for the honor. He was also the first one to rouse the interest of Europe in the great discovery.

And then began the first crude, clumsy efforts at gunmaking. Firearms were born.

The Coming of the Matchlock.

Hand bombards and culverins were among the early types. Some of these were so heavy that a forked support had to be driven into the ground, and two men were needed, one to hold and aim, the other to prime and fire. How does that strike you for a duck-shooting proposition? Of course such a clumsy arrangement could only be used in war.

Improvements kept coming, however. Guns were lightened and bettered in shape. Somebody thought of putting a flash pan for the powder, by the side of the touch-hole, and now it was decided to fasten the slow-match, in a movable cock, upon the barrel and ignite it with a trigger. These matches were fuses of some

AN UNEXPECTED MEETING
The "Kentucky Rifle" with its flint-lock was accurate, but had to be muzzle-charged.

Board of Education

Montclair, New Jersey

This Certificate is awarded to

Warren Schofield

for having attained a score of

100% Music Memory

Teacher or Supervisor of Music _Doris C. Mooney_

Director of Music _Arthur E. Ward_

Superintendent of Schools _Frank L. Pickell_

June, 1930

slow-burning fiber, like tow, which would keep a spark for a considerable time. Formerly they had to be carried separately, but the new arrangement was a great convenience and made the matchlock. The cock, being curved like a snake, was called the "serpentine."

The Gun of Our Ancestors.

Everybody knows what the flint-lock was like. You simply fastened a flake of flint in the cock and snapped it against a steel plate. This struck off sparks which fell into the flash-pan and fired the charge.

It was so practical that it became the form of gun for all uses; thus gunmaking began to be a big industry. Invented early in the seventeenth century, it was used by the hunters and soldiers of the next two hundred years. Old people remember when flint-locks were plentiful everywhere. In fact, they are still being manufactured and are sold in some parts of Africa and the Orient. One factory in Birmingham, England, is said to produce about twelve hundred weekly, and Belgium shares in their manufacture. Some of the Arabs use them to this day in the form of strange-looking guns with long, slender muzzles and very light, curved stocks.

Caps and Breech-Loaders.

Primers were tried in different forms called "detonators," but the familiar little

THE FIRST REMINGTON RIFLE

copper cap was the most popular. No need to describe them. Millions are still made to be used on old-fashioned nipple guns, even in this day of fixed ammunition. Then came another great development, the breech-loader.

From Henry VIII to Cartridges.

Breech-loaders were hardly new. King Henry VIII of England, he of the many wives, had a match-lock arquebus of this type dated 1537. Henry IV of France even invented one for his army, and others worked a little on the idea from time to time. But it was not until fixed ammunition came into use that the breech-loader really came to stay—and that was only the other day. You remember that the Civil War began with muzzle-loaders and ended with breech-loaders.

Houiller, the French gunsmith, hit on the great idea of the cartridge. If you were going to use powder, ball and percussion primer, to get your game, why not put them all into a neat, handy, gas-tight case? Simple enough, when you come to think of it, like most great ideas. But it required good brain-stuff to do that thinking.

A Refusal and What Came of It.

Two men, a smith and his son, both named Eliphalet Remington, in 1816, were working busily one day at their forge in beautiful Ilion Gorge, when, so tradition says, the son asked his father for money to buy a rifle, and met with a refusal.

The boy set his wits to work. Looking around the forge, he picked up enough scrap iron to make a gun barrel, and with this set to work to make a rifle for himself. At that time gun barrels were made, not by drilling the bore out of a solid rod of metal, but by shaping a thick, oblong sheet of metal around a rod the size of the bore, and lapwelding the edges. When the rod was withdrawn, there was your barrel.

It took him several weeks to work out this job and get it right, but he succeeded. He had no tools to cut the rifling. There was a gunsmith in Utica, and he walked there, fifteen miles over the hills, to have his barrel finished. The gunsmith was so impressed by the boy and his accomplishment that, after rifling the barrel, he fitted it with a lock. Then when Remington fitted on a wooden stock his weapon was ready.

This was the first Remington rifle, and it proved a surprisingly good one.

Neighbors tried it, and wanted guns like it. Remington made them. The first rifle—or one exactly like the first one, at least—that Remington made is still in Ilion, the property of Walter Green. Before long the demand was so brisk that Remington would take as many barrels as he could carry over to the Utica gunsmith to be rifled, bringing back a load that had been left there on a previous trip, a journey of thirty miles on foot.

When a new business grows at that rate, of course, it soon needs power. So, later, in 1816, the two Remingtons went "up the creek," building a shop three miles from home, at Ilion Gulph, which was part of the father's farm. That was the actual beginning of the plant and the industry of which the centennial was celebrated in 1916. During its early years this shop made anything in its line that could be sold in the neighborhood—rifles, shotguns, crowbars, pickaxes, farm tools. The power was taken from a water wheel in Steele's Creek, and the first grindstones for smoothing down the welded edges in gun barrels were cut from a red sandstone ledge up the gorge.

Guns sold better than all other products. Orders came from greater distances. By and by shipments were made on the new Erie Canal. For a while, as packages were small, they were taken to the canal bridge, a board lifted from the floor, and the package dropped onto a boat as it passed under. There was no bill of lading. Remington took down the name of the boat and notified his customer by mail, so the latter would know which craft was bringing his guns.

YOUNG REMINGTON AT
WORK ON RIFLE

When the trade had extended into all the surrounding counties, however, the new business needed another prime essential of industry—transportation facilities. Shipments were growing larger, and materials like grindstones, bought outside, had to be brought from the canal to Ilion Gulph. In 1828, therefore, the elder Remington bought a large farm in Ilion proper, and there, on the canal, the present plant was started. This was also the beginning of Ilion, for at that period the place was nothing more than a country corner. In 1828 the elder Remington met his death through accident, and the business was carried on by his son, who brought water for several power wheels from Steele's Creek, built a house to live in, and installed in his wooden shop quite a collection of machinery for gunmaking—the list names a big tilt hammer, several trip hammers, boring and rifling machines, grindstones, and so on.

The Beginning of Precision in Mechanics.

Not so many years before that, in England, James Watt was complaining about the difficulty of boring a six-inch cylinder for his steam engine with sufficient accuracy to make it a commercial success. No matter how he packed the piston with cork, oiled rags and old hats, the irregularities in the cylinder let the steam escape, and it was believed that neither the tools nor the workmen existed for making a steam engine with sufficient precision. When a young manufacturer named Wilkinson invented a guide for the boring tool, and machined cylinders of fifty inches diameter so accurately that, as Watt testified, they did not err the thickness of an old shilling in any part, it seemed as though the last refinement in machinery had been achieved. That was not very accurate by present-day standards of the thousandth part of an inch, for a shilling is about one-sixteenth of an inch in thickness.

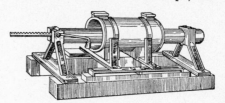

OLD BORING TOOL

Remington was right in the thick of development with a gunmaking plant, of course, for as his business grew he had to invent and adapt machines to increase output. The lap-welded barrel was standard until 1850, and he got together a battery of trip hammers for forging and welding his barrels. Finer dimensions became a factor in his business when the output grew large enough to warrant carrying a stock of spare parts for his customers, and so he improved those parts in ways that gave at least the beginnings of interchangeability.

POLE LATHE OF 1800

Materials were very crude. There was no buying of foundry iron by analysis, no high carbon steels, no fancy tool steels—nor any "efficiency experts" with their stop watches and scientific speed-and-feed tables. Iron was secured by sending teams around the neighborhood to pick up scrap, and when the scrap iron was all cleaned up, fresh metal was brought from ore beds in Oneida County. Coal was scarce, and charcoal made the chief fuel, burnt in the hills round about Ilion.

And the world was fairly swarming with inventors!

That was long before invention became a research department full of engineers. The individual inventor, with a queer-shaped factory process, carried on by a head and a rough model in his carpet-bag, had a chance to influence industry. Few of the useful contrivances had been invented yet, and almost any one of these chaps might be a genius. So, from the very first, Remington was interested in inventors. He was an inventor himself! His pioneer spirit was so strong that Ilion became a place of pilgrimage for men with ideas. Inventors came from everywhere, and Remington listened to them all. Some brought models, others drawings, still others a bare idea, and a few, of course, had just a plain "bug."

The First Government Contract.

The first government contract came in 1845. War with Mexico loomed up on the horizon. William Jencks had invented a carbine, and Uncle Sam wanted several thousand guns made in a hurry under the patent. A contract had been let to Ames & Co., of Springfield, Mass., and they had made special machinery for the job. Remington took over the contract and the machinery, added to his power, secured by putting in another water race, erected the building now known as the "Old Armory," and made the carbines.

In 1850 the art of gunmaking began to improve radically. The old lap-welded barrel gave way to the barrel drilled from solid steel. This was accomplished for the first time in America at the Remington plant, in making Harper's Ferry muskets. Then followed the drilling of small-bore barrels from solid steel, the drilling of doubled-barrel shotguns from one piece of steel, the drilling of fluid steel and nickel steel barrels, all done for the first time in this country at the Ilion shops. Three-

SHIPPING REMINGTONS IN THE EARLY DAYS

barrel guns were also made from one piece of steel, two bores for shot and the third rifled for a bullet. A customer wanted some special barrels with nine bores in a single piece of steel. These were made at Ilion, and the Remington plant soon became noted for its ability to bore almost anything in the shape of a gun, from the tiniest squirrel calibers up to boat guns weighing sixty pounds or more, which were really small caliber cannon.

Between the time when Remington made his first rifle at Ilion Gulph and the outbreak of the Civil War, most of the basic things in machine tools had been adapted to general production—the slide-rest lathe, planer, shaper, drill press, steam hammer, taps and dies, the vernier caliper that enabled a mechanic at the bench to measure to one-thousandth of an inch, and so on.

When Fort Sumter was fired upon, Uncle Sam turned to the Remington plant, among others, for help out of his dilemma of "unpreparedness." The first contract was given for 5,000 Harper's Ferry rifles, and it took two years to complete it. Five

MASTER OF THE SITUATION

The modern sportsman with his automatic rifle is prepared for all emergencies.

thousand Harper's Ferry muskets came in to be changed so that bayonet or sabre could be attached, and this particular job was finished in two weeks, every man and boy in Ilion working at it.   There was a big contract for army revolvers, and that had to be taken care of by starting a separate plant in Utica, which ran until the end of the war, when its machinery and tools were moved to Ilion.   Steam power was now installed, and the plant, increased by new buildings and machinery, ran day and night.

In 1863, the Remington breech-loading rifle was perfected, and proved to be so great an improvement over previous inventions in military arms that an order for 10,000 of them was obtained from our government.   The Ilion plant being taxed

Illustrations by courtesy of the Winchester Repeating Arms Co.

to its utmost capacity, the contract was transferred to the Savage Arms Company, of Middletown, Conn., which completed the job in 1864.

The tools and fixtures used in making Remington breech-loading rifles for the United States were brought back from Connecticut in 1866, and an inventive genius named John Rider was set to work, with a staff of the best mechanics obtainable, to develop this gun still further.   He devised the famous system of a dropping breech block, backed up by the hammer.

Uncle Sam had a great number of muzzle-loading Springfield rifles left from the Civil War.   By the Berdan system, these were turned into breech-loaders at the Ilion plant, the breech being cut out of the barrel and a breech-block inserted, swinging upward and forward.   Spain had 10,000 muskets to modernize by the same system, and the breech-block attachments were made at Ilion.

The Berdan system, with a slight alteration, was the foundation of the Allen gun, made by the United States government for the army until superseded by the Krag-Jorgensen.

The repeating rifle now seemed an interesting possibility and large sums were spent in developing a weapon of this type.   It did not prove to have merit, however.

Then James P. Lee designed the first military rifle with the bolt type of cartridge chamber, the parent of the military rifle of today.   The model was made at Ilion, but another type of bolt gun, the Keene, seemed to offer still greater possibilities at the moment, and the plant was being prepared to manufacture this.   The Lee gun was taken up at Bridgeport, but not made successfully, and finally, as the Keene

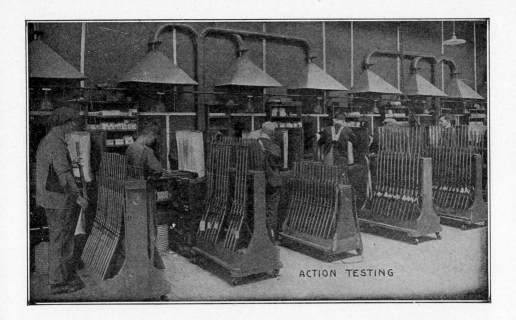

ACTION TESTING

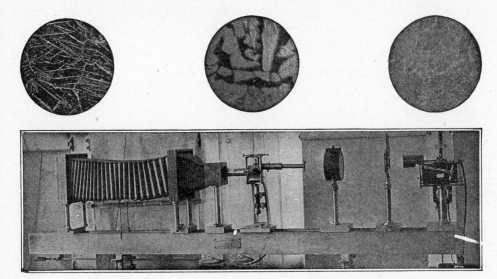

EXTREME CARE IN TESTING IS NECESSARY TO ACCURACY OF AIM IN THE FINISHED PRODUCT

Illustrations by courtesy of the Winchester Repeating Arms Co.

gun had not met expectations, falling short of government tests, the Lee type was brought back to Ilion, tools worked out and manufacture undertaken in quantities. It afterwards became the basis for the famous British army rifle, the Lee-Metford.

At this period the plant made many other interesting guns. The Whitmore double-barrel breech-loading shotgun was designed, and later developed into the Remington breech-loading shotgun. Eliott hammerless breech-loading pistols with one, two, four and five barrels, discharged by a revolving firing pin, were made in large quantities, as well as a single-barrel Eliott magazine pistol. The Eliott magazine pump rifle was perfected in Ilion, but afterwards made in New England. Vernier and wind gauge sights, attachable to any rifle, were made, and novelties like the

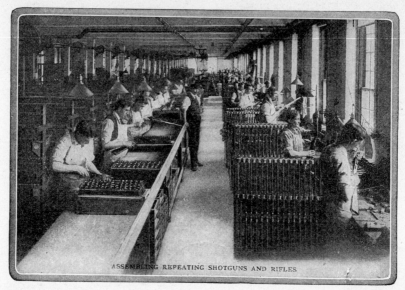

ASSEMBLING REPEATING SHOTGUNS AND RIFLES

"gun cane," which had the appearance of a walking-stick, but was a perfect firearm, carried as a protection against robbery.

Making Barrels.

One of the most important features is, of course, the making of barrels. The machines for drilling and boring are the best that money can buy, and the operatives the most skilful to be found anywhere. Care at this stage reduces the necessity for straightening later. Every point is given the minutest attention. In drilling 22-calibers, for example, the length of the hole must be from 100 to 125 times the diameter of the drill.

Improvements have made it possible to drill harder steel than formerly. This reduces the weight of the gun, and is important to the man who carries it.

Taking off 2/1000 of an Inch.

The boring is an especially delicate task. In choke-boring your shotgun, for example, the final reamer took off only 2/1000 of an inch. Think of such a gossamer thread of metal! But it insures accuracy. No pains can be too great for that.

This exquisite painstaking will be seen still more in the barrel-inspection department, to which we will go now. In passing, we must not forget the grinding shop, where is, perhaps, the finest battery of grinding machines in the United States; a-

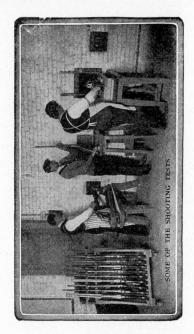

SOME OF THE SHOOTING TESTS

WEIGHING BULLETS

SHOOTING ROOM OF BALLISTIC DEPARTMENT*

CHRONOGRAPH FOR MEASURING VELOCITIES

*The bullet breaks a metal tape at the moment of leaving the muzzle.   This time and the time of striking target are electrically recorded on the Chronograph.

the polishers running at the dizzy speed of 1,500 to 1,700 revolutions per minute and making the inside of the barrel shine like glass. This high polish is important, for it resists rust and prevents leading.

Courtesy of the Winchester Repeating Arms Co.

That is the atmosphere of the whole place. Every action has its reason. There is not an unnecessary motion made by any one, and there is not one necessary thing omitted, whatever the cost or trouble.

The Making of Ammunition Today.

It is no easy matter to secure a pass to the Bridgeport plant. Its great advantage over other concerns lies, to a large degree, in the exclusive machinery that has been developed at so much pains and expense and the secrets of which are so carefully guarded. In our case, however, there will be nothing to hinder us from getting a few general impressions, provided we do not go into mechanical details too closely.

The very size of the great manufactory is impressive—sixteen acres of floor space, crowded with machinery and resounding with activity. In building after building, floor above floor, the sight is similar: the long rows of busy machines, the whirling network of shafts and belts above, the intent operatives, and the steady clicking of innumerable parts blended into a softened widespread sound. It seems

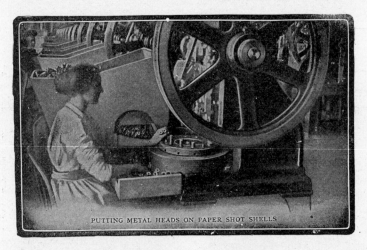

PUTTING METAL HEADS ON PAPER SHOT SHELLS

absolutely endless; it is a matter of hours to go through the plant. Stop at one of the machines and see the speed and accuracy with which it turns out its product; then calculate the entire number of machines and you will begin to gain a little idea as to what the total output of this vast institution must be.

More than once you will find yourself wondering whether there can be guns enough in the world, or fingers enough to press their triggers, to use such a tremendous production of ammunition. But there are, and the demand is steadily increasing. This old world is a pretty big place after all.

EXAMINING PAPER SHELLS

INSPECTING METALLIC SHELLS

ASSEMBLING AUTO SHOTGUNS

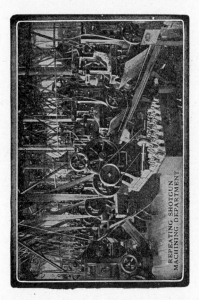

REPEATING SHOTGUN MACHINING DEPARTMENT

Handling Deadly Explosives.

Operatives, girls in many cases, handle the most terrible compounds. We stop, for example, where they are making primers to go in the head of your loaded shell, in order that it may not miss fire when the bunch of quail whirrs suddenly into the air from the sheltering grasses. That grayish, pasty mass is wet fulminate of mercury. Suppose it should dry a trifle too rapidly. It would be the last thing you ever did suppose, for there is force enough in that double handful to blow its surroundings into fragments. You edge away a little, and no wonder, but the girl who handles it shows no fear as she deftly but carefully presses it into molds which separate it into the proper sizes for primers. She knows that in its present moist condition it cannot explode.

Extreme Precautions.

Or, perhaps, we may be watching one of the many loading machines. There is a certain suggestiveness in the way the machines are separated by partitions. The man in charge takes a small carrier of powder from a case in the outside wall and shuts the door, then carefully empties it into the reservoir of his machine, and watches alertly while it packs the proper portions into the waiting shells. He looks like a careful man, and needs to be. You do not stand too close.

The empty carrier then passes through a little door at the side of the building, and drops into the yawning mouth of an automatic tube. In the twinkling of an eye it appears in front of the operator in one of the distributing stations, where it is refilled and returned to its proper loading machine, in order to keep the machine going at a perfectly uniform rate; while at the same time it allows but a minimum amount of powder to remain in the building at any moment. Each machine has but just sufficient powder in its hopper to run until a new supply can reach it. Greater precaution than this cannot be imagined, illustrating as it does, that no effort has been spared to protect the lives of the operators.

How does an Artesian Well Keep Up Its Supply of Water?

Artesian wells are named after the French Province of Artais, where they appear to have been first used on an extensive scale.

They are perpendicular borings into the ground through which water rises to the surface of the soil, producing a constant flow or stream. As a location is chosen where the source of supply is higher than the mouth of the boring, the water rises to the opening at the top. They are generally sunk in valley plains and districts where the formation of the ground is such that that below the surface is bent

ARTESIAN WELL (D) IN THE LONDON BASIN

into basin-shaped curves. The rain falling on the outcrops of these saturates the whole porous bed, so that when the bore reaches it the water by hydraulic pressure rushes up towards the level of the highest portion of the strata.

The supply is sometimes so abundant as to be used extensively as a moving power, and in arid regions for fertilizing the ground, to which purpose artesian springs have been applied from a very remote period. Thus many artesian wells have been sunk in the Algerian Sahara which have proved an immense boon to the district. The same has been done in the arid region of the United States. The water of most of these is potable, but a few are a little saline, though not to such an extent as to influence vegetation.

The hollows in which London and Paris lie are both perforated in many places by borings of this nature. At London they were first sunk only to the sand, but more recently into the chalk. One of the most celebrated artesian wells is that of Grenelle near Paris, 1,798 feet deep, completed in 1841, after eight years' work. One at Rochefort, France, is 2,765 feet deep; at Columbus, Ohio, 2,775; at Pesth, Hungary, 3,182, and at St. Louis, Mo., 3,843½. Artesian borings have been made in West Queensland 4,000 feet deep. At Schladebach, in Prussia, there is one nearly a mile deep.

As the temperature of water from great depths is invariably higher than that at the surface, artesian wells have been made to supply warm water for heating manufactories, greenhouses, hospitals, fishponds, etc. The petroleum wells of America are of the same technical description. These wells are now made with larger diameters than formerly, and altogether their construction has been rendered much more easy in modern times.

Boring in the earth or rock for mining, geologic or engineering purposes is effected by means of augers, drills or jumpers, sometimes wrought by hand, but now usually by machinery, driven by steam or frequently by compressed air.

In ordinary mining practice a bore-hole is usually commenced by digging a small pit about six feet deep, over which is set up a shear-legs with pulley, etc. The boring rods are from ten to twenty feet in length, capable of being jointed together by box and screw, and having a chisel inserted at the lower end. A lever is employed to raise the bore-rods, to which a slight twisting motion is given at each stroke, when the rock at the bottom of the hole is broken by the repeated percussion of the cutting tool. Various methods are employed to clear out the triturated rock.

The work is much quickened by the substitution of steam power, water power, or even horse power for manual labor. Of the many forms of boring machines now in use may be mentioned the diamond boring machine, invented by Leschot, a Swiss engineer. In this the cutting tool is of a tubular form, and receives a uniform rotatory motion, the result being the production of a cylindrical core from the rock of the same size as the bore or caliber of the tube. The boring bit is a steel thimble about four inches in length, having two rows of Brazilian black diamonds firmly embedded therein, the edges projecting slightly. The diamond teeth are the only parts which come in contact with the rock, and their hardness is such that an enormous length can be bored with but little appreciable wear.

Where do Dates Come From?

Besides the dried dates which we are accustomed to seeing in this country, they are used extensively by the natives of Northern Africa and of some countries of Asia.

It consists of an external pericarp, separable into three portions, and covering a seed which is hard and horny in consequence of the nature of the albumen in which the embryo plant is buried.

Next to the cocoanut tree, the date is unquestionably the most interesting and useful of the palm tribe. Its stem shoots up to the height of fifty or sixty feet without branch or division, and of nearly the same thickness throughout its length. From the summit it throws out a magnificent crown of large feather-shaped leaves and a number of spadices, each of which in the female plant bears a bunch of from 180 to 200 dates, each bunch weighing from twenty to twenty-five pounds.

The fruit is eaten fresh or dried. Cakes of dates pounded and kneaded together are the food of the Arabs who traverse the deserts. A liquor resembling wine is made from dates by fermentation.

Persia, Palestine, Arabia and the north of Africa are best adapted for the culture of the date-tree, and its fruit is in these countries an important article of food. It is now being introduced into California.

The Story of Rubber

Rubber is the coagulated sap of more than 300 varieties of tropical trees and vines—the Landolphia of Africa, the Ficus of the Malay Peninsula, the Guayule shrub of Mexico and the Castilloa of South America, Central America and Southern Mexico are all important rubber producers, but far more important than all of the others together is the Hevea, a native of Brazil.

Hevea trees are scattered through the dense forests of practically every part of the Amazon Basin, a territory more than two-thirds as large as the United States.

How was Rubber First Used?

Down in Brazil, several hundred miles up the Amazon River, there stood a great forest of trees and in this forest—the same as in forests of today—were birds and

INDIANS PLAYING WITH A RUBBER BALL WHEN COLUMBUS CAME IN SIGHT
Courtesy of the United States Rubber Co.

animals and bugs and beetles, etc. All trees are protected by nature; some are protected from bugs eating their leaves, by other bugs eating up these bugs; other trees are protected by having a thorny or bristly bark.

In these forests in which the rubber tree grows there was a wood-boring beetle, and this beetle would attack these rubber trees, boring into them; but the tree, in order to protect itself, had a poisonous juice, and as soon as the beetle bored into the tree, this juice killed him. Then the juice would fill up the hole the beetle had made, and the tree would go on growing as before.

In those days the natives around these forests (who were half Indian and half Negro) happened to find some of this juice sticking on the tree. They cut it off, rolled it together and made a ball, with which they would play games. The first

IN THE JUNGLE
LLAMA, DOMESTIC ANIMAL OF THE ANDES, USED TO CARRY RUBBER
OVER MOUNTAINS
RAILROAD AROUND THE RAPIDS OF THE MADEIRA TERMINAL
CRUDE RUBBER "BISCUITS" ON THE BANKS OF THE AMAZON
Courtesy of the United States Rubber Co.

mention of it was made by Herrera in his account of the second voyage of Columbus, wherein he speaks of a ball used by Indians, made from the gum of a tree which was lighter and bounced better than the far-famed balls of Castile.

The way they gather this rubber is very interesting. When it comes from the tree it is nothing but a milky juice. The natives of South America soon discovered that the white man was willing to pay them beads and other trinkets for chunks of this rubber, so they became active in gathering it.

ON THE BANKS OF THE RIO GUAPORE—BRAZIL
Courtesy of the B. F. Goodrich Co

What is a Rubber Camp Like?

In this locality the rubber harvest commences as soon as the Amazon falls which is usually about the first of August. When this date approaches bands of natives set out from their primitive homes and go, in many instances, hundreds of miles into the forest lowlands. There, within easy reach of the rubber trees, they set up their camp and the actual work of harvesting the rubber crop begins. It usually covers a period of about six months, extending from August to January or February.

The camps are usually great distances from the nearest town and procuring supplies is not only difficult but very expensive as well. The natives build their huts out of small poles covered with palm thatch and live in little colonies while the rubber harvest is going on. The Brazilian name for a rubber gatherer is "seringuero."

A roof and floor with the flimsiest of walls, set up on piling for coolness, defense against animals and insects, and to keep the building dry during flood season, forms the home of the rubber gatherer. The more pretentious and better furnished

RUBBER GATHERER'S HUT NEAR THE AMAZON
Courtesy of the B. F. Goodrich Co.

home of the superintendent of the "estate," together with the storehouses, etc., are called the "seringal."

The buildings are usually grouped together at a favorable spot on the banks of the Amazon or one of its tributaries.

Furniture is of the most primitive type. The laborers and their families sleep in hammocks or on matting on the floor. Food is largely made up of canned goods and the ever-present farina, a sort of tapioca flour.

The climate of the South American rubber country is usually fatal to white men, and even among the Indians the fevers, the poisonous insects and reptiles, and the other perils of a tropical forest cause a high death rate. The production of South American rubber is limited by a shortage of men rather than a shortage of trees.

In December the rainy season begins. The waters of the Amazon begin to rise and the work ceases. The superintendent and many of the workers go down the river to Para and Manaos or to villages on higher ground. However, a number of the laborers usually remain in the huts, loafing and fighting the animals and insects

A HOME OF THE RUBBER GATHERERS
Courtesy of the United States Rubber Co.

that seek refuge from the rising waters. They have but little to eat, and during the entire season practically no communication with the outside world.

At the end of the rainy season, early in May, the laborers return to their task. The quick-growing vegetation has filled the estradas and this must be cleared away and perhaps new estradas opened. An estrada is simply a path leading from one Hevea tree to another and circling back to camp. Each estrada includes about one hundred of the scattered Heveas.

After having established themselves in camp the natives take up their monotonous round, which is followed day after day as long as the rubber trees continue to yield their valuable sap. When the seringuero starts out he equips himself with a toma-hawk-like axe having a handle about thirty inches long. This is called a "macheadino."

TAPPING HEVEA RUBBER TREE—BRAZIL
Courtesy of the United States Rubber Co.

How is Rubber Gathered by the Natives?

The trees are tapped very much like maple syrup trees. Only the juice is found between the outer bark and the wood. So these men make a cut in the tree through the bark, almost to the wood. A little cup is then fastened to the tree with a piece of soft clay to press the cup against it, and the juice runs into this cup. Sometimes they have from ten to thirty cups on one tree and the average yield of a tree is ten pounds of rubber a year.

Some two hours after the tapping is done the flow entirely ceases and the tree must be tapped anew to secure a fresh flow.

ON THE BANKS OF THE AMAZON
Courtesy of the B. F. Goodrich Co.

The film of rubber that forms on the inside of the cup and the bits of rubber remaining on the tree are collected and sold as coarse Para.

The rubber gatherer carries in addition to a macheadino and many small tin

GATHERING THE RUBBER MILK—BRAZIL
Courtesy of the United States Rubber Co.

HOW THE RUBBER MILK DRIPS FROM
THE GASH IN THE TREE—BRAZIL

cups, a larger vessel for gathering the liquid and carrying it to camp. One man will tap as many as 100 trees in a single morning and then cover the same ground again in the afternoon or on the following morning, gathering the sap that drips slowly from the cuts made in the trees.   On these journeys the harvester frequently travels long distances over paths so buried by the undergrowth of the jungle that they are

A Plantation in Borneo
Courtesy of the B. F. Goodrich Co.

almost invisible to the untrained eye.   On such expeditions rubber gatherers usually go armed with rifles to protect themselves against wild animals, reptiles and savage Indians.

How is Rubber Smoked?

After the juice has been gathered in this way, the native built a fire; over it he placed a cover shaped like a large bottle with the bottom knocked out of it.   This fire is built of oily nuts found in the forest, and the thick smoke arises through what would be the neck of the bottle.

With a stick shaped something like the wooden shovels used at the seashore, he dipped into the milky juice in the bowl, then turned this stick or paddle around

Smoking Rubber on the Lower Amazon
Courtesy of the United States Rubber Co.

very rapidly in the smoke until the juice baked on the paddle.   He then added more juice and went through the same operation again and again until there were between five and six pounds of rubber baked on this paddle.   He then cut this off with a

SMOKING RUBBER—UPPER AMAZON

Courtesy of the United States Rubber Co.

wet knife which made it cut more rapidly. That formed what is called a rubber "biscuit," and he then started over again for his next five or six pounds. Later, as the demand for these "biscuits" increased, instead of the native using the paddle, he erected two short fence-like affairs about six feet apart, but parallel with each other, and in between was the smoky fire. Then he obtained a long pole, stretched it across these two rails and poured a small quantity of this juice on this pole, over where the smoke came in contact with it, and rolled the pole around until this juice was baked, adding more, until, instead of a small five- or six-pound "biscuit," he would get an immense ball. In order to get this off his pole, he would jog one end of the pole on the ground until the "biscuit" would slide off. This is the way crude rubber first came into our market and the way it comes today.

How was Vulcanizing Discovered?

Up to this time, these "biscuits," when exposed to heat, would become very soft and sticky, and when exposed to the cold, would become hard like a stone.

There was an American by the name

REMOVING BISCUIT FROM POLE AFTER SMOKING

Courtesy of the United States Rubber Co.

of Charles Goodyear who had heard how the natives of the rubber-growing countries used this milky juice in many ways for their own benefit. One use they put it to was the waterproofing of their cloaks. How could this be done so that our clothing would be made water-tight and yet not be sticky in summer or stiff in winter? Goodyear devoted a great deal of his time to solving this problem, and, like many other great inventors, he passed through many trials. His many failures caused his friends to forsake him and he was put in prison for not paying his debts. He persisted in his quest, however, and it was accident at last that opened the way to discovery of the processes of vulcanization for which Goodyear was seeking.

At Woburn, Mass., one day, in the spring of 1839, he was standing with his brother and several other persons near a very hot stove. He held in his hand a mass of his compound of sulphur and gum, upon which he was expatiating in his

INDIAN WATERPROOFING CLOTH BY "PAINTING" IT WITH RUBBER "MILK"—BRAZIL
Courtesy of the United States Rubber Co.

usual vehement manner, the company exhibiting the indifference to which he was accustomed. In the crisis of his argument he made a violent gesture, bringing the mass in contact with the stove, which was hot enough to melt India-rubber instantly; upon looking at it a moment afterwards, he perceived that his compound had not melted in the least degree! It had charred as leather chars, but no part of the surface had dissolved. There was not a sticky place upon it. To say that he was astonished at this would but faintly express his ecstasy of amazement. The result was absolutely new to all experience—India-rubber not melting in contact with red-hot iron! He felt as Columbus felt when he saw the land bird alighting upon his ship and the driftwood floating by. In a few years more his labors were crowned with success.

This great invention made it possible for us to have rubber boots and rubber shoes and many other things made of rubber.

Up to this time, all the rubber was called Para rubber, named from the town of Para in Brazil, from which all rubber was shipped. The full-grown tree is quite

PARA BISCUITS

WASHING

VACUUM DRYER

CRUDE RUBBER DEP'T
"DRYING"

Courtesy of the United States Rubber Co.

large, ranging sixty feet and over in height and about eight feet around the trunk. It has a flower of pale green color and its fruit is a capsule containing three small brown seeds, with patches of black. These seeds lose their life very quickly, so a great deal of care is necessary to pack them if they are wanted to plant in another place. The safest way is to lay them loosely in a box of dry soil or charcoal.

The rubber tree grows best in rich, damp soil and in countries where the temperature is eighty-nine to ninety-four degrees at noon-time and not less than seventy-four

Courtesy of the United States Rubber Co. RUBBER TWIGS

degrees at night, and where there is a rainy season for about six months in the year, and the soil and atmosphere is damp the year round.

The name of this species of tree is Hevea, but many years ago it was called Siphonia on account of the Omaqua Indians using squirts made of a piece of pipe stuck into a hollow ball of rubber.

How did Rubber Growing Spread to Other Places?

Back in the seventies an English botanist, Wickham by name, smuggled many Hevea seeds out of Brazil. The tree was found to grow well in the Eastern tropics and today the rubber plantations of Ceylon, Borneo, the Malay Peninsula and neighboring regions are producing more than half of the world's supply of crude rubber. Here the natives work under pleasant climatic conditions and the trees under cultivation grow better and yield better than in the forest.

On these plantations, rubber trees are cultivated just the same as other crops. All weeds are removed and great care is used with the young trees. Low-growing plants which absorb nitrogen from the air which enriches the soil, such as the passion flower and other sensitive plants, were planted around these small rubber trees, for it was found that when the weeds were removed to give the trees a chance to grow, the ground become hard and dry.

The method of tapping is different, too. Instead of ten to thirty taps, a series

MIXING OR COMPOUNDING

REFINING

UPPER CALENDER

SOLING CALENDER

Courtesy of the United States Rubber Co.

of cuts the shape of a V is made on four sides of the tree, from the bottom up to as high as a man can reach, and a cup placed at the point of the V. Another way is to make one long cut down the tree and then cut out slanting channels about one foot apart into this, and put a cup at the bottom of the long cut; another is making a spiral around the tree with the cup at the bottom.

How is Rubber Cured on Modern Plantations?

With these big plantations some other way to cure the rubber had to be devised from the smoking process used in curing the native rubber which comes from South America. The milky juice is emptied from the cups into a tank and lime juice is added and it is then allowed to stand. The juice, as it comes from the tree, contains considerable water: the lime juice is added to separate the rubber from the water.

A YOUNG RUBBER PLANTATION
Courtesy of the United States Rubber Co.

Sometimes separators are used much like our cream separators; in fact, the whole process and the appearance of the interior of these rubber "dairies" very much resembles our own dairies where real milk is made into butter, curds or cheese.

Para, at the mouth of the Amazon, and Manaos, a thousand miles up, are both modern cities of more than one hundred thousand population. They have schools, churches, parks, gardens and museums, and, except for the Indians, certain peculiarities in architecture and the ever-present odor of rubber, they differ but little from our northern cities of equal size. Here the rubber markets are located and here the rubber is carefully examined, graded, boxed and shipped to New York or Liverpool.

Plantation rubber usually comes in the form of sheets of various shapes and sizes. The rubber shown here is in oblong sheets. Sometimes it is in the form of "pancakes" or in "blocks." Often, after being coagulated, it is smoked, and "smoked plantation sheet" is, next to Para, the best rubber obtainable.

SOLE CUTTING

LINING CALENDER

CUTTING ROOM

BOOT MAKING

Courtesy of the United States Rubber Co.

How is Crude Rubber Received Here?

Crude rubber is received in many forms under various names. There are more than three hundred standard kinds, depending on source and method of handling; e. g., "Sernamby" is simply bundles of Para tree scrap and scrap from the cups where milk has cured in the open air. "Guayule" is a resinous rubber secured from a two-foot shrub that grows on the arid plains of Texas and Northern Mexico.

ANOTHER CEYLON TAPPING METHOD—
THE HERRINGBONE
Courtesy of the United States Rubber Co.

Our picture shows a bin of crude up-river Para the finest rubber known. Every "biscuit" or "ham" has been cut in two to find out whether the native has loaded it in any way.

How is Rubber Prepared for Use?

Now that we have rubber so that it can be used, we find there are a great many operations necessary between gathering the crude rubber and finally the finished rubber coat or shoe. These various operations are called washing, drying, compounding, calendering, cutting, making, varnishing, vulcanizing and packing and each one of these main operations requires several smaller operations.

The grinding and calendering department is the one in which the crude rubber is washed, dried, compounded and run into sheets ready to be cut into the various pieces which constitute a boot or shoe.

The cultivated rubber comes practically clean, but the crude rubber "biscuits" contain more or less dirt and foreign vegetable matter which have to be removed. The rubber is softened in hot water for a number of hours and then passed through the corrugated rolls of a wash mill in which a stream of water plays on the rubber as it is thoroughly masticated and formed into thin sheets. These sheets are taken to the drying loft. Here they are hung up so that the warm air can readily circulate through them and are allowed to remain from six to eight weeks, until every trace of moisture has been removed. The vacuum dryer is used where rubber is wanted dry in a short space of time.

RUBBER MARKET IN MANAOS
Courtesy of the B. F. Goodrich Co.

This is a large oven containing shelves. The wet sheets of rubber are cut in square pieces, placed on perforated tin pans and loaded into the dryer, which will hold about eight hundred pounds of rubber. The

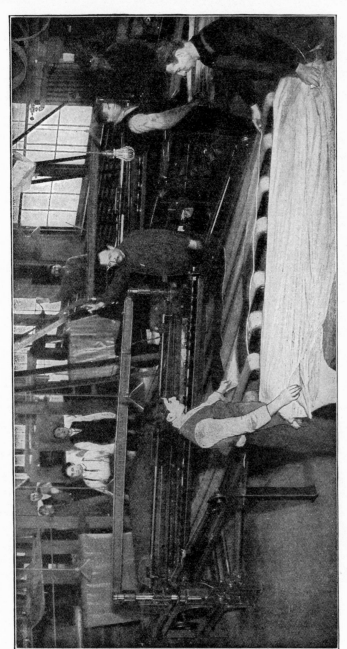

Courtesy of the United States Rubber Co.   SPECIAL DESIGNED MACHINE FOR CUTTING RUBBER

TAPPING HEVEA RUBBER TREE ON CEYLON PLANTATION
Courtesy of the United States Rubber Co.

doors are closed, fastened, and by the vacuum process the water is extracted, leaving the rubber perfectly dry in about three hours' time.

SOFTENING VATS
Courtesy of the B. F. Goodrich Co.

After the rubber is dry, and has been tested by the chemist, it goes to the grinding mills where it is refined on warm rolls and made ready for the compounding or mixing. It is impossible to make out of rubber alone, shoes or other products that will withstand extreme changes in temperature; certain amounts of sulphur, litharge and other ingredients are necessary in combination with the pure rubber to give a satisfactory material. The gum from the grinding mills is taken to the mixing mills, where, between the large rolls, the various materials are compounded into a homogeneous mass. The compounded rubber goes from the mixing mills to refining mills, to be prepared for the calenders.

SHOE MAKING

VARNISHING

VULCANIZER

PACKING

Courtesy of the United States Rubber Co.

Automobile, motorcycle and bicycle tires, belting, footwear and many other rubber articles must have a base or backbone of cotton fabric, and in order that the fabric may unite firmly with the rubber it must be "frictioned" or forced full of

rubber. This is done by drawing it between enormous iron rollers, rubber being applied on its surface as it passes through. The pressure is so great that every opening between the fibers of cotton, every space between threads is forced full of rubber.

The fabric is then ready to go with the milled rubber to the various departments of the factory to be incorpo-

THE MILL ROOM

Courtesy of the B. F. Goodrich Co.

rated into rubber goods. The calender is also used to press rubber into sheets of uniform thickness.

How are Rubber Shoes Made?

In making footwear, the linings and such parts as can be piled up layer on layer are cut by dies, usually on the large beam-cutting machines, commonly seen in leather shoe factories. The uppers are cut by hand from the engraved sheets, while metal patterns are used on the plain stock. The soles are cut by specially designed machines. The sheets of rubber from which the uppers and soles are cut are at this stage of the work plastic and very sticky. It is necessary on this account to cut the various pieces one by one and keep them separate, by placing them between the leaves

of a large cloth book. In an ordinary rubber shoe there are from twelve to fifteen pieces, while in a common boot there are over twenty-five pieces.

The various pieces are next delivered to the making department, where they are fitted together on the "lasts" or "trees" in such a way that all the joints and seams are covered and the lines of the shoe kept exactly. Consid-

MAKING RUBBER BULBS

Courtesy of the B. F. Goodrich Co.

erable skill is required to do this, as all the joints and seams must be rolled down smooth and firm to ensure a solid boot or shoe. The goods are all inspected before they are loaded on the iron cars to go to the varnishing department, where they receive the gloss which makes them look like patent leather.

From the varnishing department the shoes are taken to the vulcanizers, which are large ovens heated by innumerable steam pipes. The shoes remain in these vulcanizers from six to seven hours, subjected to extreme heat. This heating or

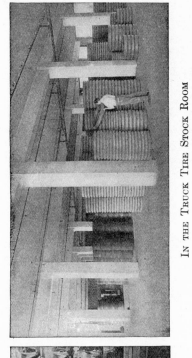

In the Truck Tire Stock Room

Inspecting Automobile Inner Tubes

Making Straightline Rubbers

Making Garden Hose (Wrapped Construction)

Courtesy of the B. F. Goodrich Co.

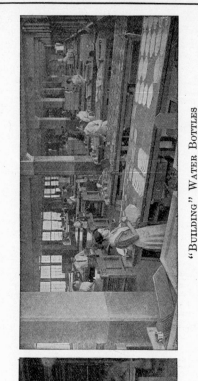

"Building" Water Bottles

Belt Press and Roll of Conveyor Belt

Insulated Wire Ready for Shipment

Vulcanizing Truck Tires

Courtesy of the B. F. Goodrich Co.

vulcanizing process fixes the elasticity of the rubber, increases its strength enormously and unites the parts in such a way as to make the shoe practically one piece.

The shoes next go to the packing department, where they are taken off the "lasts," inspected, marked, tied together in pairs, sorted and packed. They are then sent to the shipping department to be shipped immediately or stored in one of the spacious storehouses.

How are Automobile Tires Made?

In making tires, the strips of fabric are built together about a steel core to form the body or carcass of the tire. The beads are also added. The side strips, the breaker strip and finally the tread are applied. All of these pieces are sticky, and as they are laid together and rolled down by small hand rollers they adhere to each other, and when the tire is completed it looks very much like the tires you see on automobiles, but it is not yet vulcanized. The rubber is much like tough, heavy dough—there is not much stretch to it and in a cold place it would become hard and brittle.

The tire on its steel core is taken to the mold room and placed in a steel box or mold, shaped to exactly enclose it. It is then placed with many others on a steel frame and lowered into a sort of a well or oven, where it remains for a time under pressure in the heat of live steam, after which it is removed, a finished tire.

Vulcanization is simply the heating of the rubber mixed with sulphur—this causes a chemical change in the substance; it becomes tougher, more elastic and less affected by heat and cold.

This process, discovered in 1839, made rubber the useful substance it is today. The discoverer, Charles Goodyear, to whom we referred before, was never connected in any way except by name with any of the manufacturers of the present day, but his discovery was the real beginning of a great industry.

How did the Expression "Before you can say Jack Robinson" Originate?

Jack Robinson was a man in olden days who became well known because of the shortness of his visits when he came to call on his friends, according to Grose, who has looked up the subject very carefully. When the servants at a home where Jack Robinson called went to announce his coming to the host and his assembled guests, it was said that they hardly had time to repeat his name out loud before he would take his departure again. Another man, Halliwell, who has also investigated the development of the expression, thinks that it was derived from the description of a character in an old play, "Jack, Robes on."

It is also interesting to learn that the sandwiches which we all enjoy so much at picnics are so called because of the fact that an English nobleman, the Earl of Sandwich, always used to eat his meat between two pieces of bread.

What is an Aerial Railway Like?

Wonderful ingenuity has been shown in contriving a means to enable people to ascend the Wetterhorn Mountain in Switzerland. The sides of the mountain are so irregular and rough in their formation that it was found impossible to build even the incline type of railway, such as is usually resorted to where the ascent to a mountain is particularly steep. So the engineers who studied the problem finally contrived two huge sets of cables, securely fastened at the top, and fixed to a landing place a short distance from the base of the mountain. Cars, holding twenty passengers each, are carried up and down these cables, one car balancing the other, by means of a cable attached to each, which passes around a drum at the top.

THE WETTERHORN AERIAL RAILWAY
Reproduced by permission of The Philadelphia Museums.

There is probably no railway in all Europe upon which travel affords more wonderful scenery than this trip, suspended in the air, up the side of the Wetterhorn Mountain, the three peaks of which are all considerably more than two and a quarter miles high.

Why are They Called " Newspapers "?

Although something like an official newspaper or government gazette existed in ancient Rome, and Venice in the middle of the sixteenth century also had official news sheets, the first regular newspaper was published at Frankfort in 1615.   Seven years later the first regular newspaper appeared in England.

It was customary to print the points of the compass at the top of the early single-sheet papers, to indicate that occurrences from all four parts of the world were recorded.   Before very long, the publisher of one of the most progressive papers rearranged the letters symbolic of the points of the compass, into a straight line, and printed the word NEWS, and in a very short time practically every newspaper publisher decided to adopt the idea.

It is interesting to find that American colonies were not far behind England in establishing newspapers, and equally interesting to know that the most remarkable development of the newspaper has been in the United States, where, in proportion to population, its growth and circulation has been much greater than in any other country.   Practically a half of all the newspapers published in the world are published in the United States and Canada.

Every trade, organization, profession and science now has its representative journal or journals, besides the actual newspapers and magazines of literary character, and Solomon's remark might be paraphrased to read: "To the making of newspapers there is no end."

The great and rapid presses of recent years, the methods of mechanical type-setting and the cheapness and excellence of photographic illustrations, have all been necessary elements of the great sheets and enormous circulations of the present day, and the twentieth century newspaper is one of the greatest achievements in the whole field of human enterprise.

How Did the Cooking of Food Originate?

As soon as man found that he could produce fire by friction, as the result of rapidly rubbing two sticks together, he began to have accidents with his fires, just as we do today.   And it was probably because of one of these accidents, in which some food was cooked quite unintentionally, that primitive man made the great discovery that most of the meats and fruits and roots that he had been accustomed to eating raw, were far better if they were put in or near the fire for a while first.

How Far Away is the Sky-Line?

Unless you happen to be of the same height as the person standing next to you, the sky-line is a different distance away from each of you, for it is really just a question of the distance the eye can see from different heights above the sea-level A person five feet tall, standing on the beach at the seaside, is able to see about two and three-quarter miles away, while one a foot taller can see about a quarter of a mile further.

A person on the roof of a house a hundred feet high is able to see more than thirteen miles away, on a clear day, and a forty-two mile view may be enjoyed from the top of a mountain a thousand feet high.   The aviator who goes up to a level a mile above the sea is able to see everything within a radius of ninety-six miles and the further up he goes the larger the earth's circle becomes to him.

The Story of Rope[*]

Everybody knows what rope is, but everybody does not know how rope is made or of what kinds of fiber it is manufactured. And very few probably know the history of rope making, or how it developed from the simple thread to the great cable which now holds giant vessels to their wharves or aids to anchor them in ocean storms.

Let us go back and try to trace the history of the rope. It is a long one, going out of sight in the far past. In very early times men must have used some kinds of cords or lines for fishing, for tying animals, at times for tying men. These may have been strips of hide, lengths of tough, flexible wood, fibrous roots, and such gifts of nature, and in time all these were twisted together to make a longer and stronger cord or rope.

SCENE IN EGYPTIAN KITCHEN, SHOWING USE OF A LARGE ROPE TO SUPPORT A SORT OF HANGING SHELF

We have evidence of this. Tribes of savages still have in use cords made of various materials and some of them very well made. These have been in use among them for long centuries. Take the case of our own Indian tribes. They long made use of cordage twisted from cotton and other fibers, or formed from the inner bark of various trees and the roots of others, and from the hairs, skins and sinews of animals.

Good rope was made also by the old Peruvians, by the South Sea Islanders, and by the natives of many other regions. Those on the seashore made fishing

REPRODUCTION OF SCULPTURE FROM A TOMB IN THEBES, SHOWING PREPARATION OF LEATHER CORDS BY PROCESS SIMILAR TO ROPE MAKING

lines and well-formed nets, and certain tribes, among them the Nootka Indians, harpooned the whale, using cords made from the sinews of that animal, these being very strong and highly pliable. The larger ropes used by them, two inches in diameter, were made from the fibrous roots of the spruce.

Civilized Rope Makers.

All the ancient civilized peoples used ropes and cordage, made from such flexible materials as their countries afforded. We have pictures of this from ancient

[*] Illustrations by courtesy of Plymouth Cordage Co.

CORDAGE MANUFACTURE BY THE ROPE WALK METHOD

Yarns passing from bobbins through perforated plates in forming of strands.
Top truck used in laying of rope.
Forming machine making strands.
Closing tarred Russian hemp cable, 15¾ inch circumference for Argentine
Battleship "Rivadavia."

Egypt, in which the process of twisting strips of leather into rope is shown on the walls of their tombs. One workman is seen cutting a long strand from a hide which he turns round as he cuts, while another man walks backward with this, twisting it as he goes. The Egyptians also made ropes from papyrus and palm fibers, of which specimens still exist. Only by the use of large and strong ropes could they have moved the massive stones seen in their pyramids and temples.

When men began to move boats by sails, ropes of some kind must have been needed, and the early ships no doubt demanded long and strong cordage. We have pictures of these from several centuries before the Christian era, and we are told by Herodotus that Xerxes, when he built his famous bridge of boats across the Hellespont, 480 B. C., fastened them together by enormous cables which stretched

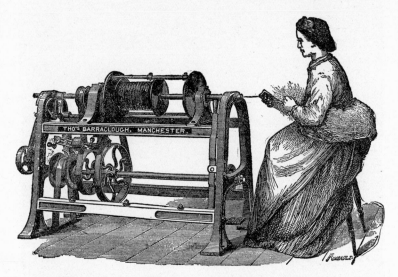

EARLY TYPE OF MACHINE FOR SPINNING ROPE YARN

from shore to shore, a distance of nearly a mile. Twelve of these ropes were used, about nine inches thick, some of them being made of flax and others of papyrus.

During the medieval and later centuries rope making was an active industry and America was not long settled before the rope maker became active. John Harrison, an English expert in this line, set up a ropewalk in Boston in 1641 or 1642, and for many years had a monopoly of the trade. But after his death the art became common and in 1794 there were fourteen large ropewalks in that city. In 1810 there were 173 of these industries in the United States, and from that time on the business has grown and prospered.

Hand Spinning.

In the period referred to all the work was done by hand, machine spinning being of later date. American hemp was used, this softer fiber being spun by hand long after Manila hemp was spun by machines. The hand-making process, long used, is an interesting one. The first step was to "hackle" the hemp. The hackle was a board with long, sharp steel teeth set in it. This combed out the matted tow of the hemp into clean, straight fiber. The instrument used in spinning was a large wheel, turned by hand, and setting in motion a set of "whirls" or revolving spindles,

FOUR-STRAND COMPOUND LAYING MACHINE MAKING STRANDS AND LAYING
ROPE IN A SINGLE, CONTINUOUS OPERATION

which twisted the hemp by their motion. The spinner wrapped a quantity of the hackled hemp around his waist and attached some of the fibers to the whirls, which

SIXTEEN-INCH TOWLINE WITH EYE SPLICE

twisted the hemp as he walked backward down the ropewalk, pulling out new fiber from his waist by one hand and pressing it into form and size with the fingers of the other.

In forming a small rope, two of the yarns thus formed were twisted together

FORMATION OF SLIVER (FOR SPINNING) ON FIRST BREAKER

in a direction opposite to that of the first twist. Then a second twisting followed, the direction being again reversed. Thus rope making may be seen to consist in a series of twisting processes, each twist opposite to the former, the rope growing in size and strength at each operation. Horse power or water power was used when the ropes became too large to be made by hand.

INTERIOR OF PRESENT-DAY ROPEWALK

Machine-made Ropes.

The old ropewalk is today largely obsolete, the rope-making machine taking the place of the hand-making process, which was not adapted to produce the large cables which in time were called for. Steam-driven machines were first introduced about 1838. These are now used alike in making fine threads and yarns and in large ropes.

There are two methods in the modern system of rope making. In one the strands are formed on one type of machine and twisted into a rope on another. In the second method both operations are performed on a single machine. The latter saves space, but is not so well fitted for large ropes as the former. A plant for the two-part method comprises two or more horizontal strand-forming machines, several bobbin frames, and a vertical laying-machine. The former twists several strands into a rope, the latter several ropes into a cable.

The yarns, which are wound around bobbins, are drawn from them through perforated plates, these so placed that the yarns converge together and pass into a tube. In this they are compressed and at the same time twisted by the revolution of a long carriage or flyer, which can be made to vary in speed and direction. After being twisted the strands are wound around reels in readiness for the second, or laying process.

In this the full reels are lifted by overhead chains and are placed in the vertical flyers of the laying-machine. Here again the strands are made to pass through openings and converge into a central tube, through which they pass to the revolving flyers which perform the final duty of twisting them into rope. The finished product is delivered to a belt-driven coiling reel on which it is wound.

REMOVING REEL WITH COMPLETED STRAND
FROM FORMING MACHINE

The most complete rope-making machine yet reached is that in which these two machines are combined into one. It economizes space, machinery and workmen, and also is more rapid in reaching the final result. But there are disadvantages which render it unfit for the larger sizes of rope, and it is therefore used only on a limited range of sizes.

American Hemp.

Among the fibers employed in rope making that of the hemp plant long held the supremacy, though in recent years it has been largely supplemented by other and stronger fibers. This plant is a native of Asia, but is now grown largely in other

HOW PINE TAR IS MADE IN THE SOUTH ATLANTIC STATES

1. Building the kiln.
2. Starting fire.   3. Racking back coals.
4. Tar coming from kiln.
5. Dipping and barreling.   6. Working around kiln.
7. After hard day and night.
8. Tar makers at home.   9. Burning completed.

continents, taking its name from the country in which it is raised, as Russian hemp, Italian hemp, and American, or Kentucky, hemp, it having long found a home in the soil of Kentucky. It differs from the Manila fiber, which has now very largely supplanted it, by being much softer, though of less strength. In the old days of the sailing vessel hempen rope was largely used for the rigging o' merchant and war ships, but the use of other fibers and of wire for rigging has greatly reduced the market for Kentucky hemp. There are various other fibers known under the name of hemp, the New Zealand, African, Java, etc., but the Manila and Sisal fibers, since the middle of the last century, have largely taken their place.

Manila and Sisal Fibers.

Manila hemp, as it is called, is a product of our Philippine dependency, being obtained from a species of the banana plant which grows abundantly in those islands.

AMERICAN HEMP STACKED IN FIELDS

Its fiber is very long, ranging from six to ten feet, and is noted for its smoothness and pliability, a feature which makes it ideal for rope making. Gloss and brilliancy are also characteristics of good quality Manila.

Manila hemp is obtained from the leaf stalks of the Philippine plant known as the Abacá, the leaf stems of which are compressed together, and constitute the trunk of the plant. It is obtained by scraping the pulp from the long fibers, drying these when thoroughly cleaned, and baling them for market.

The high price of the Manila product, however, has brought a cheaper fiber, of American growth, into the market; this being that known as Sisal, extracted from henequen, a cactus-like plant of Yucatan. As a substitute for or rival of Manila hemp it has come into common use. Its cheapness recommends it despite the fact that it is not of equal strength, and also that its fibers are shorter, being from two to four feet in length. Sisal also lacks the flexibility of Manila, being much more stiff and harsh. The development of the self-binding reaper on our western grain-fields has opened a gold mine for Sisal cordage. Of the annual import of this fiber to the United States, 300,000,000 pounds in quantity, a large proportion finds its way

PHILIPPINE HEMP CART

LOADING FIBER FROM SISAL FIBER PLANT ONTO PLANTATION CAR

to the wheat fields of the West. It is also used in all other wheat-yielding countries.

Henequen is now grown on large plantations, the plant being about five years old before the long, sword-like leaves are ready to cut. It continues to yield a supply for ten or twenty years, this lasting until the flower stalk, or "pole," appears, after which the plant soon dies. As Manila fiber is at times adulterated with Sisal, so has the latter its adulterant in a plant called Istle, which grows in Mexico and has hitherto been chiefly used in brush making.

These are the chief plants used in rope making. To them we may add coir, obtained from the brush of the cocoanut, which has been long used in India, and

NEW ZEALAND HEMP OR FLAX

CRUDE HAND METHOD OF CLEANING MANILA FIBER ON PLANTATION

has come into use in Europe in recent years. It is fairly strong and has the advantage of being considerably lighter than hemp or Manila. And, unlike these, it does not need to be tarred for preservation, as it is not injured by the salt water. Two other rope-making fibers of importance are the Sunn hemp of India and cotton, ropes of the latter being largely used for certain purposes, such as driving parts of textile machinery.

Wire Ropes.

We have not completed the story of rope making. There is the wire rope to consider, a kind of cordage now largely used in many industries, in which it has

STACKING BALES OF MANILA FIBER WITH PORTABLE COMPRESSED AIR ENGINE

superseded hemp ropes and chains. These seem to have originated in Germany about 1821. In the bridge at Geneva, built in 1822, ropes of untwisted wire, bound together, were used, and some fifteen years later "stranded" wire ropes were employed in the Harz mines. These at first were made of high-class wire, but only steel is now used in their manufacture. A strand of wire rope generally consists of from six to nine wires and sometimes as many as eighteen, but much larger ropes are made by twisting these strands together. They are generally galvanized to prevent them from rusting.

The applications of wire ropes are very numerous, an important one being for winding and hauling purposes in mines. For aerial ropeways they are extensively employed, and are of high value in bridge building, the suspension bridge being sustained by them. The strength of the steel wire used for ropes varies from

HANK OF MANILA FIBER TWELVE FEET LONG

seventy to over one hundred tons per square inch of sectional area, the weight of a hemp rope being about three times that of a wire rope of equal strength.

Pine Tar for Ropes.

Who does not know of the tarred rigging that once meant so much to the rope maker? Its very odor seems to cling to the pages of seafaring books. When steam power took the place of wind power in ships the use of tarred rigging naturally declined, yet tarred goods still form an important branch of the rope business. Pine tar is the kind best suited for cordage, the yellow, longleaf, or Georgia pine holding the first rank in the United States for tar making. This tree is found along the coast region from North Carolina to Texas.

In tar-kiln burning only dead wood is used, the green tree yielding less tar and of lower quality. It is a slow process, as a brisk fire would consume the wood without yielding tar. As the tar comes from the kiln it is caught in a hole dug before the outlet and is dipped up and poured into barrels, the average yield being one barrel of tar to the cord of wood. As above said, it is indispensable to protect cordage exposed to the effects of moisture, except in the case of coir ropes. Oiling is also an important process in the manufacture of ropes from hard fibers, as Manila, Sisal

INSPECTING MANILA FIBER AT DOCK

SHIPPING PLATFORM OF A LARGE FACTORY

and New Zealand. This softens them and makes them more workable, and it also acts as a preservative.

Why does Rope Cling Together?

This is probably due to a degree of roughness in the surface of fibers, often imperceptible to the eye, yet preventing them when in close contact from slipping easily upon each other. This is greatly increased by twisting the fibers together, and is added to by the toughness of the fibers themselves, the whole giving to rope a great resisting power. In the case of wire rope it is the firmness with which the metal holds together that gives it its great resisting strength. It is also not unlikely that the pressure of gravitation takes part in rope making, by holding the fibers in close contact, even if we do not know how this force operates.

What is Rope Used for?

This is a question that has already been answered in great part. Its uses, in fact, are innumerable. It serves to hold things together, and also to hold them apart; to lift things into the air and to hold them down to the ground; to pull things forward and pull things back—but not to push things forward. For the latter something less flexible than rope is needed. Animals are tied or tethered by it and led by it, and man, himself, is one of its victims. This is especially the case in the dismal way in which man's career upon earth has so often been ended by lifting him from the ground by the aid of a rope loop around his neck. It is of some comfort to know that this brutal use of the rope is being replaced by more humane methods of ending the lives of condemned criminals.

How did the Expression " A-1 " Originate?

We have all become so accustomed to hearing the term "A-1" used to designate a thing as perfect that it does not occur to many of us to wonder how it originally came to be used in that connection. Its first use was as a symbol in the code by which vessels were graded in the register of shipping kept by Lloyd's, the originators of marine insurance. "A-1" was the best rating given to the highest class vessels, "A" standing for perfect condition of the hull of the ship and "1" meaning that the rigging and whole equipment was complete and in good order.

How has Man Helped Nature Give Us Apples?

The original of all the varieties of the cultivated apple is the wild crab, which is a small and extremely sour fruit, and is native of most of the countries of Europe. We use the crab-apple for preserving even now, although man's ingenuity has succeeded in inducing nature to give us many better tasting kinds.

The amazingly large number of different varieties which we have today have all been brought into existence through the discovery of the process of "grafting." There are a half a dozen or more different methods of grafting. The method most commonly practiced in working with apple trees is called "bud-grafting," and consists of transferring a plate of bark, with one or more buds attached, from one tree to another.

The wood of apple trees is hard, close-grained and often richly colored, and is suitable for turning or cabinet work. Apple-growers classify apples into three different kinds, each consisting of a great many separate varieties. The three general divisions are—table apples, which are characterized by a firm, juicy pulp, a sweetish acid flavor, regular form and beautiful coloring; cooking apples, which possess the quality of forming by the aid of heat into a pulpy mass of equal consistency, and also by their large size and keeping properties; and cider apples, which have a considerable astringency and a richness of juice.

IN THE LAND OF THE APPLE

The Rogue River Valley, Oregon, in one section of which this photograph was taken, is known all over America for its wonderful apples. One apple-raiser in this district gathered two hundred bushels of apples per acre from his six-year-old trees.

The University of Pittsburgh

The Story of Self-Loading Pistols*

Colt Pistols.

The machine gun of the present day, the murderous weapon which numbered its victims by the hundreds of thousands during the World War, had its origin in the mind of a man whose birth dates back to almost exactly one hundred years before this war began, that of Samuel Colt, born at Hartford, Conn., on July 19, 1814.

The small arm of the previous period, the old "Brown Bess," used in the British army for 150 years, was a muzzle-loading, flint-lock musket of the crudest mak

CUSTER'S LAST STAND

The revolver played a large part in Indian warfare.

The only important improvement made in it during that long term of service was the substitution of the percussion cap for the flint lock. This took place in the last period of its use. A breech-loading rifle was also invented about this time. This was the "Needle Gun," of which 60,000 were issued to the Prussian army in 1841, and which was first used in 1848, in the German war with Denmark.

The Colt pistol had appeared before this date. The idea of it grew in the mind of young Colt when he left his father's silk mill and shipped as a boy sailor in the ship "Carlo," bound from Boston to Calcutta. While on this voyage the conception of a revolving pistol came to him, and he whittled out a rude model of one with a penknife from a piece of wood.

*Illustrations by courtesy of Colt's Patent Fire Arms Manufacturing Co.

THE ORIGINAL PATTERSON MODEL, 1836

SINGLE ACTION ARMY AND FRONTIER REVOLVER— THE "COWBOY'S FRIEND"

OLD MODEL "POWDER AND BALL" REVOLVER USED IN MEXICAN AND CIVIL WARS

When he returned he sought in vain to interest his father and others in his idea of a pistol with a revolving cylinder containing six chambers to be discharged through a single barrel. This boyish notion won no converts. and at the age of eighteen

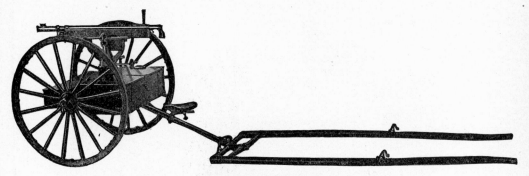

GUN MOUNTED ON LANDING CARRIAGE WITH SHAFT ATTACHMENT

he went on a lecture tour on chemistry, under the dignified title of Dr. Coult. These lectures met with success, and he used the money made by them in developing his pistol, which was in a shape to patent by 1835. Patents were taken out by him in

PACK SADDLE FOR CARRYING AUTOMATIC MACHINE GUN AND COMPLETE EQUIPMENT

this and the following year in the United States, Britain and France, and in 1836 he established the "Patent Arms Company" at Paterson, N. J., with a paid-in capital stock of about $150,000. This was a bold move by the young inventor, then just escaped from boyhood.

AUTOMATIC MACHINE GUN MOUNTED ON LIGHT LANDING CARRIAGE, AMMUNITION CHESTS OPEN, SHOWING HOW FEED BOXES, ETC., ARE CARRIED

Young Colt tried in vain to interest government officials in his new weapon, their principal objection being that he used in it the new percussion caps instead of the time-honored flintlock. But success came during the Seminole War of 1837, when some of the officers, who had seen the new revolving pistol, decided to give it a trial and sent to the factory for a supply.

Its value was soon proved. The Indians looked on this weapon that could be fired six times after one loading, as something magical. It was too much for their philosophy and the war soon came to an end. At a later date it was used by the Texans in their war against Mexico, and from that time on every Texas ranger wanted a revolver. It has ever since been the favorite weapon of the cowboy and frontiersman.

But wars ran out, the market closed, and the "Patent Arms Company" failed. What put Colt on his feet again was the Mexican war a few years later. General Taylor offered Colt a contract for one thousand revolvers at $24 each, and though the young inventor was looked upon as a ruined man he took the contract, got together the necessary capital, and built a factory on the Connecticut at Hartford. From that time on there was no want of a market. The "Forty-Niners" took revolvers to California, foreign governments sent orders for them, and armories were built in England and in Russia for their manufacture. Colt died in 1862, but the Civil War had previously opened a great market for his pistols, and before the conflict ended the Colt factory at Hartford was in a highly flourishing state. In the following years the revolver be-

AUTOMATIC PISTOL—GOVERNMENT MODEL, CALIBER .45

In this model the slide remains open after firing the last cartridge. When reloading the arm in this position, insert the magazine, then press downward the slide stop (to the rear of the trigger as illustrated). The slide goes forward, inserting a cartridge without any movement of the slide by hand. The slide stop is operated by the thumb of the hand holding the pistol.

POLICE-POSITIVE REVOLVER

Adopted by the Police Departments of the principal cities of the United States and Canada.

AUTOMATIC PISTOL—POCKET MODEL, HAMMERLESS

The action of this pistol is automatic except that the trigger must be pulled to fire each shot; continued discharge will not result from one pull of the trigger.

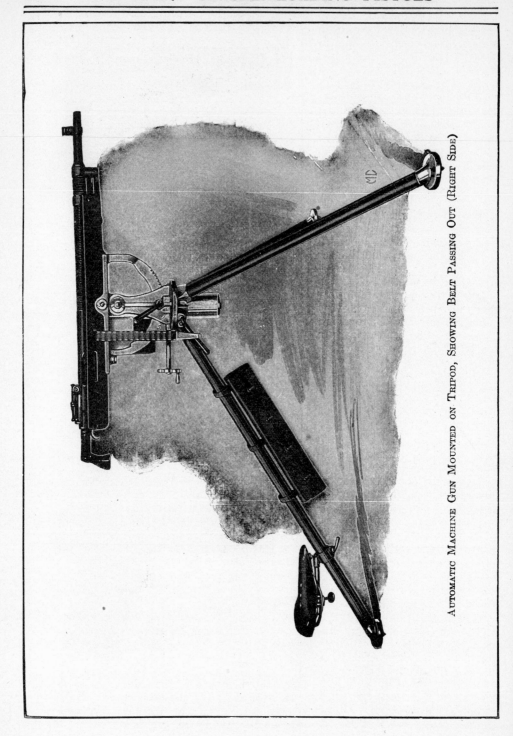

Automatic Machine Gun Mounted on Tripod, Showing Belt Passing Out (Right Side)

came a prime necessity in dealing with the Indians of the West, and a school-book statement of that date was to the effect that: "The greatest civilizer of modern times is the Colt revolver." Another writer, speaking of the "Peacemaker," an effective weapon produced after 1870, said: "It has the simplicity, durability, and beauty of a monkey-wrench."

Machine Guns.

The revolving idea was applied to guns about 1861 by Richard J. Gatling, the first Gatling guns fitted for use with metalling ammunition being produced by the Colt Company in 1870. These guns had ten barrels revolving around a central shaft and in their developed form were capable of being fired at the rate of one thousand shots a minute. The first of these to be used prominently in warfare was the French

AUTOMATIC GUN MOUNTED ON AUTOMOBILE

mitrailleuse, used by France in the war of 1870–71. The Gatling soon made its way widely, and its rapidity of fire became a proverb. If anything moved quickly it was said to "go like a Gatling" or "sound like a Gatling."

Other guns of this type are the Hotchkiss, the Nordenfeldt and the Gardner, and a more recent one is the Maxim, which, after the first shot is fired by hand power, continues to fire shot after shot by means of the power derived from the explosion of each successive cartridge. In the early form of the revolver the empty cartridge cases had to be ejected from the cylinder singly by an ejector rod or handy nail. In 1898 a new type was introduced with a lateral swinging cylinder which permitted the simultaneous ejection of all the empty shells.

Near the time of the Spanish-American War appeared what is known as the Colt automatic gun, operated by the action of the powder gases on a piston and lever near the muzzle of the barrel. This could be fired at the rate of 400 to 500 shots a minute, and by reason of its light weight could be very easily carried. The British used it effectively in the Boer War.

Today the Colt Company manufacture revolvers in which the simultaneous ejection of the cartridge-cases and recharging of the chambers is combined with a strong, jointless frame; automatic magazine pistols in which the pressure of the powder gases, as above said, is utilized after giving the proper velocity to the projectile, it requiring only a slight continued pressure on the trigger for each shot; automatic machine guns firing at will single shots or volleys while requiring only a slight pull upon the trigger; and the improved manually-operated Gatling gun firing the improved modern ammunition. The cartridges are carried on a tape which feeds them with the necessary rapidity into the barrel.

What would be the history of the European War without the machine gun is not easy to state, but as a highly efficient weapon of war its quality has been abundantly proved.

How does the Poisonous Tarantula Live?

When the National Guardsmen from all over the Union were concentrated along the Mexican border, many reports were sent home of thrilling experiences with tarantulas, to whose bite the natives of Mexico, Italy and many other warmer countries have ascribed a disease called "tarantism." The Italian peasants believe that this disease can only be cured by a certain kind of music.

The tarantula, like many other members of the spider family, is an expert in the making of burrows. Its burrows are artfully planned. At first there is a sheer descent four or five inches in depth, but at that distance below the surface the tunnel turns aside before dipping straight down again to its termination. It is at the angle or elbow of the tunnel that the tarantula watches for the approach of enemies or prey, like a vigilant sentinel, never for a moment off its guard, lying hidden during the day, if nothing disturbs it, and coming out at nightfall to seek its prey.

Unlike most other spiders, it hunts its game without the aid of webs or snares. It does, however, possess the ability to spin the silk which we have all seen other spiders make, for, in digging its hole, it makes neat little packages of the dirt it has scraped up, bound together with silk and slime from its mouth, and flips them to one side out of the way. When it comes to hunting, it makes sure that it can pounce on its prey, by building the entrance of its hole about two inches in diameter and up from the surface an inch or so, so that it can spread its legs for the leap.

How do the Indians Live Now?

The Indians of the United States are now largely gathered into reservations and their former dress, arms and habits are being gradually changed for those of the whites. Civilization is invading their homes and driving out their older characteristics. This is especially the case with the large numbers now dwelling in the former Indian Territory, now Oklahoma, although those confined in the reservations of Arizona, New Mexico and Montana are clinging more to their old modes, as is shown in the accompanying illustrations.

In ancient times the body was covered with furs and skins according to the seasons, but now the white man's clothes and blanket have generally superseded the native dress; though the moccasin of deer or moose hide, and, in the wilder tribes, the ornamental leggings and head-dresses are still retained. Their dwellings are made of bark, skins and mattings of their own making, stretched on poles fixed in the ground. The arms of the wilder tribes consist of the bow and arrow, the spear, tomahawk and club, to which have been added the gun and knife of the whites. Canoes are made of logs hollowed out, or of birch bark stretched over a light frame, skilfully fastened with deers' sinews and rendered water-tight by pitch.

The American Indian is described as of haughty demeanor, taciturn and stoical; cunning, brave and often ferocious in war; his temperament poetic and imaginative, and his simple eloquence of great dignity and beauty. They have a general belief in Manitous, or spiritual beings, one of them being spoken of as the Great Spirit,

MORE PICTURESQUE THAN BEAUTIFUL

The Apaches, formerly one of the most powerful and warlike of the Indian tribes, are now confined to reservations in Arizona and New Mexico.

A PICTURESQUE CAMP

Blackfeet Indians in camp on St. Mary Lake.

They believe in the transmigration of the soul into other men and into animals, and in demons, witchcraft and magic. They believe in life after death, where the spirit is surrounded with the pleasures of the "happy hunting grounds." They adopt a "totem" or symbol of the family and this is generally some animal, the turtle, bear and wolf being favorites.

The number of Indians in the United States at the taking of the Federal Census in 1910, was 265,683; and there are about 130,000 in the British possessions, 1,500,000 in Central America and 4,000,000 in Mexico. In all North America there are somewhere about 6,000,000 and there are probably 10,000,000 more in South America, many of them being more or less civilized.

How does the Beach Get Its Sand?

Most of the sands which we find on the beaches and in other places are the ruins of rocks which have come apart, usually as the result of the action of water. A large part of the ocean bottom is made up of "sandstone" and the continual washing of the water over this causes particles to break away and float off, whereupon they are swept up upon the beaches by the waves.

Sands differ in color according to the rocks from which they are derived. In addition to the sands on the beaches, they occur very abundantly in many inland locations, which were formerly sea bottoms, and very extensively in the great deserts of the world.

Valuable metallic ores, such as those of gold, platinum, tin, copper and iron, often occur in the form of sand or mixed with that substance. Pure siliceous sands are very valuable for the manufacture of glass, for making mortar, filters, ameliorating dense clay soils, for making molds in founding and for many other purposes.

The silica, which is the principal ingredient of sand, as well as of nearly all the earthy minerals, is known as "rock crystal" in its naturally crystallized form. Colored of a delicate purple, these crystals are what we call "amethysts." Silica is also met with in the "carnelian" and we find it constituting jasper, agate, cat's-eye, onyx and opals. In the latter it is combined with water. Many natural waters present us with silica in a dissolved state, although it is not soluble in pure water. The resistance offered by silica to all impressions is exemplified in the case of "flint" which consists essentially of silica colored with some impurity.

How did Nodding the Head Up and Down Come to Mean "Yes"?

Like a multitude of other things, the signs which we give by the movements of our heads to indicate "yes" and "no" were copied from animal life.

When the mother animal brought her young a choice morsel of food she would hold it up temptingly before its mouth and the quick forward movement of the head, with mouth open, showed the young animal's desire and acceptance of the offer. Even today when we make a forward movement of our heads to indicate "yes" it is observed that the lips are usually quite unconsciously opened a little.

In much the same manner, when the young had been well fed and were no longer hungry, a tightly closed mouth and a shaking of the head from side to side were resorted to, to keep the mother from putting the food into their mouths. Our natural impulse now is to slightly clinch our teeth when we shake our heads to mean "no."

Why do We Call a Man "a Benedict" When He Marries?

We call men "benedicts" when they become married because that was the name of a humorous gentleman in Shakespeare's play, "Love's Labour's Lost," who was finally married to a character named "Beatrice."

The Story in Firecrackers and Sky-Rockets[*]

The blaze and noise, indispensable to patriotic celebrations among all peoples, was produced a century ago in America by simple agencies. Washington's Birthday was ushered in by cannon salutes in every garrisoned place in the United States, and boys the country over built bonfires as they still do in old New England towns to celebrate the day. But the Fourth of July was the great hurrah time of the year, when every youth who owned a gun or could borrow one, brought it into use as a contribution to the general noise. He might lack shoes and be short of shot and bullets for hunting, but for this occasion no young man was so poor as to have failed to lay in a hornful of powder, and at the stroke of twelve midnight, which began the day, he and his companions blazed away with guns loaded to the danger point, and kept up their fusillade as long as ammunition lasted. For demonstrations on a larger scale, a small cannon was secured if possible, but lacking this, two black-smith's anvils were made to do the same service, the hole in the top of one being filled with powder, a fuse laid into it and the second anvil placed as a stopper upon the first before the charge was exploded.

A favorite firearm for celebration purposes was one of the old "Queen's Arm" muskets which were common in country communities, being trophies captured from the British during the Revolutionary War. One of these cumbersome flintlock pieces might be loaded halfway to the muzzle and fired without bursting, and would roar in the discharge in a way highly pleasing to patriotic ears.

It was near the close of the eighteenth century that Chinese firecrackers first came into use in celebrating the American Independence Day. For many years they were used sparingly and only in large cities. They had been known in the New England coast cities ever since the year 1787, when Elias Haskett Derby's ship of Salem, the first American vessel to engage in deep-water commerce, returned from her voyage to Calcutta, China and Isle of France. Among the things she brought back—more as a curiosity than as an article of cargo—was a consignment of Chinese firecrackers. Their capabilities in aiding the uproar on the Fourth of July were quickly recognized, and thereafter every ship that made the voyage from Massachusetts Bay to India or China brought back firecrackers with the tea, silks and rice. In time, rockets, squibs and torpedoes were included in the consignment, but it was not until the middle of the nineteenth century that their use became general in America.

The time when the more complicated fireworks, which we owe both to Europe and the Orient, came into vogue in this country, no one perhaps could now definitely tell. Their use was known to our seafaring men in the "forties," for it was in that decade that Capt. Decimus Forthridge, of the American brig "Independence," showed his Yankee pluck and resource in defeating an attack of Malay pirates with no other armament than fancy fireworks. During his voyage in the East Indies he had laid in a supply of fireworks with which to celebrate the Fourth of July in a manner worthy an American captain. For some reason no ammunition was available for swivels or muskets, when, in the mid-watch of the night, two war proas, deeply laden with armed Malays, were seen coming quickly up on the vessel's

* Illustrations by courtesy of Consolidated Fireworks Company of America.

Interior of Rocket Finishing Shop

Interior of Shell Finishing Shop

INTERIOR OF TORPEDO SHOP

quarter as she lay becalmed off Firabader Point in the Island of Sumatra. The cry of "All hands on deck to repel pirates" brought the crew on deck in haste, but without ammunition the chance that they would beat the enemy off was a long shot compared with the probability that the throat of every man on board would be cut as a preliminary to plundering and scuttling the vessel. Even in their extremity the crew laughed and jeered when the captain ranged them along the quarter rail with boarding pikes and empty muskets in hand to give the enemy the idea that they were ready for business, and then, opening the box of fireworks, he began to shoot rockets and roman candles at the pirates. If the crew laughed, the Malays did not, and when the captain of one of the proas was struck by a rocket, both crafts rested oars and came no nearer. But while Captain Forthridge was attending to these, a third proa came up unobserved under the port quarter, and the first that was known of its presence was the attempt of its occupants to board the vessel by the chains. To make matters worse it was discovered that the paper wrappings of the fireworks in the box were on fire. While the crew with clubbed muskets and boarding pikes kept the Malays outside the rails, Captain Forthridge picked up the blazing box, carried it to the chains, and while the mate and sailors warded the spears and krises from him, dropped it into the proa. The box was blown to pieces the minute it struck, scattering the fireworks through the proa, and with firecrackers snapping and jumping and fiery serpents running round among their bare legs, the Malays chose to take their chances with the sharks, and all hands went overboard into the water at double-quick. A little breeze came up and the brig drew away from the pirates, leaving the two proas to pick up those Malays from the water that the sharks had missed.

In the days of the China clippers, those famous ships sailed many a race from Hong Kong and Canton, with New York as the goal, to get there with "first tea" and to forestall the Fourth of July market with a cargo of firecrackers.

In China and the East Indies, fireworks, like "the fume of the incense, the clash of the cymbal, the clang and the blaze of the gong," are a part of the worship of the gods, as well as a feature of coronations and weddings. China is the birthplace of fireworks. From China the knowledge of them spread to India, and in both these lands rockets were used as missiles of war as early as the ninth century. The Chinese war rocket was a long, heavy affair, fitted at the end with a barb-like arrow, and to a foe unacquainted with firearms, it must have seemed a formidable missile. After gunpowder was introduced in Europe, fireworks came into use on the continent, and the use of both explosives undoubtedly was learned from the Chinese.

Fireworks were manufactured in Italy as early as 1540, and in France we have accounts of their employment in great celebrations between the years 1606 and 1739. Long before this time, some form of rocket, now unknown, that would burn in water, constituted the famous Greek fire which struck terror to the hearts of invaders from Northern Europe in medieval times when the Saracens launched it against their ships. Early in the present century during the Napoleonic Wars, the rocket perfected by Sir William Congreve was used in the siege of Boulogne and in the battle of Leipsic. The conditions of modern warfare have so changed that the rocket is no longer of practical use in fighting except as a signal. In case of shipwreck it is often employed to carry a line from the shore to a stranded vessel. It is noteworthy that while almost every kind of fireworks is manufactured in Europe and the United States, the small firecrackers are still imported from China. But larger quantities are now manufactured in the United States, and it is only a matter of time when the "Young American" salute will take the place of the Chinese firecrackers.

It was about ten years before the Civil War that "set pieces" began to form a

INTERIOR OF ROLLING SHOP

INTERIOR OF ROMAN CANDLE SHOP

INTERIOR OF BALLOON SHOP

part of fireworks celebrations. In those days the most famous pyrotechnic display in the whole country was given on Boston Common on the Fourth of July, and the country boy who was so lucky as to see that display, with the miracle of George Washington's benign face illuminated amid spouting flames and a shower of fireballs and rockets, had something to talk about for the rest of the year.

The American Civil War which did so much toward the modern development of firearms and munitions of war, brought also a great advance in pyrotechny, and soon after the close of the struggle, extensive manufacture of fireworks began in this country, with New York as the headquarters of the principal firms engaged in the business.

In 1865 the first displays of fireworks in the United States, illustrating historical events, were made by a company in New York City. They were the pioneers in this line of displays. Their success was immediate, and from these displays has grown the successes of today in pyrotechnics.

Fireworks now enter into the celebration of every important event in our national, political and business life. The celebrations at Washington, D. C., at the inaugurations of our Presidents, the coronations of emperors and kings in lands beyond our borders, are all brought to a close by brilliant displays of fireworks.

The writer, in visiting the plant of a large fireworks manufacturer, found that they were turning out large quantities of time fuses and primers for shrapnel shells for the foreign powers, and are working night and day on orders for the United States government on aeroplane bombs and signals. They have also worked out a searchlight projectile which is arranged to burst in the air, throwing out a number of luminous bodies that light up the surrounding country and reveal the movements of the enemy.

All large displays of fireworks are now fired by electricity and every known color and effect is produced by the pyrotechnist of the present day.

The water displays are scarcely less varied, consisting of flying fish, diving devils, prismatic fountains, floating batteries, fiery geysers and submarine torpedoes, all of which, being ignited and thrown into the water, go through their stunts as readily as other kinds do on land and in the air.

From every part of the civilized world, from Mexico, Central and South America and Europe, orders for fireworks come in increasing numbers to American firms, who now lead the world in this art. The Philippines will soon be a customer for them, and with the general opening up of China to modern civilization, from causes now in operation, it will not be strange if some day we should supply fireworks to the land of their origin.

What Makes a Chimney Smoke?

Smoky chimneys are usually caused either by the presence of other buildings obstructing the wind and giving rise to irregular currents of air, or by improper construction of the fireplace and adjacent parts of the chimney.

The first may generally be cured by fixing a chimney-pot of a particular construction, or a revolving cowl, on the chimney top, in order to prevent the wind blowing down; in the second case the narrowing of the chimney throat will generally create a better draft.

The longer a chimney is, the more perfect is its draft, provided the fire is great enough to heat the column of air in it, because the tendency of the smoke to draw upwards is in proportion to the difference of weight between the heated air in a chimney and an equal column of external air.

The first we hear of chimneys, for the escape of the smoke from a fire or furnace, is in the middle ages.

FLOATING DRY DOCK "DEWEY"

This dry dock, which is capable of floating the largest battleship, was towed from Sparrow's Point, Maryland, to Olangapo, Philippine Islands, a voyage of 13,000 miles. In operation, the dock is sunk by admitting water into its tanks until the ship can be floated in. The water is then pumped out and the dock with the ship inside rises to the proper level as shown.

U. S. Battleship "Mississippi" in Dry Dock at League Island

What are Dry Docks Like?

Although divers are able to go down under the water to examine the bottom of a ship while it is afloat, it is usually necessary to have it up on dry land when thorough inspections or repairs have to be made. So a berth something like a huge box stall in a stable is built, with the part where a horse would stand in the stall full of water, and a door, either made like swinging gates opening in the middle, or a caisson which is operated up and down like a window, at the end. The ship is floated into the dock and then after the door is shut to prevent any more coming in, all of the water is pumped out until the vessel rests on a lot of great big wooden blocks and supporting props with which the bottom and sides of the dock are lined. Supports are also placed between the vessel and each side of the dock. Then, when the work has been finished, and the ship is ready to go to sea, water is let back either by pumping it in or else by gradually opening the door at the end, and the vessel is able to float out into the river or harbor again.

Although all of the navy yards and some private corporations in this country have docks of this kind, they are not of as much importance here as in England, where they are used, without pumping out the water, for the loading and unloading of vessels, because of the very great rise and fall of the tides there straining and otherwise damaging ships tied up to ordinary docks.

There are nine important navy yards in the United States, located at Brooklyn, N. Y.; Boston, Mass.; Portsmouth, N. H.; Philadelphia, Pa.; Portsmouth, Va.; Mare Island, Cal.; New London, Conn.; Pensacola, Fla.; Washington, D. C., and Port Orchard, Wash.

There is another kind of dry dock, called "floating docks," which float on the surface of the water and may be sunk sufficiently to allow of a vessel being floated into them, and then raised again by pumping the water out of the tanks around the sides. They are usually built of iron, with water-tight compartments, and not closed in at either end. They are sunk to the required depth by the admission of water into so many of the compartments, till the vessel to be docked can float easily above the bottom of the dock, and then they are raised by pumping out the water until the ship can be propped up as in the land dry dock.

Why does a Lightning Bug Light Her Light?

The lightning bugs or fireflies which are seen so often on summer evenings in the country and among the trees in the parks of the city, are similar to the species of beetle called the glowworm in Great Britain, although the glowworm there does not give as much light as the firefly in America.

In reality it is only the female which is the lightning bug, for the male is not equipped with any lighting power. He has the bad habit of going out nights, and so the female has had to make use of her ability to make part of her body shine with a sort of a phosphorus green light in order to show him the way home, very much as a dweller in a poorly-lighted street keeps a light in the window or on the porch to guide visitors or the late home-comer to the proper house. She seems to possess the power of moderating or increasing the light at will.

The most brilliant fireflies are found only in the warmer regions of the world. The ordinary firefly to which we are accustomed gives off a very much brighter light if placed in warm water. Fine print may be read by the light of one kind which is found in the West Indies; in Cuba the ladies have a fashion of imprisoning them in bits of netting or lace of a fine texture and wearing them as dress ornaments, and in Hayti they are used to give light for domestic purposes, eight or ten confined in a vial emitting sufficient light to enable a person to write.

11

The Story in the Making of a Picture*

Let us suppose, for the purposes of explanation, that as far as *seeing* goes, any object is made up of countless infinitesimal points of light, and that the business of the eye is to gather them in and spread them out at the back of the eye in exactly the same relation they bore to each other on the object. The points of light, so duplicated, would thus form the image of the object.

The camera works very much the same way. The lens at the front of the camera is the eye, and the plate or film at the back of the camera corresponds to the back of the eye. The lens collects all the points of light of the object we wish to photograph, and directs them to the plate or film in such fashion that they occupy exactly the same relative position that they did before. An image of the object is formed.

Now if we could look inside the camera and the image were visible, we would see that it was upside down. The reason for this is very simple, as the accompanying diagram shows. The ray of light from "A" at the bottom of the object passes through the lens at an angle, and continues in a straight line until interrupted by the film or plate. It started at the bottom of the object and ended at the top of the image. The position of all the points of light is just reversed, although their relative position remains the same.

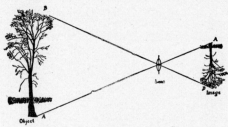

SHOWING INVERSION OF THE IMAGE

"Then here," you say, "is where your analogy between the camera and the eye falls down."

Not at all. It is true that we do not see things upside down, but this is because of mental readjustment during the passage of the impressions from the eye to the brain.

Now let us suppose that we have our camera loaded with film, and that mother has succeeded in keeping the baby quiet long enough for us to uncover the lens for an instant and let the points of light through to the film. The next question is, how are we going to make the resulting image permanent. We know that it is there, but in its present state it is not going to do us a great deal of good. In fact, if we should peek in the back of the camera, and to do so would ruin the exposure, we could not even see it.

But let us go back a bit. We ought to know a little something about the composition of this film on which the image has been projected.

In brief, film is a cellulose base coated with silver bromide and gelatine. If we were using a plate the only difference would be that instead of cellulose as a base we would have a sheet of glass. The gelatine is there to afford lodgment to this sensitized silver. The silver, being sensitive to the action of light, is there to record the image. As soon as one of these silver particles has been touched by light, it becomes imbued with the power of holding whatever the lens has transmitted to it. The image was formed, we remember, by points of light grouped in the same relative positions as the points of light of the object we were photographing. Consequently

* Illustrations by courtesy of Eastman Kodak Company.

it is only those silver particles within the image-forming area that are affected, because that is where the light struck.

The lens, then, gathered in the points of light and dispersed them on the film so as to form an image. The silver particles held this image, but not visibly—it is a latent image, and it is the purpose of development to bring it out.

It is the particular business of a chemical called "pyro" to release this latent image. When attacked by pyro, those silver bromide particles which have been affected by light—and only those—change to black metallic silver. After all the silver bromide particles, the ones that held the image, have been transformed into metallic silver, another chemical called "hypo" effectively disposes of all the silver bromide that was not affected by light. Now only the image-forming silver bromide particles remain, and these have been transformed to metallic silver. The result is a permanent image—a negative.

But it *is* a negative, so called because everything in it is reversed—not only from left to right, but in the details of the image. Mother's dark blue gown looks light, for example, and baby's white dress, dark.

To get our picture as it should be, we must place the negative in contact with a sheet of paper coated with a gelatine containing silver. This emulsion, as the coating is called, is, as we might readily infer from the presence of the silver, sensitive to the action of light in much the same manner as was the original film. We place the negative and paper in contact, then, in what is called a printing frame, so that light may shine through the negative and impress the image on the sensitive paper. It is obvious that the light parts of the negative will let through the most light, and that consequently the silver emulsion on the paper underneath will be most blackened, while the dark parts will hold back the light and the emulsion on the paper underneath will be less affected. In other words, the very faults that we noted in the negative, from a picture point of view, automatically right themselves. Mother's dress looks dark and baby's dress white—just as the lens saw it.

We then have the picture in its finished form.

The story of the making of the camera is as interesting as that of the making of the pictures by the camera.

Back in 1732, J. H. Schulze discovered that chloride of silver was darkened by light and all unwittingly became the father of photography. In 1737, Hellot, of Paris, stumbled on the fact that characters written with a pen dipped in a solution of silver nitrate would be invisible, until exposure to light, when they would blacken and become perfectly legible. However, it was not until early in the nineteenth century that these two discoveries were put to any practical use, as far as photography was concerned.

People of an artistic turn of mind had been in the habit of making what were called "silhouettes." The sitter was so posed that the light from a lamp threw the profile of his face in sharp shadow against a white screen. It was then easy enough to obtain a fairly accurate silhouette, by either outlining the profile or cutting it out from the screen.

It occurred to a man by the name of Wedgwood that this profile might be printed on the screen by using paper treated with silver nitrate, and he not only succeeded in accomplishing this, but also in perfecting what was then called the "camera obscura," the forerunner of the kodak of today. The camera obscura consisted of a box with a lens at one end and a ground glass at the other, just like a modern camera. It was used by artists who found that by observing the picture on the ground glass they could draw it more easily. Wedgwood tried to make pictures by substituting his prepared paper for the ground glass, but the paper was too insensitive to obtain any result. Sir Humphrey Davy, continuing Wedgwood's experiments, and using chloride of silver instead of nitrate, succeeded in making

ARTOTYPE COPY OF THE EARLIEST SUN-
LIGHT PICTURE OF A HUMAN FACE

Miss Dorothy Catherine Draper, taken by her brother, Prof. John W. Draper, M.D., LL.D., in 1840.

photographs through a microscope, by using sunlight. These were the first pictures made by means of a lens on a photographic material. But none of these pictures were permanent, and it was not until 1839 that Sir John Herschel found that "hypo," which he had himself discovered in 1819, would enable him to "fix" the picture and make it permanent.

At about this time, Daguerre announced discoveries that gave photography at least a momentary impetus, but the Daguerre process did not long survive, as it was slow, costly and troublesome. The daguerreotype was made on a thin sheet of copper, silver plated on one side, polished to a high degree of brilliancy, and made sensitive by exposing it to the fumes of iodine. The first daguerreotype made in America, that of Miss Catherine Draper, was exposed for six minutes in strong sunlight, and the face of the sitter thickly

powdered, to facilitate the exposure. An exposure today with a modern camera, under similar conditions, could be made in 1/1000 of a second.

It was impossible, of course, to find many sitters as patient as Miss Draper—try keeping perfectly quiet for even a minute if you would know why Miss Draper should be ranked as a photographic martyr—and many experiments were made in an attempt to materially shorten the time of exposure. The only real solution, of course, was to find some method where the light had to do only a little of the work, leaving the production of the image itself to chemical action.

The first great step in this direction was taken by Fox Talbot in 1841. He found, that if he prepared a sheet of paper with silver iodide and exposed it in the camera, he got only a very faint image, but if, after exposure, he washed over the paper with a solution of silver nitrate and gallic acid, the faint image was built up into a strong picture. And not only was Fox Talbot the first to

OLD-FASHIONED PHOTOGRAPHIC
EQUIPMENT

develop a faint or invisible image; he was also the first to make a negative and use it for printing.

In spite of all these advances, photography was almost exclusively a studio

The First Kodak (1888), Showing Roll Holder and Roll Film for 100 Exposures

The First Daylight Loading Method

The First "Folding Kodak" Fitted for Plates or Roll Film

"Dope" Barrel

proposition, when, in 1880, experiments were begun which were to result in photography that could be universally enjoyed—photography as we know it today. Of course there were amateurs even in those early photographic days, but they were few and far between. There was something about the bulk and weight of the old-time photographic outfit that failed to beget general enthusiasm.

RAW STOCK ROLLS, KODAK PARK

THE CINE-KODAK

Easy threading is an impressive feature of the new Cine-Kodak. The take-up reel fits over the shaft shown in the right half of the illustration. The supply roll is placed in similar position beside the motor, beyond the partition.

Pocket Motion-Picture Cameras.

Cameras weighing only five pounds loaded, automatically cranked, and the same size as an ordinary portable camera, are now available.

Load the camera with daylight film, obtainable in either 50 or 100-foot reels—it takes but a second—wind the spring, point the camera at scene or subject, release the lever and the movie's in the making—instantly.

Close-ups follow distant views, action follows action, without any adjustment for focus or time. When ready to make the movie, there's only one thing to consider: which of four diaphragm openings to use—a turn of a dial makes that adjustment, and an exposure guide beneath the dial tells which stop to choose for the prevailing light condition.

To lighten the camera burden, and to simplify the various photographic processes, were the problems that confronted the American inventor. The first step toward film photography—and it was film photography that relegated camera bulk to the scrap heap—was a roll film made of coated paper to which a sensitive emulsion was applied, but the real goal was reached when cellulose was substituted as a film base. This made practicable the present flexible, transparent film with its attendant convenience and dependability.

The kodak was the natural outcome of the roll film system. The first one appeared in 1888, and its development, which proceeded simultaneously with the film discoveries, soon reached the point where the loading and unloading could be done in daylight. Daylight developing soon followed, and the dark room, as far as the kodaker was concerned, took its proper place as a relic of the dark ages.

With 1914 came autographic photography, so that now with a kodak in one pocket and a handful of film in the other, the amateur is equipped for a picture-making tour of the world—not simply a pictorial record, but a written record as well, for autographic photography permits the dating and titling of each negative directly after exposure.

Photography, not so many years ago an exclusive pleasure for the few, is now easy fun for millions.

FILTER ROOM, KODAK PARK

Cellulose Acetate Manufacturing

How Deep is the Deepest Part of the Ocean?

Man has not been able to tell definitely just what the greatest depth of the ocean is, because it would be a practically unending task to go over every bit of it to take measurements. A great many exploring expeditions have been sent out to determine that interesting information so far as possible, however, and one of these, the Murray-Challenger expedition, has reported that the greatest depth that could be found in the Atlantic Ocean is 27,366 feet, in the Pacific Ocean 30,000 feet, in the Indian Ocean 18,582 feet, in the Southern Ocean 25,200 feet and in the Arctic Ocean 9,000 feet. They also stated that the Atlantic Ocean has an area in square miles, of 24,536,000; the Pacific Ocean, 50,309,000; the Indian Ocean, 17,084,000; the Southern Ocean, 30,592,000 and the Arctic Ocean, 4,781,000.

Why do We Say "Get the Sack"?

The use of the expression "get the sack," when we mean "to be discharged," originated through the impression made upon people in this country when stories were brought to them of the way the Sultan of Turkey disposed of members of his harem of whom he had tired. When he wanted to get rid of one of his harem he was said to have had her put into a sack and thrown into the Bosporus. People who heard of this report repeated it to others and they became so used to telling the tale that they slipped quite naturally into the habit of saying "to get the sack" when they meant that they expected to be put out of a position suddenly.

In very much the same way the phrase "Hobson's choice" is supposed to have resulted from the story told here of a livery-stable keeper at Cambridge, England, called Hobson, who obliged each customer to take the horse nearest the stable door, when a wish to hire one was expressed, even though he might permit customers to make the rounds of all the stalls, examining and perhaps selecting other horses. Since the interest inspired by that report, "Hobson's choice" has come to mean a choice without any alternative, or the chance to take the thing which is offered or nothing.

Why do We Call Them X-Rays?

At the time the discovery of X-rays was announced by Prof. Wilhelm Conrad Röntgen of the University of Würzburg, Germany, he was not sure of their exact nature, and so he named them "X-Rays," because "X" has always been understood to be the symbol for an "unknown quantity."

They are invisible rays transmitted through the air in a manner similar to light. They are produced by passing unidirectional electric current of from twenty to one hundred thousand volts pressure through a specially constructed high vacuum tube, within which rays radiating from the surface of a concave cathode (the negative electrode of a galvanic battery), are focused upon and bombard a target of refractory material such as tungsten, iridium, or platinum, from which focus spot the X-rays radiate in all directions.

They are used in medicine and surgery, to photograph the skeleton and all the internal organs of the human body, as an aid in diagnosis; also to destroy diseased tissue without the aid of surgery. Cancers and tumors of certain kinds and a number of skin diseases are said to be made to disappear by their use. When the apparatus is used, the subject is placed on a long table and the X-ray tube, in its lead glass shield container, is brought over the part of the body to which the rays are to be applied.

The most up-to-date apparatus consists of a high-tension transformer and rectifier, driven by a rotary converter, which derives power from direct-current electric service and delivers alternating current to the high-tension transformer.

Kᴜʜɪᴏ Bᴀʏ Rᴀɴɢᴇ Lɪɢʜᴛ, Hᴀᴡᴀɪɪ

Automatic Lighthouses.

In modern lighthouses the attendant need not remain awake all night to watch a fixed light. It is supplied with a piece of mechanism that will call him whenever anything is wrong. He has but to light up at dusk and then, remaining within call, may pound his ear or play pinochle to his heart's content.

If this light burns too strongly it will cause a metallic finger to advance until an electrical contact is made, which will ring an alarm, bringing the keeper up into the tower on the jump. Or perhaps the light may burn too low. If this happens the finger will sag until another electrical contact is made, and the alarm again is sounded.

In old-time lighthouses a fire of wood or coal or pitch was kept burning at the top of the tower—an uncertain and ineffectual glow. When the Boston Light was established in 1716 the oil-burning lamp had come into use. The lamp commonly employed was called the spider lamp. It had a solid wick dipped in fish oil and was swung by chains in a lantern, consisting of a wooden frame with heavy panes of glass. By 1812 whale oil had come into general use and a reflector had appeared, turning the rays seaward.

It is hard to realize that wicks dipped in lard constituted the highest development in lighting known up to the '40's. It was then that kerosene began to be used. The old single-strip wick was eventually replaced by a circular; and double wicks were employed to augment the illumination.

Kerosene is still in use in great stations, such as those at Navesink and Cape Hatteras. Wicks, however, have gone out of style, giving way to an incandescent oil vapor lamp, which converts the kerosene into a gas. This gas burns under a mantle that becomes incandescent and gives off more light than could be obtained from kerosene direct. These incandescent mantles are still monarchs of the lighthouse tower.

The development of lenses has been marked. The first step in this direction was achieved by means of a reflector. The device was primitive. Fresnel, a Frenchman, invented a lens that surrounded the light and directed its beams. The Lighthouse Service perfected this lens, set it to revolving, and timed its flashes. Lighthouses equipped with this kind of lamp require keepers. The air pressure must be regulated so that the liquid may be forced up into the vaporizer in the proper way.

Acetylene, once popular with bicyclists, is no longer produced in the messy fashion of the '90's. There are factories today whose task it is to generate the gas and store it in cylinders. The Government buys these charged cylinders, installs them and simply lets them run until they are exhausted. This super-bicycle lamp is making lighthouse keepers unnecessary.

A device now in use turns off the light when the sun shines and turns it on again when darkness comes. Two rods are placed side by side, one of them coated with lampblack. This blackened rod absorbs the heat rays that strike it. The other is highly polished and expels heat rays. When the sun shines, the rod that absorbs heat warms and lengthens. In doing so it turns off the supply of acetylene. As twilight comes on, the black rod cools, assuming its accustomed length. This shrinkage opens the gas valve and the light resumes.

Then there is selenium, one of those unfamiliar metals that sometimes lend themselves to peculiar uses. Selenium will carry an electric current in daylight but refuses to do so in the dark. Selenium has been adopted by some automatic stations.

The Story in a Newspaper[*]

Among the marvels of machinery of the present day there are none more complicated and bewildering in appearance than that by which the news of the world is sent adrift within the daily newspaper and none more marvelously effective in its operation. If we go back to the days when the seeds of the modern press were planted, we find them in the hand-printing done by the Chinese with their engraved blocks, and with the simple press used by Gutenberg about 1450, when he printed the first book from movable types.

His press consisted of two upright timbers held together by cross pieces at top and bottom. The flat bed on which the types rested was held up by other cross timbers, while through another passed a wooden screw, by the aid of which the wooden "platen" was forced down upon the types. The "form" of type was inked by a ball of leather stuffed with wool, the printer then spread the paper over it, laying a piece of blanket upon the paper to soften the impression, after which the screw forced the platen down on the paper and this on the type. This press was not original, since similar cheese and linen presses were then in use.

The Blaew Press, 1620

For 150 years this crude method of printing continued in operation, the first known improvement being made by an Amsterdam printer about 1620, he adding a few parts to render the work more effective. Such was the simple press still employed when Benjamin Franklin began his work as a printer a century later. In 1798 the Earl of Stanhope had a cast-iron frame made to replace the wooden one and added levers to give more power to the pressman. Woodcuts were then being printed and needed a stronger press.

We must go on with the old Gutenberg method and its tardy improvements, for another century, or until about 1816, when George Clymer, a printer of Phila-

*Illustrations by courtesy of R. Hoe & Co.

delphia, did away with the screw and employed a long and heavy cast-iron lever, by the aid of which the platen was forced down upon the type, the operation being assisted by accompanying devices.

As will be seen, the growth of improvements had until then been very slow. From this time forward it became far more rapid, some useful addition to the press being made at frequent intervals. The "Washington" press, used at this time by R. Hoe & Co., of New York, embodied these improvements, and became one of the best hand-printing presses so far made. The first steam-power press was introduced by Daniel Treadwell, of Boston, in 1822, the bed and platen, or its successor, the cylinder, being used in these and in the improved forms that followed until after the middle of the century.

The idea of replacing the platen by a cylinder was not a new one. It was employed in printing copper-plate engravings in the fifteenth century, a stationary wooden roller being employed, beneath which the bed, with its form and paper, was moved backward and forward, a sheet being printed at each movement. With this idea began a new era in the evolution of the

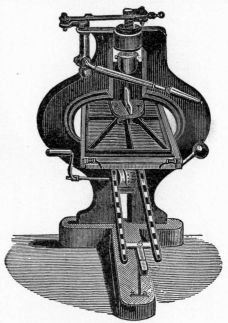

STANHOPE PRESS, 1798

printing press. A vast number of patents have since been issued for printing machines in which the cylinder is connected with the bed and later for the operation of two cylinders together, one holding the form of type and the other making the impression. But all these were for improvements, the underlying principle remaining the same. The conception of a press of this character in which the paper was to be fed into the press in an endless roll or "web" goes back to the beginning of the nineteenth century, though it was not made available until a later date.

Meanwhile, however, patent after patent for the improvement of the cylinder press were taken out and the art of printing improved rapidly, the firm of Hoe & Co. being one of the

CLYMER'S COLUMBIAN PRESS, 1816

most active engaged in this business, the United States continuing in advance of Europe in the development of the art. The single small cylinder and double small cylinder introduced by this firm proved highly efficient, the output of the former reaching 2,000 impressions per hour, while the double type, used where more rapid work was needed, yielded 4,000 per hour.

But the demands of the newspaper world steadily grew and in 1846 a press known as the Hoe Type Revolving Machine was completed and placed in the office of the *Public Ledger*, of Philadelphia. By increasing the number of cylinders the product was rapidly added to, each cylinder printing on one side 2,000 sheets per hour.

In 1835 Sir Rowland Hill suggested that a machine might be made that would print both sides of the sheet from a roll of paper in one operation. A similar double process had been performed for many years in the printing of cotton cloth. This remained, however, a mere suggestion until many years later, and the one-side printing continued. But, by adding to the number of cylinders, a speed of 20,000 papers thus printed was in time reached.

PETER SMITH HAND PRESS, 1822

To prevent the possible fall of types from a horizontal cylinder, the vertical cylinder was introduced by the London *Times*, but this danger was overcome in the Hoe presses, and by the subsequent invention of casting stereotype

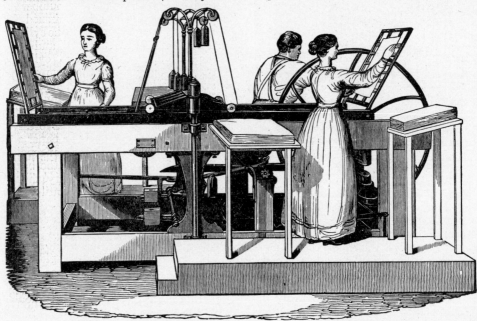

TREADWELL'S WOODEN-FRAME BED AND PLATEN POWER PRESS, 1822

plates in a curve the final stage of perfection in design was reached. In 1865 William Bullock, of Philadelphia, constructed the first printing press capable of printing from a web or continuous roll of paper, knives being added to cut the sheets, which were then carried through the press by tapes or fingers and delivered by the aid of metal nippers. There were difficulties in this series of operations, but these were overcome in the later Hoe press, in which the sheets were merely perforated by the cutter, and were afterward fully separated by the pull of accelerating tapes.

The old-time rag-paper had disappeared for newspaper work, being superseded by wood-pulp paper, the cheapness of which added to the desire to produce presses of greater speed and efficiency. It was also desirable that papers should be delivered folded for the carrier, and this led to the invention of folding machines, one of the earliest of which, produced in 1875, folded 15,000 per hour.

We have in the foregoing pages told the main story of the evolution of the printing press from the crude machine used by Gutenberg in 1450 to the rapid cylinder press of four centuries later. There is little more to be said. Later changes were largely in the matter of increase of activity, by duplication and superduplication of presses until sextuple and octuple presses were produced, and by adding to the rapidity and perfection of their operation, and the extraordinary ingenuity and quickness with which the printed sheets were folded and made ready for the convenience of the reader. Sir Rowland Hill's dream of a press which would print both sides of the paper at one operation in

WASHINGTON HAND PRESS, 1827

due time became a realized fact, while vast improvements in the matter of inking the forms, and even the addition of colored ink by which printing in color could be done, were among the new devices.

What we have further to say is a question of progress in rapidity of action rather than of invention. The 20,000 papers printed per hour, above stated, has since been seen passed to a degree that seems fairly miraculous. The quadruple press of 1887 turned out eight-page papers at a running speed of 18,000 per hour, these being cut, pasted and folded ready for the carrier or the mails. Four years later came the sextuple press (the single press six times duplicated) with an output of 72,000 eight-page papers per hour, and in a few years more the octuple press, its output 96,000 eight-page papers per hour. Larger papers were of course fewer, but its capacity for a twenty-page paper was 24,000 per hour.

As may well be conjectured, the twentieth century has had its share in this career of progress, the perfected press of 1916 being credited with the astounding output of 216,000 eight-page papers in an hour, all folded, cut, and counted in lots.

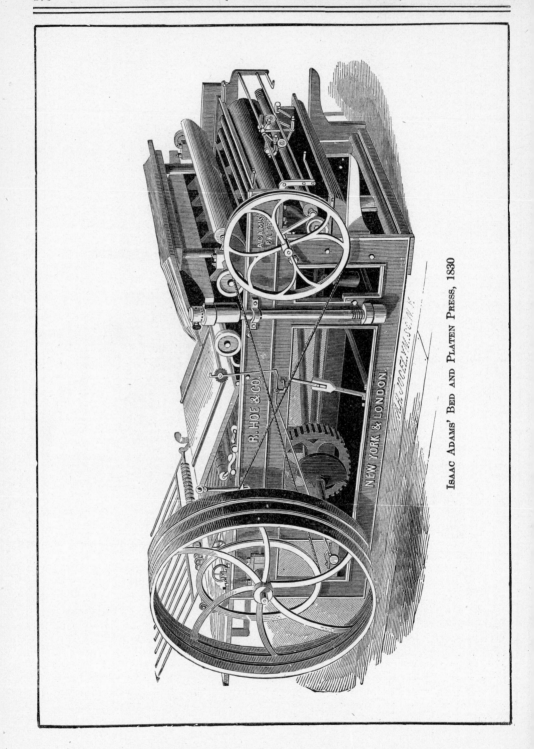

ISAAC ADAMS' BED AND PLATEN PRESS, 1830

Single Large Cylinder Press, 1832–1900

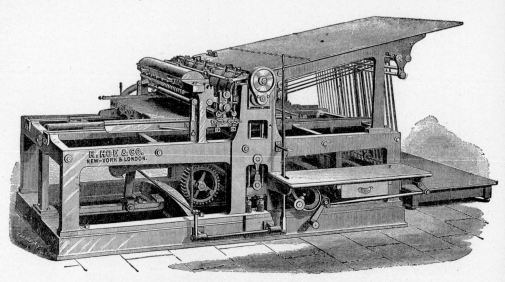

SINGLE SMALL CYLINDER PRESS, 1835–1900

DOUBLE CYLINDER PRESS, 1835–1900
These presses were built up to 1900 and this picture shows the latest design brought out about 1882.

THE LARGEST PRINTING PRESS IN THE WORLD, 1926
The Hoe 24-Cylinder Universal-Unit Multi-Color and Black Press

Where part of the pages are printed in three colors this press has still a running speed of 72,000 per hour. This machine is composed of 27,100 separate pieces, it being 47 feet long, 8 feet wide and 13 feet high, while such a mighty complication of whirling wheels and oscillating parts nowhere else exists.

A word more and we are done. To feed such giant presses the old hand method of setting and distributing type has grown much too slow. The linotype machine has added greatly to the rapidity of this centuries-old process. To this has been added the later monotype, of similar rapidity, while type distributing has become in large measure obsolete, the types, once used, going to the melting pot instead of to the fingers of the distributors.

What do We Mean by the " Flying Dutchman "?

The Flying Dutchman is a phantom ship said to be seen in stormy weather off the Cape of Good Hope, and thought to forbode ill luck. One form of the legend has it that the ship is doomed never to enter a port on account of a horrible murder committed on board; another, that the captain, a Dutchman, swore a profane oath that he would weather the Cape though he should beat there till the last day. He was taken at his word, and there he still beats, but never succeeds in rounding the point. He sometimes hails vessels and requests them to take letters home from him. The legend is supposed to have originated in the sight of some ship reflected from the clouds. It has been made the ground-work of one or two novels and an opera by Wagner.

Why does a Duck's Back Shed Water?

Nature has provided the duck with a protection against water just as she has so wisely protected all animals against such elements as they have to live in.

The feathers on a duck are very heavy and close together, and at the bottom of each feather is a little oil gland that supplies a certain amount of oil to each feather. This oil sheds the water from the back of a duck as soon as it strikes the feathers.

Canvasback ducks are considered the finest of the water-fowls for the table. The canvasback duck is so called from the appearance of the feathers on the back. They arrive in the United States from the north about the middle of October, sometimes assembling in immense numbers. The waters of Chesapeake Bay are a favorite locality for them. Here the wild celery, their favorite food, is abundant, and they escape the unpleasant fishy flavor of the fish-eating ducks.

Why doesn't the Sky ever Fall Down?

The sky never falls down because there is nothing to fall. What we see and call the sky is the reflection of the sun's rays on the belt of air that surrounds the earth. That beautiful blue dome that we sometimes hear spoken of as the roof of the earth is just the reflected light of the sun on the air.

The atmosphere of the earth consists of a mass of gas extending to a height which has been variously estimated at from forty-five to several hundred miles, possibly five hundred, and bearing on every part of the earth's surface with a pressure of about fifteen pounds per square inch.

How are Sand-Dunes Formed?

Sand-dunes are composed of drift sand thrown up by the waves of the sea, and blown, when dry, to some distance inland, until it is stopped by large stones, tree roots or other obstacles. It gradually accumulates around these, until the heaps become very large, often forming dunes or sand-hills.

What do We Mean by an " Eclipse "?

Any good dictionary will tell us that an eclipse is an interception or obscuration of the light of the sun, moon or other heavenly body by the intervention of another and non-luminous heavenly body. Stars and planets may suffer eclipse, but the principal eclipses are those of the sun and the moon.

An eclipse of the moon is an obscuration of the light of the moon occasioned by the interposition of the earth between the sun and the moon; consequently all eclipses of the moon happen at full moon; for it is only when the moon is on that side of the earth which is turned away from the sun, and directly opposite, that it can come within the earth's shadow. Further, the moon must at that time be in the same plane as the earth's shadow; that is, the plane of the ecliptic in which the latter always moves. But as the moon's orbit makes an angle of more than five degrees

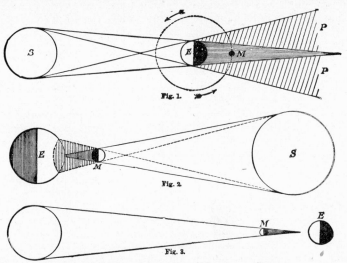

DIAGRAMS ILLUSTRATING THE THEORY OF ECLIPSES.

with the plane of the ecliptic, it frequently happens that though the moon is in opposition it does not come within the shadow of the earth.

The theory of lunar eclipses will be understood from Fig. 1, where S represents the sun, E the earth, and M the moon. If the sun were a point of light there would be a sharply outlined shadow or umbra only, but since the luminous surface is so large, there is always a region in which the light of the sun is only partially cut off by the earth, which region is known as the penumbra (P P). Hence during a lunar eclipse the moon first enters the penumbra, then is totally eclipsed by the umbra, then emerges through the penumbra again.

An eclipse of the sun is an occultation of the whole or part of the face of the sun occasioned by an interposition of the moon between the earth and the sun; thus all eclipses of the sun happen at the time of new moon.

Fig. 2 is a diagram showing the principle of a solar eclipse. The dark or central part of the moon's shadow, where the sun's rays are wholly intercepted, is here the umbra, and the light part, where only a part of them are intercepted, is the penumbra; and it is evident that if a spectator be situated on that part of the earth where the umbra falls there will be a total eclipse of the sun at that place; in the penumbra there will be a partial eclipse, and beyond the penumbra there will be no eclipse.

As the earth is not always at the same distance from the moon, and as the moon is a comparatively small body, if an eclipse should happen when the earth is so far from the moon that the moon's shadow falls short of the earth, a spectator situated on the earth in a direct line between the centers of the sun and moon would see a ring of light around the dark body of the moon; such an eclipse is called annular, as shown in Fig. 3; when this happens there can be no total eclipse anywhere, because the moon's umbra does not reach the earth.

An eclipse can never be annular longer than twelve minutes twenty-four seconds, nor total longer than seven minutes fifty-eight seconds; nor can the entire duration of an eclipse of the sun ever exceed two hours.

An eclipse of the sun begins on the western side of his disc and ends on the eastern; and an eclipse of the moon begins on the eastern side of her disc and ends on the western.

The average number of eclipses in a year is four, two of the sun and two of the moon; and as the sun and moon are as long below the horizon of any particular place as they are above it, the average number of visible eclipses in a year is two, one of the sun and one of the moon.

What are Dreams?

The dictionary tells us that a dream is a train of vagrant ideas which present themselves to the mind while we are asleep.

We know that the principal feature, when we are dreaming, is the absence of our control over the current of thought, so that the principal of suggestion has an unlimited sway. There is usually a complete want of coherency in the images that appear in dreams, but when we are dreaming this does not seem to cause any surprise.

Occasionally, however, intellectual efforts are made during sleep which would be difficult to surpass when awake.

It is said that Condillac often brought to a conclusion in his dreams, reasonings on which he had been employed during the day; and that Franklin believed that he had been often instructed in his dreams concerning the issue of events which at that time occupied his mind. Coleridge composed from two to three hundred lines during a dream; the beautiful fragment of "Kubla Khan," which was all he had committed to paper when he awoke, remaining as a specimen of that dream poem.

The best thought points to the fact that dreams depend on natural causes. They generally take their rise and character from internal bodily impressions or from something in the preceding state of body or mind. They are, therefore, retrospective and resultant, instead of being prospective or prophetic. The latter opinion has, however, prevailed in all ages and among all nations, and hence the common practice of divination or prophesying by dreams, that is, interpreting them as indications of coming events.

What Makes Our Teeth Chatter?

When one is cold there is apt to be a spasm of shivering over which the brain does not seem to have any control. The spasm causes the muscles of the jaw to contract very quickly and as soon as they are contracted, they let the jaw fall again of its own weight. This occurring many times in rapid succession is what causes the teeth to chatter.

There are two kinds of spasms, "clonic" and "tonic." In the former, the muscles contract and relax alternately in very quick succession, producing an appearance of agitation. In the latter, the muscles contract in a steady and uniform manner, and remain contracted for a comparatively long time.

The Story in a Honey-Comb*

When one thinks of honey one instinctively closes the eyes and a mental picture of fruit trees laden with snowy bloom, of beautiful clover fields, of green forests in a setting quiet and peaceful, comes before the mind so realistic that the delicate perfume of the fragrant blossoms is almost perceptible and the memory of the musical hum of the little honeybee as she industriously flits from blossom to blossom, or wings her homeward way heavily laden with the delicious nectar, rests one's jaded nerves.   Into this picture fits closely the old bee master among his old-fashioned skeps, with the atmosphere of mystery that has so long been associated with the master and his bees that one is almost reluctant to think of the production of honey as a great commercial industry, employing great factories in the manufacture of bee-hives and other equipment necessary for the modern beekeeper that he may take full advantage of the wonderful and almost inconceivable industry of the honeybee in storing the golden nectar of the blossoms.

The development of the industry has been very slow; only during the past fifty years has real progress been made, although honey formed one of the principal foods of the ancients, which was secured by robbing the wild bees.   During the early history of the United States, beekeep-ing was engaged in only as a farmer's side line, a few bees being kept in any kind of a box sitting out in the backyard, boarding themselves and working for nothing.   Even under such conditions amazing results were often obtained.   Lovers of nature and the out-of-doors were attracted by the study of bee life, and early beekeepers were invariably bee lovers.   The mysteries of

FERTILIZING ᴌ PUMPKIN FLOWER

the hive as revealed in the story of the family life of the bee—typical in many ways of our modern city life—is as fascinating as a fairy tale.

The average population of the modern beehive varies from forty to sixty thousand, with a well organized system of government.   Intense loyalty to the queen mother is apparent in all their activities and arrangements.   The close observer will discover a well-defined division of labor, different groups of bees performing certain operations.   The housekeeping operations seem to be delegated to the young bees under sixteen days old, while the policemen are the older ones whose dispositions are not so mild and who would be more likely to detect a stealthy robber.   It was this intensely interesting side of bee life that attracted the attention of a clergyman in failing health, forced to seek out-of-door occupation, in the early forties.   He began to investigate bee life from a commercial standpoint, and about 1852 devised the movable hanging frame, which entirely revolutionized the bee business, making modern commercial beekeeping possible.   Up to this time the box hive and straw skep were the only ones known, the combs being fastened to sticks, or the roof of the box, making it impossible to have any control over the activities of the hive.   The new device or frame to which the bees fastened their combs in which brood was

*Illustrations by courtesy of the A. I. Root Co.

(183)

AN ITALIAN ARMY OF BEES

ITALIAN DRONE ITALIAN QUEEN ITALIAN WORKER

(All are enlarged to about three times their size.)

reared could be removed, one or all, at any time desired. This opened up undreamed-of possibilities in the bee business, which up to this time could hardly be called an industry.

The man who has been most active in developing practical bee culture and who has contributed more to the growth of the industry in the United States than any other person, lives in Medina, Ohio. In 1865 this man was a successful manufacturer

A STRANGE HOME—BUT THE BEES ARE MAKING HONEY

of jewelry in the village of Medina. One day his attention was attracted to a swarm of bees flying over. One of his clerks noticing his interest asked what he would give for the bees. He replied that he would give a dollar, not expecting that by any means the bees could be brought down. Shortly after, he was much astonished to have the workman bring the bees safely stored inside a box and demand his dollar, which he promptly received, while his employer had the bees and soon developed a lot of bee enthusiasm. The returns from that swarm of bees convinced him that there were possibilities in the bee business, and very soon he gave up the jewelry business

A Happy Home of the Honey Bees

to engage in the bee business and manufacture of beehives. In this new move he encountered the opposition of his family and friends, for the general impression was that any man who would spend money or time on bees was either lazy or a fool. Know-ing that this particular man wasn't lazy he was called a fool to risk so much on an uncertain enter-prise. In his defense he remarked that he expected to live to see the time when honey would be sold in every corner grocery; but we doubt if he expected to see his prophecy fulfilled to the extent it has been, for not only is honey sold over every grocer's counter, but his own private brand is sold in all the principal markets of the United States.

"ALL HAIL, THE QUEEN"

Shortly after securing his first swarm of bees he commenced the manufacture of beehives in the same room where he had his jewelry business, using a large windmill for power. Soon the business outgrew the small quarters and was moved to the present location of the plant. Hardly a year has passed that additions or new buildings have not been added, and the mammoth plant as it stands today covers sixteen acres of floor space, giving steady employment to several hundred people, and for many years modern agricultural appliances have gone from this factory to all parts of the world.

The old method of straining honey has long since been replaced by the centrifugal honey extractor, which simply empties the cells of honey, not injuring the combs. The combs are then replaced in the hive to be refilled by the bees, thus saving them the labor of rebuilding the costly structure, increasing the quantity of extracted honey which a single colony can produce, while comb honey is produced so perfect in appear-ance as to cause some to believe it to be manufactured by machinery; but comb honey, nature's most exquisite product, comes in its dewy freshness untouched by the hand of man, from the beehive to the table, a food prepared in nature's laboratory fit for the Gods.

As beekeeping developed as an industry, the close relationship to fruit growing and horticulture became apparent, as bees were discovered to be the greatest pollen carry-ing agents known. The government than began to spend more money on the develop-ment of the various branches of agriculture; a Department of Apiculture was established and through the work of this department beekeeping is recognized as one of the most profitable branches of agriculture.

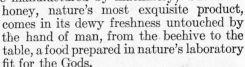

THE RESULT OF A BEE'S STING

The intense enthusiasm of this pioneer beekeeper was contagious and resulted in many taking up beekeeping. As no attention had been given to developing a market for honey and production increased, older beekeepers became alarmed and raised the cry that he was making too many beekeepers. Seeing the need for some means of increasing the demand for honey, a small honey business was started to dispose of the product of customers who had no market. Soon a definite educational campaign on the value of honey as a food was

A Large Swarm of Italians on a Young Locust Tree

Arrangement of Cells in Comb

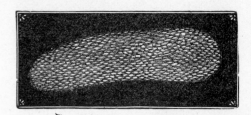

Highly Magnified Egg

started, enlisting the co-operation of beekeepers wherever possible. Immediately the necessity for more care in selecting and marketing honey was apparent.

The introduction of Italian bees into the United States in the early sixties marked an epoch in beekeeping, as they soon demonstrated their superiority as honey gatherers,

An Old-Style Hive—What is inside?

their gentleness and other traits proving them more adaptable to domestication and to modern methods of beekeeping. The marked superiority of some colonies over others attracted the attention of beekeepers to the possibility of race improvement by careful breeding, which gradually developed a new branch of beekeeping aside from honey

LOADING AN UP-TO-DATE CENTRIFUGAL EXTRACTOR

IN ACTION—FOR A FEW MINUTES ONLY

production—that of queen rearing—as it was discovered that improvement of stock must come through the queen mother. The average production of honey per colony has been materially increased, due not alone to improved methods, but to improvement in stock by careful breeders; and there are many beekeepers engaged exclusively in this branch of the industry who enjoy international reputation as breeders of

A MAN-SIZE HIVE OF ITALIAN BEES.

superior strains of queens, and many thousands are annually sent through the mails to all parts of the world. Live bees are shipped by express as easily as poultry or other live stock.

The honey industry is unique in this respect, that there is hardly a part of the United States where one cannot engage in it with profit. Locality has much to do with the flavor and quality of honey, owing to the different sources from which it is

We Must Brush the Bees Off So that We Can See
the Comb

After Cell Cappings are Cut Off—Ready to Extract

produced.   Honey is simply blossom nectar gathered by the bees, distilled or evaporated in the beehive with the same distinctive flavor as the perfume of the blossoms from which it was gathered; consequently we have as many different flavors of honey as plants that bloom in sufficient profusion to produce honey.   For this reason it is easy to recognize the distinct flavors of honey produced in different localities.   In California orange honey we get the delicate aroma of the orange blossoms, and the water-white honey from the mountain sage has its characteristic flavor.   Throughout the states east of the mountains and west of the Mississippi, are produced the well-known vari-

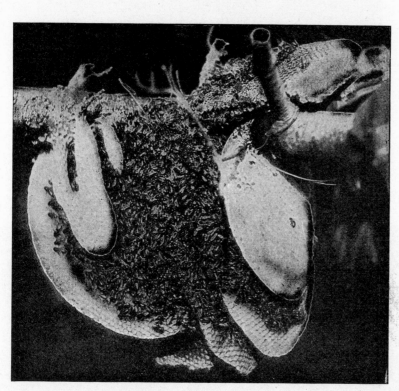

"FRESH AIR BEES"—No hive needed.

eties of honey—alfalfa, sweet clover and other honeys from fall flowers.   From the Middle West and Eastern states comes the matchless white clover honey, basswood and the dark aromatic buckwheat.   The Southern states produce a multitude of different honeys, the sweet clover, tupelo, and the palmetto being the most common. The total annual production of honey in the United States as given by the best authorities is approximately 55,000,000 pounds.   This, compared with other crop reports, may appear very small, but when considered from the standpoint of the enormous amount of bee labor represented, it is stupendous.   Undoubtedly present reports will greatly exceed those given.

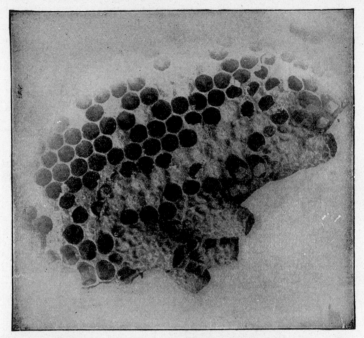

QUEEN CELLS—Note size compared with worker cells.

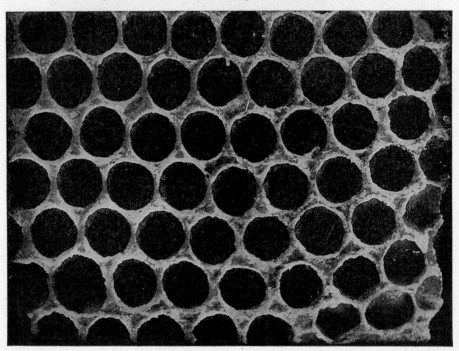

MAGNIFIED VIEW OF SECTION OF HONEYCOMB

SOME OF THE BEST HONEY COMES FROM SUCH LOCALITIES

A NICE, EVEN FRAME OF BEES

A MODEL ARRANGEMENT FOR KEEPING BEES FOR PLEASURE

REMOVING BEES FROM COMB

SECTIONS OF HONEY AS TAKEN FROM THE SUPERS

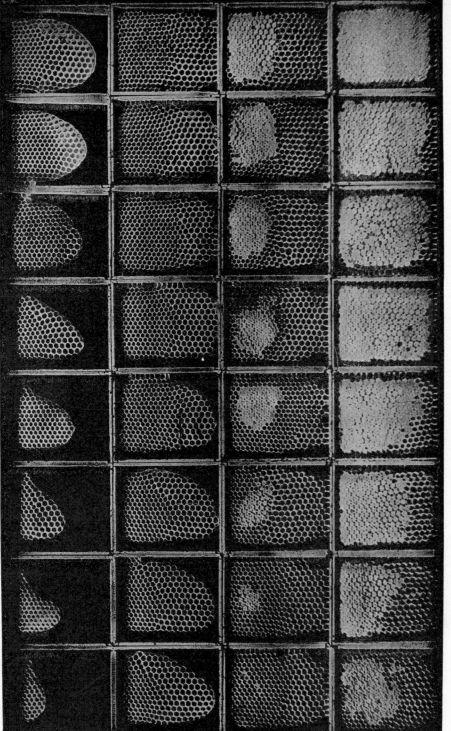

STAGES OF WORK IN BUILDING A SECTION OF HONEY

Uruk Girls Spreading Figs

Typical Smyrna Fig Orchard

Where do Figs Come From?

The fig tree, which is of the mulberry family, belonged originally in Asia Minor, but it has been naturalized in all the countries around the Mediterranean. It grows from fifteen to twenty, or even thirty, feet high.

In good climates it bears two crops in a season; one in the early summer, from the buds of the last year; the other, which is the chief harvest, in the autumn, from those on the spring growth.

Figs, particularly dried figs, form an important article of food in the countries of the Levant, and are exported in large quantities to America and Europe. The best come from Turkey.

What are " Fighting Fish "?

Fighting fish are a small fish and belong to the climbing perch family. They are natives of the southeast of Asia and are remarkable for their pugnacious propensities.

In Siam these fish are kept in glass globes, as we keep goldfish, for the purpose of fighting, and an extravagant amount of gambling takes place about the result of the fights.

When the fish is quiet its colors are dull, but when it is irritated it glows with metallic splendor.

How is the Exact Color of the Sky Determined?

An instrument called a "cyanometer," meaning "measurer of blue," is used for ascertaining the intensity of color in the sky.

It consists of a circular piece of metal or pasteboard, with a band divided by radii into fifty-one portions, each of which is painted with a shade of blue, beginning with the deepest, not distinguishable from black, and decreasing gradually to the lightest, not distinguishable from white. The observer holds this up between himself and the sky, turning it gradually round till he finds the tint of the instrument exactly corresponding to the tint of the sky.

What is a " Divining Rod "?

A divining rod is a wand or twig of hazel or willow used especially for discovering metallic deposits or water beneath the earth's surface.

It is described in a book written in 1546 and it has also a modern interest, which is set forth by Prof. W. F. Barrett, F.R.S., the chief modern investigator. The use of the divining rod at the present day is almost wholly confined to water finding, and in the hands of certain persons it undoubtedly has produced results along this line that are remarkable, to say the least. The professional water-finder provides himself with a forked twig, of hazel, for instance, which twig, held in balanced equilibrium in his hands, moves with a sudden and often violent motion, giving to the onlooker the impression of life within the twig itself. This apparent vitality of the twig is the means whereby the water-finder is led to the place where he claims underground water to exist, though its presence at that particular spot was hitherto wholly unsuspected. While failure is sometimes the outcome of the water-finder's attempts, success as often and, indeed, according to the testimony of Professor Barrett, more often crowns his efforts. Various explanations, scientific and other, of the phenomenon have been advanced. Professor Barrett ascribes it to "motor-automatism" on the part of the manipulator of the divining rod, that is, a reflex action excited by some stimulus upon his mind, which may be either a subconscious suggestion or an actual impression. He asserts that the function of the forked twig in the hands of the water-finder may be to act as an indicator of some material or other mental disturbance within him. While a hazel or willow twig seems to be preferred by the professional water-finders, twigs from the beech, holly or any other tree are employed; sometimes even a piece of wire or watch spring is used, with apparently as good results.

The Story of Electricity in the Home*

How wonderful to youth always has been the magical story of Aladdin and the wonderful lamp which, through its supernatural powers, he could gently stroke and thereby make genii of the unknown world his slaves.

In the rush of modern affairs there is that which is even more fascinating, even more wonderful, than the story of Aladdin and the magical power exerted through his lamp, but which is given but a passing thought because of the rapid changes through which we are passing.

Mythical as it may sound, yet nevertheless it is true, that man has harnessed for his use every snowflake that falls in the mountain tops and settles itself in the banks of perpetual ice and snow. How man has tapped the mountain fastnesses and converted the melting snows into a servant more powerful, more magical, more easily controlled, than Aladdin's genii, should be known to everyone. This servant is electricity.

This silent, invisible servant is ever present, always ready at the touch of a button or the snap of a switch, without hesitation, without grumbling, to do silently, swiftly, without dirt, without discomfort, without asking for a day off or for higher wages, the work which is laid out for it.

The use of electricity is so common today that the average person does not stop to think of it as a magical power wielding a tremendous influence for betterment in everyday affairs.

Electricity has rapidly found its way into the home for domestic purposes, eliminating at its entrance a host of cares of the household.

So recently, as to seem almost yesterday, the genius of man's brain coupled electricity with mechanical devices for the comfort and efficiency of the home.

Although a number of attempts have been made to build appliances for use in the home that would utilize electricity, the real beginning of the present almost universal use of electrical appliances seems to have been in the manufacture of the electric iron. One instance, at least, coupled with the manufacture of this household necessity, offers something of romanticism.

To a certain western state, a young electrical engineer betook himself, obtaining a position as superintendent of an electric power company and establishing his abode in a tent far up a canyon, more for the benefit of his wife's health than for the thought of being near the power plant and his work. The melting snow which gathered in little rivulets made a roaring mountain stream which generated such an excess of power for the company, that the young electrical engineer began looking about for other means of utilizing it than for lighting the homes of the villages below the mouth of the canyon. He designed a crude electric iron, placed a number of them in use, and found they gave fairly good service and at the same time enabled the power company to sell additional current. Development of the device was rapid, so rapid, in fact, that the young engineer's time was soon taken up with it and he resigned from his position with the power company to organize a small concern for the purpose of manufacturing electric irons which at first were sold to the consumers of the power company and later to a large near-by city.

These irons met with such a ready reception and were so popular with housewives because of the time saving and the convenience, that attention was next turned to other appliances which could be used in the home and which would assist

* Illustrations by courtesy of the Hotpoint Electric Heating Co.

the power company in the sale of current. About one hundred electric cooking sets were manufactured, consisting of ovens and crude round stoves. These were distributed among the customers of the power company and thenceforth their operation was carefully watched and improvements made from time to time, using always the suggestions offered by the housewives to make an appliance that would meet the needs of the home.

This particular company, which was started but little more than ten years ago in a small room of a store building in a small town of Southern California, has grown rapidly from that time when its complete office and factory force consisted of a man and two boys. It now places in homes well toward a million appliances each year.

Since the home can now be operated almost exclusively with electrical appliances, including everything from the electric iron to the modern labor-saving electric range, it is well to note briefly some of the many reasons for the success of electrically-heated appliances.

Perhaps most noticeable is cleanliness and the absolute absence of dirt and grime in using pure electric heat. There is no soot, no smoke nor discoloration. There are none of the bad effects so often caused by the air becoming vitiated, due to the burning up of oxygen in the air by gas and other fuels. There is no corrosion, oxidization or other form of deterioration.

Perfect and absolute control of heat seems to be secured. The easy snap of the controlling switch on the electric burner gives a certain intensity of heat which remains at that temperature so long as the switch remains in that position. Thus, with modern appliances, the housewife operates them at high, medium or low to suit her desires.

ORIGINAL ELECTRIC IRON

Fire risk is reduced to a minimum, because there are no matches, no kindlings, no kerosene cans, no oil barrels and nothing of the sort to endanger life and property.

The efficiency obtained through the operation of electrical appliances soon becomes evident to the user. The heat generated for ironing, for instance, is all utilized. This is true as well with heating or cooking appliances, and this utilization of practically all of the heat units naturally results in economy in operation in communities where the lighting or power company has made a favorable rate.

Because the electric iron seems to have been the forerunner of electrical appliances for the home, it is well first to describe briefly the processes of manufacture necessary before the iron can be placed in the home and take its position as one of the modern labor-saving devices.

One of the first irons to be manufactured, an illustration of which is shown herewith, did not offer the pleasing appearance nor give the service of its youngest sister, the illustration of which is also shown. One of the first problems was to control the heat at the iron, and to do this a separable switch plug was developed, enabling the operator to connect or disconnect the current supply at the iron.

The real problem, the one of most vital importance from the point of efficiency, was that of the heating element that would do more than heat the center of the sole plate. One of the pioneer manufacturers, after numerous experiments, concluded that, since the point or nose of an iron comes first in contact with the damp goods, naturally it should have first and most heat applied to it. The result was a double heating element in the form of a V, the resistance wire used being symmetrically wound on a flat, thin mica core. This V-shaped element, the point of the V coming up into the nose of the iron, insured a hot point, as well as hot sides, center, back and heel, where the terminals were connected with the switch plug receptacle. Another development which followed was that of an attached stand, eliminating the necessity

ELECTRIC IRONS, 1916

FIG. 1.—POURING MOLTEN METAL INTO MOLDS FOR CASTING IRON SOLE PLATES

FIG. 2.—WORKMAN POLISHING SOLE PLATES

of lifting the iron on and off a stand many times during the ironing. At first the iron was heavy and clumsy, being built of cast iron, but modern manufacture has made it possible to build the sole plate of cast iron and the top of pressed steel.

The illustrations show some of the steps necessary before the iron reaches the shipping room. Fig. 1 shows the workman pouring an earthen ladle of molten metal into the molds in which the sole plates are cast. Fig. 2 shows the sole plate in the hands of the workman, held against a rapidly revolving polishing wheel, after it has been run through a milling machine and ground to a perfect size. Fig. 3 shows a huge punch press which cuts the blank of steel that is afterwards drawn to the shape of the iron top. The workman is seen holding in his hand the blank cut from a sheet of steel (Fig. 4).   The blanks of flat steel of such irregular shape are next passed to a mammoth draw press which draws blanks into the perfect shape to be fitted over the top of the pressure plate which holds the heating element firmly against the sole plate.   At the operator's left hand is a stack of blanks and in his left hand he holds one ready to be placed in the draw press.   In his right hand is a top just pulled from the press, and at the extreme right a large truck full of finished tops ready for the polishing wheels.

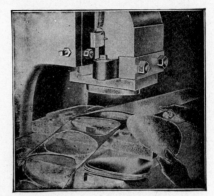

Mica, which so many people know as isinglass, is one of the most important materials in the manufacture of the standard electric iron. The highest grade mica comes from India and the open box in the picture shows thin, transparent pieces just tumbled out (Fig. 5).   At the edge of the table is a stack of mica strips known as cores.   Hanging over the top of the board are several cores on which the resistance wire has been wound, showing the V-shaped heating element.

FIG. 3.—BLANKING THE STEEL TOPS

One of the most important and yet seemingly simple parts of an electric iron is the switch plug which connects the electric light socket with the iron.   The operator in Fig. 6 is shown assembling switch plugs and is in the act of driving home a screw which holds in place the fiber bar over which the cord bends.

FIG. 4.—DRAWING THE BLANKS INTO THE PERFECTLY SHAPED TOPS

FIG. 5.—SHOWING A BOX OF IMPORTED MICA

Above on the table, a stack of "cores" and several elements ready for insertion in the iron.   Notice the V shape.

OPERATOR HOLDING ELEMENT BEFORE STRONG LIGHT TO DETECT DEFECTS IN THE MICA

INSPECTOR WITH CAREFULLY TRAINED, SENSITIVE FINGERS INSPECTING FINISHED IRONS BEFORE THEY ARE ENCASED IN THE CARTON

FIG. 6.—OPERATOR ASSEMBLING SWITCH PLUGS

FIG. 7.—ELECTRIC BOUDOIR SET THREE-POUND IRON

Stand for converting the iron into small stove, curling tongs heater, felt bag.

A standard six-pound iron consists of seventy-nine parts and represents two hundred and ten distinct factory operations. Every part is carefully inspected before being routed to the assembling department, and after being fully assembled the irons are placed on a traveling table where each is examined in its turn by an inspector with carefully trained fingers, sensitive as those of a miller who tells the quality of flour by pinching it between his thumb and forefinger. This inspector can quickly detect in the handsome finish a defect that is unnoticeable to the average person.

The Traveler's Iron.

Electric current is so nearly universally obtainable that milady who travels much has come to carry in her grip or suitcase a light-weight iron, usually of about three pounds, and to aid to further convenience, the manufacturer has supplied with this iron, curling tongs, curling tongs heater and an attached stand so that the iron can be inverted and its sole plate used as a small disc stove. The entire outfit is placed in a neat felt bag as shown by Fig. 7.

Electric Cooking Appliances.

It is stated that not until the reign of Queen Elizabeth did women begin to take over generally the handling of the kitchen work. Their absence from this important part of the household is not so much to be wondered at when we consider the size of the joints served prior to the time of that well-known queen and the crude methods of preparing the meal. On the other hand, it may

ELECTRIC TOASTER STOVE

have been due to the fact that the Armada called for men, and the women had to go into the kitchen irrespective of conditions. Be that as it may, we naturally conclude that the evolution of the kitchen and kitchen work began at about that time, for very shortly after the open fire gave way to some of the more crude methods of contained fire pots.

It was many years after Good Queen Bess' reign that electricity was introduced in England for cooking purposes; in fact, not until as late as 1891, when H. J. Dowsing, one of the pioneers of electric cooking, exhibited electric cookers and heaters at the Crystal Palace Electrical Exposition in London, was much interest manifested.

Divided into Three Classes.

Electric cooking appliances can very conveniently be divided into three classes: table appliances, and the light and heavy duty kitchen appliances; the latter being those requiring special wiring. Among table appliances are toasters, coffee percolators, electric teapots, chafing dishes and numerous other articles that add to the convenience of preparing food. These are termed light-duty appliances, as they operate from the light socket.

It might be well to explain that the lamp-socket appliances are those operating from the light socket and are built to carry not over 660 watts of current. Should you attach an appliance of heavier wattage to a light socket you will doubtless "blow" a fuse.

Electric Toaster.

In the rush and hurry of modern life, we are inclined to go back to the days of barbarism, when real home life was unknown. Instead of all members of the family gathering about the breakfast table when the meal is ready, they come straggling in one by one. This made it very difficult for the housewife to serve the breakfast hot, and particularly the toast, which is a favorite dish of our breakfast table. The necessary steps back and forth from the breakfast room to the kitchen to prepare hot, crunchy toast made this portion of breakfast-getting a not agreeable feature. The thought, taken up by electrical engineers, brought out an electric toaster, rectangular in shape, with handsome frame, nickel supports and wire heating element. This was indeed very efficient and could be used also as a small stove. This type of toaster was followed a little later by an upright toaster (Fig. 8). The heating element is of the radiant type, made of flat resistance wire wound on mica and placed in a vertical position between the two bread racks. When the current is switched on, the heating element becomes red and the bread is inserted under the gravity-operated bread clamps on each side. The bread clamp is simply raised at the edge of the slice of bread, and holds the bread firmly in place. This appliance toasts bread evenly, rapidly, and costs very little to operate. The flat top can be used for keeping a plate warm for the toast.

FIG. 8.—ELECTRIC UPRIGHT TOASTER

Electric Coffee Percolator.

Lovers of good coffee want it served hot, but boiling spoils coffee. The modern electric percolator, which can be operated on the dining table, has solved coffee-making problems. The particular style of percolator shown in Fig. 9 has no valves or floats or traps that continually get out of order and that make the cleaning of a percolator so disagreeable. This valveless percolator is very easily cleaned and requires no brush. The heating element of this type percolator is in the bottom of the pot in the center of the water space, and is of the immersion type, protruding up from the center of the bottom of the pot. The heating element is made of flat ribbon resistance wire wound on mica, then bent into the form of a cylinder to fit into the German silver shell. A screw-operated spreader in the center presses the heating element tightly against the entire surface of the shell and insures rapid conduction of the heat from the element to the water. A study of the illustration showing the inside of the percolator (Fig. 10) will make clear to you the method of operation. With this style of electric percolator, percolation begins within thirty seconds after the water has been placed in the pot and

FIG. 9.—ELECTRIC NICKEL VALVELESS PERCOLATOR

the current turned on, and delicious coffee, clear as amber, is ready to pour in ten minutes.

Percolators of this type are made by the manufacturer from sheet copper spun in perfect shape, and also aluminum spun. The latter makes an especially desirable percolator.

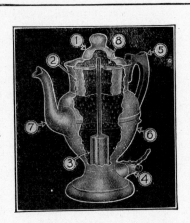

FIG 10.—X-RAY SHOWING THE VALVELESS MECHANISM, ELECTRIC PERCOLATER

The above gives a comprehensive insight into the general construction, equipment and operation of valveless Percolators. 1—Glass globe. 2—Aluminum coffee basket. 3—Element, with German-silver shell—completely surrounded by water. (Highly efficient.) 4—Interchangeable switch-plug. 5—Ebonized wood—always-cool handle. 6—Copper body—nickeled and highly polished. 7—White metal spout. 8—Lid—securely fastened hinge.

FIG. 11.—ELECTRIC MACHINE TYPE VALVELESS PERCOLATOR

Machine Type Percolator.

Because some prefer to draw coffee from a faucet rather than pour it from a spout, manufacturers have made a percolator of this type called the machine style. These are sold in various patterns from the Colonial design, like the illustration shown (Fig. 11), to those patterned after the Grecian urn.

We have already mentioned how an electrical engineer, shortly after placing irons in the homes of his customers, followed them with a number of small stoves and ovens. These required special wiring, as the wattage was too heavy to allow of their operation from the light socket. Principally, they were used in the kitchen on one end of the table or on a small shelf. This method necessitated carrying considerable food to the dining room after it was cooked, and brought out the thought of a means of preparing breakfast or a luncheon at the dining table. For this purpose a small stove seemed desirable, and the result was a small disc stove made of cast iron, highly nickel plated and polished.

On this little stove, herewith illustrated (Fig. 12), minor cooking operations can be performed, such as frying, boiling, etc., and it is used by many for toasting bread by placing a piece of metal screen on top. It is also very serviceable for frying hot cakes. The heating element is of the same construction as that in the iron; the mica is clapped tightly against the metal top and below this is a plate of asbestos which prevents the downward radiation of the heat.

This disc stove was first made in single heat, but the later improved stoves of this same type are made in three-heat style.

Many improvements have been made on the disc stoves and they are sold not only as single, but as double or twin, and triple discs.

One often finds it inconvenient, when traveling, to obtain hot water whenever needed. The light four-inch disc stove has proved to be a very desirable possession in cases of this kind. Its size makes it very convenient to pack in trunk or grip, and since it operates from any light socket, it is very handy, not only for the traveler and in the kitchen, but is a boon to many a bachelor man or maid.

FIG. 12.—ELECTRIC DISC STOVE

Perhaps, before going further, it is well to explain the meaning of single and three-heat. Let us suppose that you are operating one of the small disc stoves and that the stove will carry 600 watts of current. If that stove is equipped with a single heat, you will be using the full 600 watts whenever the switch is on. If it is equipped with a three-heat switch, it can be adjusted to 600 watts at full, 300 at medium and 150 at low, which means a great saving in current for most small cooking operations.

Two Distinct Types of Heating Elements.

There are two very distinct types of electric heating elements or burners, the disc or closed type, and the open-coil type. These two types operate on entirely different principles. The disc stove conveys the heat to the food by the principle of conduction, i. e., the heated metal top of the stove in turn conducts the heat to the metal of the dish and thereby heats the food within the dish.

The open-coil type of element operates on the principle of radiant heat. The heat rays from the element are focused on the dish in which the food is being prepared. In the former style burner, sufficient time is required to heat the metal top of the stove before the heat can be utilized, while in the latter, the heat is almost instantaneously effective. Below the coils of the radiant type of grills and heaters shown in this section is placed a highly polished, nickeled disc which serves to reflect all the heat units that are directed downward, back to the dish in which the food is being prepared, thereby utilizing a maximum of the heat units produced.

One very distinct advantage in the open-coil over the disc type is that in the former practically all the utensils found in the average home can be satisfactorily used, granite and enamel-ware being especially desirable, while in the disc-type stoves, it is necessary to have dishes with smooth, clean bottoms and that they fit very closely in order to make metallic contact over the entire surface.

The lightness, convenience, and general utility of the small open-coil stove has been responsible for a number of designs being manufactured and sold in enormous quantities, these being made up not only as stoves, but as grills. The accompanying illustration (Fig. 13) is of a rectangular grill, made of pressed steel and highly polished, designed to operate from any electric light socket. The heating element is of the open-coil reflector type and is so placed in the frame that cooking can be done both above and below the glowing coils at the same time. This is a convenience and economy, as one is able to cook two dishes of food at the cost of one. This particular grill is furnished with three dishes, any one of which can be used either above or below the coils. When cooking above the coils only is desired, the small flat pan is placed in a groove below the coils to reflect to the cooking operation any heat that would be thrown downward from the heating element. The shallow pan also serves as a cover for either of the deeper dishes or for a hot-cake griddle.

This radiant grill is light in weight, occupies a small space and is a most desirable appliance in the home, to be used in either the living room or dining room for the preparation of a light luncheon or afternoon tea service.

Of the same manufacture is the radiant grill shown in Fig. 14. This grill, you will note, is round, which particularly adapts it to the use of utensils ordinarily found in the kitchen of the average home. You will note that there are two dishes to this grill, a top dish with a broiling grid, to be used underneath the coils for broiling chops, and a shallower dish to be used above the coils

FIG. 13.—ELECTRIC RECTANGULAR GRILL

FIG. 14.—ELECTRIC THREE-HEAT GRILL

FIG. 15.—ELECTRIC RADIANT STOVE

for frying operations. There is furnished also a reflector which is so designed that it serves equally well as a cover for either dish and makes a very choice griddle for baking hot cakes.

While this particular grill is furnished with a wattage providing for operation from a lamp-socket, it is of the three-heat style already spoken of as so desirable in appliances of this character. A companion grill to this is of the same design, excepting that it is furnished in single heat only and lists at a somewhat lower price.

You will remember that in explaining the many advantages of the open-coil type of burner, it was stated as one of these that the housewife could use cooking utensils ordinarily found in the home, and because of this peculiar adaptability the round grills here spoken of and illustrated are having an exceedingly large sale. These open-coil grills are also very efficient as toasters, the bread being placed on

FIG. 16.—ELECTRIC CHAFING DISHES

top of the grating, which protects the coils from injury. Where only chops, toast and coffee are to be had for breakfast, chops can be prepared below the coils, the toast above, while the coffee gurgle-gurgles in the percolator.

Some people who have not felt any need of a grill have desired an open-coil stove, and of this same general type of manufacture there is the open-coil radiant stove herewith illustrated (Fig. 15). It is equipped with the same kind of a burner or element with a reflector underneath, and can be used very efficiently with ordinary cooking utensils and is also very serviceable as a toaster. Using this stove in combination with the ovenette, which will be illustrated further on, the owner is provided with a table range which meets most of the requirements in a small family.

A line of cooking utensils would not be complete without suitable designs of chafing dishes, and these are made in several styles, both with and without heating elements, the latter being used on the disc and open-coil stoves already illustrated, while the former contains a heating element very much along the lines of the percolator. These are furnished, as you will note from the illustration (Fig. 16), with suitable cooking pans for the preparation of chafing-dish dainties.

Baking and Roasting.

It is only natural to suppose that manufacturers of electric stoves of both light and heavy duty should next turn their attention to ovens, since oven cooking is even primary to cooking that is done on open burners and is now coming to be even of more importance. The first oven herewith shown (Fig. 17) is of the lamp-socket type, equipped with three heats, providing a very efficient oven for small operations. The second one illustrated (Fig. 18) is of standard size and accommodates a quantity of food equal to that of any large range oven. It is provided with a heavy wattage and therefore requires special wiring.

To meet the requirements of the many families in which such a small amount of baking is done, and to cater particularly to apartment-house dwellers, the manufacturers of the line of radiant stoves described and illustrated have brought forth a small cylindrical oven called the ovenette. This little oven fits either the radiant stove or the round radiant grill. It is made of pressed steel and finished in highly polished nickel. This ovenette, in combination with either the radiant stove or the round radiant grill, provides complete cooking equipment upon which an entire meal can be prepared, whether it be heating rolls and preparing crisp bacon or chops for breakfast, or baking a roast, a loaf cake or even bread for the dinner. It will bake pies, cake, biscuit, potatoes, roast meats, etc., up to its capacity, at a less

FIG. 17.—ELECTRIC LAMP-SOCKET OVEN   FIG. 18.—ELECTRIC STANDARD OVEN

current cost than is possible with the larger oven and in less time. This ovenette has what is called a middle ring, which makes it adjustable to two sizes when large or small quantities of food are to be prepared.

So you see, the woman of today who utilizes current furnished through the light socket, can bring to her command genii as wonderful as those at the command of Aladdin when he stroked the wonderful lamp. Her household duties are made easier. There is far less preparatory work and she is able to place her home on a much more efficient basis than with ordinary methods.

The home electrical is not complete without containing at least some of the electrical appliances which have been designed for the purpose of alleviating pain. One of these is an electric heating pad made of steel units, so hinged as to make the appliance sufficiently flexible to be wrapped around an arm or limb and to conform to the curves of the body. The other is a pad made of aluminum which is concave on one side and convex on the other and may be used in a wet pack. Each of these heating pads is covered with a high-grade cover of eiderdown which provides a soft contact for the skin.

Perhaps next in importance along this line of electrical appliances is the small immersion heater shown in Fig. 19, and which requires so little space that it can be easily carried even in a woman's handbag. This style of heater will quickly heat a glass of water by simply immersing the heater in the water. This device is very extensively used by mothers in heating milk for the baby, by men in heating water for shaving, and by doctors and dentists who require small quantities of hot water for sterilizing and other uses.

One thing most desirable in connection with practically all of the lamp-socket appliances described and illustrated in this section is the very small cost of operation. Lighting companies have so reduced the cost of current within the last two or three years that a breakfast may now be prepared electrically for not more than a couple of cents, while one of the pads may be used an entire night at a cost of less than one cent in soothing rheumatic pains or in driving away the chill for outdoor sleepers.

But one of the hardest domestic tasks is that of keeping the house clean.   To obviate the difficulties encountered in this connection and to make the home sanitary,

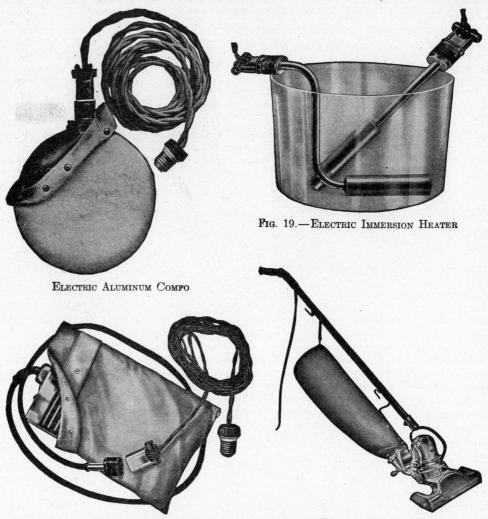

ELECTRIC ALUMINUM COMFO

FIG. 19.—ELECTRIC IMMERSION HEATER

ELECTRIC FLEXIBLE COMFO (Metal)

FIG. 20.—ELECTRIC VACUUM CLEANER

electric vacuum cleaners are provided by several manufacturers, a very recent acceptable type being illustrated in Fig. 20.   This type of vacuum cleaner, which is reasonable in price, is made of steel and finished in very highly polished nickel. It operates from any light socket and consumes but a very small amount of current, much less than is consumed by a toaster.   It can also be purchased with different attachments with which curtains, radiators, clothes and walls may be cleaned. The possession in the home of one of these vacuum cleaners makes it unnecessary to take up rugs, carpets, tear down curtains and go through the semiannual worry, wear and tear of house cleaning. The vacuum cleaner will do it better and many times quicker without removing a single article of furniture or disturbing a rug or curtain; and instead of scattering the germ-laden dust in the air, to be drawn into the nostrils and lungs of the family, the cleaner sucks them up into a dust-tight bag from which they can be deposited on a paper and burned.

The evolution in cooking and heating appliances for the home in the last ten years has indeed been rapid, but it is very recently indeed that the housewife has been able to satisfy the longing and the desire that has kept getting stronger from day to day, since first she began to use electric cooking appliances. She has been dreaming of that which would make her kitchen a domestic-science laboratory, and her dream can come true because now she can purchase an elec-

FIG. 21.—ELECTRIC RANGE

tric range patterned in general style after the more acceptable gas or other fuel ranges, but infinitely more efficient.

The particular type of range herewith illustrated (Fig. 21) uses a burner of the open-coil type, both for the surface burners and for the oven. The ovens are highly insulated with a thick packing of best grade mineral wool, which reduces air leakage to a minimum and retains the heat generated for a long period. Many cooking operations which are performed in ordinary ovens with the burners on, can be prepared in this particular style of oven by using stored heat for the last half of the operation. The range is simplicity itself in operation. Each burner is operated by an indicating snap switch which has three separate heats, full, medium and low; medium being one-half of full and low one-half of medium. There are no matches; there is no danger from fire. There is no vitiated, foul air because of noxious gases from ordinary cooking stoves. There is no soot or grime, no ashes, no wood or coal to carry; there are fewer steps; there is less watching of the range; practically none at all, because when a burner is turned to medium, for instance, you know that you have a certain degree of heat for just as long as the switch is in that position. Results are eminently satisfactory and there is a sufficient saving in the weights and the nutritive value of foods cooked, especially in the oven, to make the electric range indeed a most desirable and economical addition to any home.

Today, the housewife, whether the provider of the home be a laborer or a merchant prince, can, with a simple touch of the button or a snap of the switch, bring to her immediate command, and subservient to her wishes, that subtle something which came in the snowflake, and which, while invisible, yet provides the greatest boon to mankind—electricity.

Why is there Always a Soft Spot in a Cocoanut Shell?

A cocoanut shell always has a soft spot at one end because this is the provision nature has made to allow the embryo of the future tree to push its way out of the hard shell.

Cocoanuts, as most of us know, have a thick, hard shell, with three black scars at one end. The soft scar may easily be pierced with a pin; the others are as hard as the rest of the shell. Outside of this hard shell we are accustomed to seeing another covering of considerable thickness, of an extremely fibrous substance. When cocoanuts are picked, however, they have still another covering—an outer rind which has a smooth surface.

The tree which produces the cocoanut is a palm, from sixty to a hundred feet high. The trunk is straight and naked, and surmounted by a crown of feather-like leaves. The nuts hang from the summit of the tree in clusters of a dozen or more together.

Food, clothing and the means of shelter and protection are all afforded by the cocoanut tree. The kernels are used as food in a number of different forms, and when pressed, they yield an oil which is largely used in candle making and in the manufacture of soaps. When they are dried before the oil is pressed out they are known as "copra."

We have given the name "milk" to the sweet and watery liquid, of a whitish color, which is inclosed in considerable quantity in the kernel.

By boring the tree itself, a white, sweetish liquid called "toddy" exudes from the wound. This yields one of the varieties of the spirit called "arack" when distilled. A kind of a sugar called "jaggery" is also obtained from the cocoanut juice.

The fibrous coat of the nut is made into a preparation called "cellulose," which is described in another story in this book, and also into the well-known cocoanut matting. The coarse yarn obtained from it is called "coir," and it is also used for cordage. The hard shell of the nut is polished and made into cups and other domestic utensils. The fronds are wrought into baskets, brooms, mats, sacks and many other useful articles; and the trunks are made into boats, and furnish timber for the construction of houses. Altogether the cocoanut palm will be seen to be a very useful member of the plant kingdom.

How does a Gasoline Motor Run an Electric Street Car?

A gasoline-electric railroad train was introduced in Germany in 1913. It comprises a power car and ten other cars, each of a five-ton capacity, which trail along behind. The power car carries two gasoline engines of a hundred and twenty-five horse-power each which drive a dynamo installed in the center. The current is transmitted to the electric motors, actuating each of the wheels of the power car and the trailers. The General Electric Company has perfected a similar car for use on the suburban branches of street railroads in this country. Most of them are equipped with a two hundred horse-power gasoline engine directly connected to a dynamo from which power is generated and transmitted to the motors, which are located on the car axles. Cars of this type can be made of a larger seating capacity than is customary and can easily attain a speed of a mile a minute.

Gasoline engines offer great advantages over steam because of the absence of boilers, coal and ashes, and a much higher efficiency is obtainable, a consumption of one pint of gasoline per horse-power hour being good practice for well-designed motor engines and a total efficiency of from ten to thirty-five per cent of the energy in the fuel being available, as against one to twenty per cent for steam averages. The utilization of the gasoline engine to generate electric power for surface cars, in instances where it is not practical to transmit energy from power stations, presents wonderful possibilities.

A Suburban Railway Car of the Gasoline-Electric Type

How do " Carrier Pigeons " Carry Messages?

The real carrier pigeon is a large bird with long wings, a large tuberculated mass of naked skin at the base of the beak, and a circle of naked skin round the eyes, but the variety generally employed to carry messages more resembles an ordinary pigeon.

The practice of sending letters by pigeons belongs originally to Eastern countries, though in other countries it has often been adopted, more especially before the invention of the electric telegraph. An actual post-system in which pigeons were the messengers was established at Bagdad by the Sultan Nureddin Mahmud, who died in 1174, and lasted till 1258, when Bagdad fell into the hands of the Mongols and was destroyed by them.

These birds can be utilized in this way only in virtue of what is called their "homing" faculty or instinct, which enables them to find their way back home from surprising distances. But if they are taken to the place from which the message is to be sent and kept there too long, say over a fortnight, they will forget their home and not return to it. They are tried first with short distances, which are then gradually increased. The missive may be fastened to the wing or the tail, and must be quite small and attached so as not to interfere with the bird's flight.

By the use of microphotography a long message may be conveyed in this way, and such were received by the besieged residents in Paris during the Franco-Prussian War of 1870–71 the birds being conveyed out of the city in balloons.

Seventy-two miles in two and one-half hours, a hundred and eighty in four and one-half, have been accomplished by carrier pigeons. Large numbers of these birds are now kept in England, Belgium, France, etc., there being numerous pigeon clubs which hold pigeon races to test the speed of the birds. These pigeons are also kept in several European countries for military purposes.

What Family has Over 9,000,000 Members?

Each female cod has more than 9,000,000 eggs, but the numbers are kept down by a host of enemies.

The most interesting species is the "Common" or "Bank Cod." Though they are found plentifully on the coasts of other northern regions, such as Britain, Scandinavia and Iceland, a stretch of sea near the coast of Newfoundland is the favorite annual resort of countless multitudes of cod, which visit the "Grand Banks" to feed upon the molluscous animals abundant there, and thus attract fleets of fishermen.

The spawning season on the banks of Newfoundland begins about the month of March and terminates in June; but the regular period of fishing does not commence before April, on account of the storms, ice and fogs. The season lasts till the end of June, when the cod commence their migrations.

The average length of the common cod is about two and one-half or three feet, and the weight between thirty and fifty pounds, though sometimes cod are caught weighing three times as much. The color is a yellowish gray on the back, spotted with yellow and brown; the belly white or red, with golden spots in young specimens.

Few members of the animal creation are more universally serviceable to man than the codfish. Both in its fresh state and when salted and dried, it is a substantial and wholesome article of food. The tongue is considered a delicacy. The swimming-bladders or "sounds," besides being highly nutritious, supply, if rightly prepared, isinglass equal to the best of that which is brought from Russia. The oil, which is extracted from the liver, is of great medicinal value, and contributes considerably to the high economic value of the cod.

The finest and palest oil is made from fresh and carefully cleaned liver, the oil being extracted either in the cold or by a gentle heat. Only the pale oils are used in medicine; the dark oils are too rank and acrid, and they are only used in dressing leather.

The Story in the Telephone*

On March 10, 1876, Alexander Graham Bell, standing in a little attic at No. 5 Exeter Place, Boston, sent through his crude telephone the first spoken words ever carried over a wire, and the words were heard and understood by his associate, Thomas A. Watson, who was at the receiver in an adjacent room. On that day the telephone was born, and the first message went over the only telephone line in

DR. ALEXANDER GRAHAM BELL AT THE OPENING OF THE TRANSCONTINENTAL LINE

In front of Dr. Bell is the replica of his original telephone, and to his left is the glass case containing a piece of the wire over which Dr. Bell and Mr. Watson carried on the first telephone conversation in the world.

the world—a line less than a hundred feet long. On January 25, 1915, less than forty years later, this same Alexander Graham Bell, in New York, talked to this same Thomas A. Watson, in San Francisco, over a wire stretching 3,400 miles across the continent.

In that memorable year of 1876, Dom Pedro, Emperor of Brazil, while visiting the Philadelphia Centennial, was attracted to Bell's modest telephone exhibit, picked up the receiver, listened as Professor Bell talked at the other end of the room, and, amazed at the wonder of the thing, cried out, "My God—it speaks!"

*Illustrations by the courtesy of the American Telephone and Telegraph Co.

From that time, the first telephone exhibit became the center of attraction at the exposition. Had Dom Pedro lived to see the Panama-Pacific Exposition he might have listened to Professor Bell talking not merely from the other end of a room, but from the other side of a continent.

Some idea of the rapid growth of the telephone business in the United States may be gathered from the statistician's figures, which show that in 1880 there were less than 100,000 telephones in use in this country, and in 1922 there were more than 13,500,000 owned and connected stations in the Bell system alone—nearly two-thirds of all the telephones in the world. There are more telephones in New York City than in the whole of any foreign country, excepting only Great Britain and

CENTRAL TELEPHONE EXCHANGE, NEW YORK CITY, 1880

Germany. Chicago has more telephones than France, Spain and Portugal combined. As for rural telephones, practically the only farm telephones in the world are in the United States, where the number is now over 2,500,000. Elsewhere this field of service has been almost wholly neglected.

Essential Factor in American Life.

Such broad use is made of the telephone service of America that the progress in telephony is an essential factor in all American progress.

A visiting Englishman envying the light, airy accommodations in the tall office buildings in American cities, has sagely said that the skyscraper would be impossible without the adequate telephone service which is here provided.

In the housing of the people the telephone is a pioneering agent for better conditions. In the cities telephone service is indispensable in apartment houses and hotels which raise people above the noise and dust of the street. In the suburbs the telephone and the trolley make the waste places desirable homes, and although a

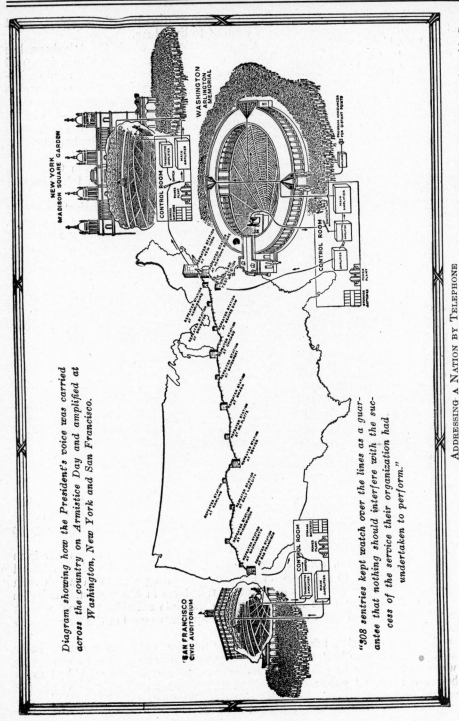

Diagram showing how the President's voice was carried across the country on Armistice Day and amplified at Washington, New York and San Francisco.

"308 sentries kept watch over the lines as a guarantee that nothing should interfere with the success of the service their organization had undertaken to perform."

ADDRESSING A NATION BY TELEPHONE

On Armistice Day, 1921, the President of the United States, speaking at Arlington, over the body of the Unknown Soldier, was heard in San Francisco and New York, by means of the telephone system and amplifiers. This diagram shows the telephone route, with repeater stations.

man may walk some distance to reach some transportation line, the telephone must enter his own dwelling place before he is content to live there.

This desirable decentralization of the population in which the telephone has been so important a factor extends beyond the suburbs to the rural districts, and the American farmer with his wife and family is blessed by facilities for communication unknown in any other part of the world. The fact that the farms and ranches in this country, and especially in the west, have been of comparatively large area, has had a tendency to make American farm life particularly lonely. It is safe to say that nothing has done more to relieve this loneliness and prevent the drift from the farms to the cities, than the widespread establishment of rural telephone service.

The telephone development of the United States is not confined to the large centers of population, but is well distributed, the large number of farm telephones in this country being in strong contrast to the small number of farm telephones in European countries.

It is obvious that the ordinary methods of commerce and manufacture would have to be radically made over if the telephone service should lose any of its present efficiency or if it should fail to advance so as to meet the constantly increasing demands made upon it. With the first day of telephone congestion ordinary business would come to a standstill, and when an adjustment was made, everybody would find himself slowed down, doing less work in longer hours and at greater expense, and being unable to take advantage of opportunities for advancement which he had come to consider an inalienable right.

Not only would methods be changed, but the physical structure of business, especially in cities, would be completely metamorphosed. The top floors of office buildings and hotels would be immediately less desirable. In tall buildings the multitude of messengers and the frequent passing in and out would demand the increase in elevator facilities and even the enlargement of halls and doorways. Many of the narrower streets would be impassable. Factories and warehouses now located in the open country where land is cheap and the natural conditions of working and living are most favorable, would be relocated in cities as close as possible to their administrative and merchandising headquarters.

It would be hard to find a line of business where progress would not be seriously retarded by an impairment of the present telephone efficiency.

America Leads in Telephone Growth.

It is a far cry from Bell's first telephone to Universal Service.

Bell's invention had demonstrated the practicability of speech transmission, but there were many obstacles to overcome and many problems to be solved before the telephone could be of commercial value and take its place among the great public utilities.

Professor Bell had demonstrated that two people could talk to each other from connected telephones for a considerable distance. In order to be of commercial value, it was necessary to establish an intercommunicating system in which each telephone could be connected with every other telephone in the system. This has been accomplished through the invention of the multiple switchboard and a great number of inventions and improvements in all the apparatus used in the transmission of speech.

But it was an unexplored field into which the telephone pioneers so courageously plunged. There were no beaten paths, and the way was beset with unknown perils; there was no experience to guide. A vast amount of educational work had to be done before a skeptical public would accept the telephone at its true value, yet courage and persistency triumphed. Discoveries and inventions followed scarcely less important than Professor Bell's original discovery.

Courtesy New York Telephone Co.

THE WORLD'S LARGEST TELEPHONE BUILDING

This remarkable building, which is a notable unit in New York's skyline, is the Central Office and Administration Building of the New York Telephone Co. It covers an entire block, the ground dimensions being 212 by 257 feet. The total gross area is 28 acres. Each of the first ten floors covers an acre. There are 5 floors below the street level, 31 above. The 20,000 tons of steel used in its construction would fill 1000 railroad freight cars in a train 9 miles long. A unique feature is an arcade 17 feet wide.

That the United States has from the beginning far outstripped the rest of the civilized world in the growth of the telephone is shown by comparison.

In Great Britain and Ireland there are only 2 telephones to every 100 inhabitants. In the United States there are 13.6 to every 100 inhabitants. Sweden shows the highest percentage of telephones of any European country, having 6.4 to every 100 people. Norway has 4.4 and Denmark 3.9 per hundred population. Germany, at the beginning of the World War in 1914, had 2.2 telephones to every hundred inhabitants; since then the percentage has increased slightly. Receipts of telephone companies in the United States amount in a single year to over $400,000,000, the annual expenses for equipment reaching $100,000,000.

The total number of telephones in all other European countries is considerably

POLE LINE RUNNING THROUGH PRINCIPAL   A TYPICAL EXAMPLE OF AMERICAN POLE
STREET IN AN ITALIAN TOWN   LINE CONSTRUCTION

less than may be found in two American cities, Chicago and Philadelphia; all of South America has less than Boston, and the remainder of the world, including Asia, Africa and Oceanica, has less than the City of New York.

American Telephone Practice Superior.

The superior telephone development in America is largely due to the efficiency of American telephone equipment and practice. The mechanical development has not only kept pace with public needs, but has anticipated them.

It is the practice of the Bell System, for example, to make what are called "fundamental development plans," in which a forecast is made of the telephone requirements of each American city twenty years ahead. The construction in each city is begun with these ultimate requirements in view. Underground conduits are built, central offices located and cables provided with an eye to the future, and if these plans are carried out important economies are obtained. If the plans are

AMERICAN METHOD OF RAISING POLES BY DERRICK WITH POWER FURNISHED BY MOTOR-TRUCK.

ONE OF THE VARIED TYPES OF DESK TELEPHONES USED IN FRANCE

THE STANDARD AMERICAN DESK TELEPHONE

TILE CONDUITS USED IN AMERICAN UNDERGROUND CONSTRUCTION

abandoned, the loss may be very great. Furthermore, there are sure to be times when the service will be interrupted and seriously impaired if such plans for the future are not made and consistently carried out.

It is characteristic of the best telephone management that while it cannot always perfectly forecast the direction of immediate growth, it should be built far enough ahead of present requirements to have a pair of wires ready for each new customer. The fact that New York and other large American cities have a considerable investment in telephone plant constructed to meet a prospective demand,

THIS PRIVATE SWITCHBOARD, IN ONE AMERICAN HOTEL, IS LARGER THAN MANY A SWITCHBOARD ABOARD, WHICH SERVES A WHOLE CITY

is the price which must be paid by any telephone management which really supplies the wants of the American people. Every additional subscriber that is connected with the system, requires sooner or later an outlay of new capital for his proportionate share of the whole plant, including equipment, wires, poles, cables, switchboards and real estate. In America the new subscriber finds his need anticipated and the facilities provided.

It is characteristic of private management that plans can be made for the future with reasonable assurance that the necessary funds will not be arbitrarily withheld, or that the work of the past will not be ruthlessly cast aside.

Another factor of telephone service in America is promptness. Local connections are made in a few seconds. In the case of interurban and long-distance calls, to prevent the long waiting for a turn, which abroad sometimes is a matter of hours, the American engineer provides enough long-distance trunks, so that, except in cases of accident, customers at the busiest times of the day are connected with distant points without delay.

The First Transcontinental Line.

The opening of the first transcontinental line between New York and San Francisco on January 25, 1915, was an epoch-making event in telephone history. The line is 3,400 miles long. It crosses thirteen states; it is carried on 130,000 poles. Four hard-drawn copper wires, .165 of an inch in diameter, run side by side over the entire distance, establishing two physical and one phantom circuit. The ordinary

THIS PICTURE SHOWS THE DIFFICULTIES ENCOUNTERED IN HAULING POLES IN A MOUNTAINOUS SECTION ALONG THE TRANSCONTINENTAL LINE OF THE BELL SYSTEM

telephone connection consists of two wires technically called a telephone circuit, each wire constituting one "side" of the circuit. A phantom circuit is a circuit superimposed on two ordinary circuits by so connecting the two wires or "sides" of each ordinary circuit that they can be used as one side of the phantom circuit. By the new multiplex method five practical talking circuits can be obtained from one pair of wires. One mile of single wire used in the transcontinental line weighed 435 pounds. Important improvements in cables have been made since then, and it is now possible to give even better transmission over circuits having only 80 pounds of copper per mile of circuit.

It was, perhaps, little more difficult to string wires from Denver to San Francisco than from New York to Denver, but the actual construction of the line was the least of the telephone engineer's troubles. His real problem was to make the line "talk," to send something 3,000 miles with a breath as the motive power. In effect, the voyage of the voice across the continent is instantaneous; if its speed should be accurately measured, a fifteenth of a second would probably be nearly exact. In other words, a message flying across the continent on the new transcontinental line, travels, not at the rate of 1,160 feet per second, which is the old stagecoach speed of sound, but at 56,000 miles per second. If it were possible for sound to carry that far, a "Hello" uttered in New York and traveling through the air without the aid of wires and electricity would not reach San Francisco until four hours later. The telephone not only transmits speech, but transmits it thousands of times faster than its own natural speed.

But while the telephone is breaking speech records, it must also guarantee safe delivery of these millions of little passengers it carries every few minutes in the way of sound waves created at the rate of 2,100 a second. There must be no jostling or crowding. These tiny waves, thousands and thousands of varying shapes, which are made by the human voice, and each as irregular and as different from the other as the waves of the sea, must not tumble over each other or get into each other's way, but must break upon the Pacific coast as they started at the Atlantic, or all the line fails and the millions of dollars spent upon it have been thrown away. And in all this line, if just one pin-point of construction is not as it should be, if there is one iota of imperfection, the miles of line are useless and the currents and waves and sounds and words do not reach the end as they should. It is such tremendous trifles, not the climbing of mountains and the bridging of chasms, that make the transcontinental line one of the wonders of the ages.

The engineer in telephony cannot increase his motive power. A breath against a metal disk changes air waves into electrical currents, and these electrical currents, millions of which are required for a single conversation, must be carried across the continent and produce the same sound waves in San Francisco as were made in New York. Here is a task so fine as to be gigantic. It was to nurse and coax this baby current of electricity 3,000 miles across the continent, under rivers and over mountains, through the blistering heat of the alkali plains and the cold of snow-capped peaks, that has taken the time and thought and labor of the brightest minds of the scientific world.

This great problem in transmission was due to the cumulative effect of improvements, great and small, in telephone, transmitter, line, cable, switchboard and every other piece of apparatus and plant required for the transmission of speech.

The opening of the transcontinental telephone line has been followed by the extension of "extreme distance" transmission into all the states of the Union, by applying these new improvements to the plant of the Bell System. It is now possible to talk from points in any one state to some points in every other state of the Union, while over a very large part of the territory covered by the Bell System, it is possible for any subscriber to talk to any other subscriber, regardless of distance.

Addressing a Nation by Telephone.

On Armistice Day, November 11, 1921, President Harding stood at the bier of the Unknown Soldier at Arlington, and, epitomizing one of the most significant ceremonies in all American history, paid to the nation's dead the tribute of more than one hundred million people. The words of his address, and indeed every detail of the impressive service, were carried by the telephone wire system and the telephone amplifier not only to the vast assemblage of people surrounding the amphitheatre at Arlington, but to other huge gatherings at New York and San Francisco. It is estimated that 100,000 heard the ceremony at Arlington, while 15,000 in Madison Square Garden, New York, and an additional 20,000 in the park adjoining listened to the addresses and the music as they came over the wires. In the Civic Auditorium and the Plaza, San Francisco, 20,000 people heard every word of the impressive service, until taps sounded over the resting place of the Unknown Soldier.

To link three distant cities by telephone and to send over thousands of miles of wire every word of the memorial program, spoken or sung; and so to amplify the currents reaching the terminals of this vast span of wire that they might carry to the very outskirts of the huge throngs gathered to hear them, was a tremendous task. The tools with which this task was undertaken were of two kinds: the existing long-distance wires and other equipment of the Bell Telephone System used in transmitting the voice currents from Arlington to New York and San Francisco; and the special apparatus used at Arlington and at the two distant cities in magnifying or amplifying these currents up to the volume and intensity required to produce the desired result. To guard against unseen dangers, every foot of line between Washington and New York, and New York and San Francisco was gone over, literally inch by inch, several weeks before Armistice Day. A few days before the ceremony another inspection was made. And on November 11th the entire length of line was patrolled by a force of linemen who stood ready to hasten on a moment's notice to any point where trouble might develop and make the necessary repairs.

In many respects the principles underlying the operation of the telephone amplifying apparatus and that of the long distance telephone itself are strikingly similar. In each the telephone circuit is derived from a transmitter containing loosely packed carbon granules whose agitation by the waves of the voice gives rise to an electric current the variations of which are an exact copy of the sound waves. Each has a receiver of electromagnetic type which converts the ripples of telephone current back into sound waves, and an amplifier which increases the telephone current as it comes from the transmitter. In both cases the essential feature of the amplifying apparatus is a series of vacuum tubes. Stripped of its technical details, the amplifier may be described as an electric valve so extremely sensitive that by means of it one electric current may be made to control another current which may be as much as a million times larger.

The receiver used in connection with the amplifying apparatus differs in many respects from the ordinary telephone receiver used on a long distance circuit. Not only is it much larger and more powerful but attached to it is a large wooden horn or sound projector which acts as a megaphone in projecting the sound through the air to great distances and at the same time directing it to the desired section of the audience. To reach a large audience several receivers and projectors are used. These projectors are usually arranged in a group or cluster, as a more natural reproduction of the speaker's voice is thus obtained.

Since each projector supplies a portion of the audience it is necessary that the volume of sound from each one be capable of individual control. To attain this end the circuit from each receiver is brought into a central control room where attendants provided with switches can increase or diminish the sound coming from any projector. These attendants of the control room are in constant communication with others who are stationed at listening posts in the audience.

Radio and the Telephone.

The characteristics of radio and wire transmission are fundamentally different. Each, due to its unique capabilities, is performing a service for which the other is unsuited, and each is supplementing the other to the end that all important needs for communication are being provided for as rapidly as they arise. For the large amounts of traffic on land, both telegraph and telephone, which must be handled with certainty and a minimum of cost, the use of wires is necessary. But as an agency for communicating over wide stretches of water, with moving conveyances generally, for a host of maritime and military purposes, and for the broadcasting of information, lectures, concerts, sermons, etc., radio today is rendering services of the greatest value, and all considerations point to the conclusion that in these fields its use will become of ever greater importance. (The Story of Radio is given in detail in another part of this work.)

The first two wireless telephone stations available for public use were erected on the California coast. These stations supply every-day telephone service between the Island of Santa Catalina and the mainland, and are an integral part of the Bell System so that a subscriber on the Island can call any number in Los Angeles, or in fact any number throughout the entire Bell System.

At a demonstration given in honor of the delegates to the international Communications Conference, conversation was exchanged between Catalina in the Pacific Ocean and the S. S. *Gloucester* in the Atlantic. Speech was transmitted by radio telephone from the *Gloucester* through the New Jersey station, and thence by wire across the continent to Los Angeles, and thence by radio telephone to Catalina. More recently, apparatus has been developed whereby a single land station can maintain a different two-way conversation with each of three ships at the same time.

POWER AMPLIFIER TUBES

A circular bank of fifteen high power water-cooled tubes used in the first commercial radio service across the Atlantic.

Perhaps the greatest achievement in radio telephony was signalized by the opening to the public of regular radio telephone service between New York and London which was inaugurated on January 7, 1927. Scientific experimenters had accomplished this feat before but never on a commercial scale. Traffic originating in New York was carried by wire to Rocky Point, Long Island, thence transmitted by radio telephone to Wroughton, England, and by wire from there to London. Traffic from London went to Rugby by wire, thence by radio to the American receiving station at Houlton, Maine, and by wire to New York. The radio transmission was on wave lengths of 5,000 meters and 22 meters, employed simultaneously in both directions. The equipment used in this epoch-making achievement cost over $5,000,000 and employed great banks of high power radio tubes which have only recently been perfected. When one realized that this accomplishment came less than a dozen years after the first New York-San Francisco conversation, and fifty years from the first use of the telephone, the remarkable progress of telephone engineering can be appreciated. This service makes it feasible for any telephone station in the United States to be connected with any station in England, the voice spanning the ocean in the brief space of .018 seconds.

The extensive experience of the Bell engineers in transoceanic and ship-to-shore radio telephony and in supplying commercial radio telephone service on the Pacific coast, has provided trustworthy data whereby they can judge concerning the practicability of radio in the various fields in which it might be applied. Their studies show that the characteristics of wireless transmission are such as to make it particularly useful as a means of supplementing the wire systems in those instances where, from the nature of the case, it is impossible or impracticable to employ wires.

The Bell research laboratories have worked on the problem of applying to radio telegraphy the quick cipher or secret method of wire telegraphy which their engineers developed and which was used with marked success upon wires by the Signal Corps during the war. It is a secret means of telegraph communication, and while the ciphered message may be heard at all radio stations, it can be interpreted only by those who have the cipher apparatus and key. This instantaneously enciphers the message at the sending end and deciphers it at the receiving end, where it appears immediately in printed page form ready for use. The work done upon this system of secret telegraphy by the engineers of the Bell System promises to be generally available and for the benefit of radio telegraphy.

The Bell engineers have also attacked the problem of privacy in radio telephony and have given an experimental demonstration of a method which they have devised, whereby ordinary receiving stations can hear nothing but unintelligible sounds; yet at all stations equipped with the necessary apparatus and in possession of the requisite operating information, the spoken words can be understood.

Photo by Brown Bros.

LONG RIBBONS OF LIGHT

The giant scintillator erected on the shore of the bay was not the least wonderful of all the wonderful sights of the Panama-Pacific Exposition at San Francisco.

How Far can a Powerful Searchlight Send Its Rays?

Searchlights have recently been made capable of being seen nearly a hundred miles away. Such lights are very valuable for signaling purposes in time of war, and they are also much used on warships, enabling the officers to detect the approach of an enemy in the dark and to guard against torpedo boats.

We are all familiar with the less powerful ones which are universally used on automobiles for night driving and in a multitude of other every-day practices. The illustration shows a battery of powerful searchlights, the use of which furnished some very effective displays during the Panama-Pacific Exposition at San Francisco in 1915.

Searchlights are ordinarily electric arc lights of great candle-power, arranged with a parabolic reflector so that the rays are sent almost wholly in one direct line, forming a path of light which may be projected for miles.

What Started the Habit of Touching Glasses Before Drinking?

Just as athletes shake hands before the beginning of a contest today, the people who fought duels in the olden days used to pause before their fighting long enough to each drink a glass of wine furnished by their friends. In order to make sure that no attempt was made to forestall the results of the duel by poisoning the wine in either cup, they developed the habit of pouring part of the contents of each glass into the other, so that if either contestant was poisoned the other would be too.

This habit has continued up to the present time, although there is no thought given now to the danger of poison, and in the present day the ceremony of actually pouring the drink from one glass to another has been omitted, merely the motion, as if to touch the glasses, sufficing as an expression of friendliness and good will.

Touching glasses together in drinking, preparatory to a confidential talk, has come to be nicknamed "hob-nobbing" because of the equipment incidental to that action years ago. A "hob" was the flat part of the open hearth where water and spirits were warmed; and the small table, at which people sat when so engaged, was called a "nob."

Why are Windows Broken by Explosions?

When the large cannons in the forts on our coast are discharged during target practice, there are usually a lot of windows broken in the nearby houses. In Jersey City, N. J., several freight cars and boats loaded with dynamite and ammunition full of high explosives furnished the power for an explosion which, in July, 1916, broke considerably over a hundred thousand dollars worth of windows in the lower part of New York City.

The force of an explosion, whatever its source, throws back the air in huge waves, very much like the waves of the ocean, and whatever they come in contact with must have a sort of a tug-of-war with them, the weaker side being crumpled up and pushed back by the other. Broad expanses of glass, unprotected and without any support, except at the extreme edges, present an easy mark for air waves, therefore, and the amount of damage done to windows by explosions is usually only limited by the power of the explosives which produce the force of air waves.

The earth beneath, and the roof and walls of a building above, all receive the effects of these air waves in exactly the same way as do windows, and the resulting disaster is in direct proportion to their resisting capacity as against the pressure caused by the explosion. Many striking examples of the power of explosives have been accidentally furnished of late, in the course of making munitions for the European war.

The Story in Elevators and Escalators*

Going up and down stairs is a duty every man, woman and child finds it necessary to perform daily and in many cases hourly, and some means for doing this is necessary in every modern household. Even in the old-time one-story house, steps from the outside to the inside were usually necessary, and when the two or more storied houses came into use the stairway became an indispensable feature. In modern times the art of building has had such an upward trend that edifices looming far into the air, hotels, stores, apartment houses, office buildings, etc., have come into use, one notable specimen, the Woolworth building in New York, towering

IN ORDER TO ASCEND MORE EASILY, MAN DEVISED THE STAIRWAY, FROM WHICH, IN TURN, WAS DEVELOPED THE ESCALATOR, IN ORDER TO FURTHER ELIMINATE PHYSICAL EFFORT

PRIMITIVE MAN PULLED HIMSELF UP A LADDER WHEN HE WANTED TO GO FROM ONE LEVEL TO ANOTHER

upwards to fifty-four stories in height. This upward tendency has rendered the elevator, or lifting apparatus, an indispensable necessity, alike for passengers and freight, and it has been installed abundantly in all our large cities.

The elevator is not exactly a new idea. Its pioneer form may be traced back to the Middle Ages, when heavy weights were lifted by aid of an apparatus worked by hand power. But it was not until well on into the nineteenth century that the steam-power elevator came into service. The first example is said to have been produced by Elisha Graves Otis, who applied steam power to an elevating machine in a little shop at Yonkers, on the banks of the Hudson, New York. A few years later, at the International Exhibition of 1853 in New York, he displayed the first elevator with a safety device to prevent the car from falling in case of a broken cable.

The elevator was then a novelty. It has long since grown into a necessity. It is to be seen in all hotels and high buildings, and the art of getting up stairs has in very many cases changed into that of being lifted up by a moving car in an enclosed shaft or cage. The steam elevator, at first used, has now in great measure been replaced by the electric elevator, the first moved by an electric motor being

*Illustrations by courtesy of the Otis Elevator Co.

the Otis elevator installed in the Demarest Building, New York, in 1889.   This is still in active use.

The first electric elevators were confined to the drum type of machine, these having a grooved drum around which the hoisting cables were wound, the drum being revolved through worm gearing by an electric motor.   But the erection of buildings, ranging from 200 to 700 feet in height has put this type of traction out of business on account of the great size of drums required and the necessary slowness of motion. It has been replaced by the electric traction elevator.   In this the hoisting cables from which the car is suspended have at the other end a counterweight and pass around driving sheaves in place of a drum.   This, in its latest form known as the gearless traction elevator, does away with all intricate machinery, and yields a machine moving with equal speed whatever the height.

AN ELEVATOR OF THE MIDDLE AGES
History tells us this form of elevator was used in monasteries for hoisting passengers and supplies.

ELEVATOR INSTALLATION IN THE WOOLWORTH BUILDING, NEW YORK

To obviate danger from accidents, safety devices are installed for gripping the rails in case of the car attaining excessive speed. Another feature of security is the oil cushion buffer. One of these is placed in the hoistway under the car and one under the counterweight, they being capable of bringing a car to rest from full speed without discomfort to those in the car. The oil in the buffer is driven by the impact of the car from one chamber of the buffer to another, but this is made to take place at a fixed rate of retardation, the oil acting as a liquid cushion which stops the car gradually and without shock.

To do business in the modern lofty building without the aid of elevators (or lifts, as they are called in England) is today out of the question, while the great grain-transporting edifices in cities in which our annual crops are lifted and lowered, are known by the specific name of elevators. There is, however, another means of getting up and down stairs which is coming somewhat rapidly into use and in which the old stairway is restored. It is one in which the stair itself does the moving instead of the passengers upon it. This new and interesting device is known as an escalator.

A STEAM-DRIVEN ELEVATOR OF EARLY DATE

The Escalator.

The earliest way to get upward from the ground was that adopted by climbing animals in clambering up tree trunks, and by man himself in "shinning" up trees by aid of his arms and legs. This was followed by the plank leading from a lower to a higher level, by the ladder, and finally by the stairway. In our days the stairway has been put on a set of revolving wheels and moves upward itself, carrying its passengers with no need on their part to use their feet. This simple but effective device is known as the escalator.

It is a very useful contrivance for tired shoppers needing to make their way from floor to floor in the great department stores, for travelers on subway or elevated railways, for large mills, theaters, or other places where easy getting up and down stairs is necessary. The escalator is a simple device. No intricate machinery is needed. It is so arranged as to be always going, traveling upwards or downwards, and returning out of sight below. It has been called "an elevator with the doors always open." It is capable of carrying all the passengers who can crowd upon it,

Battery of Elevators in a Department Store

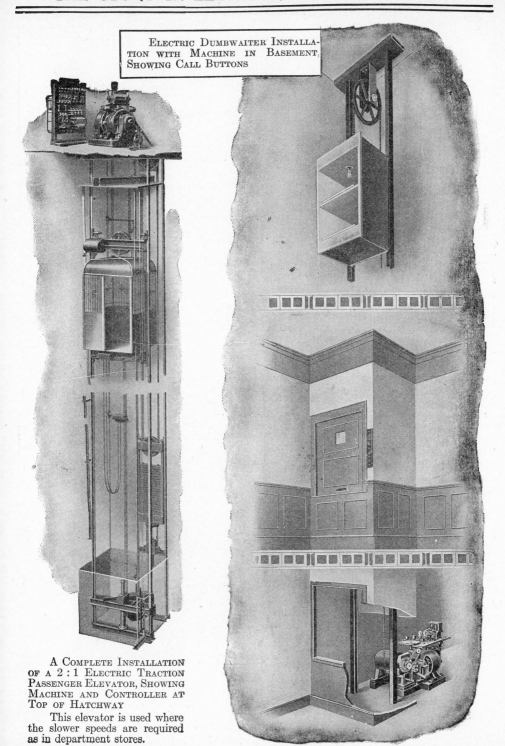

ELECTRIC DUMBWAITER INSTALLATION WITH MACHINE IN BASEMENT, SHOWING CALL BUTTONS

A COMPLETE INSTALLATION OF A 2 : 1 ELECTRIC TRACTION PASSENGER ELEVATOR, SHOWING MACHINE AND CONTROLLER AT TOP OF HATCHWAY

This elevator is used where the slower speeds are required as in department stores.

ESCALATOR OR MOVING STAIRWAY AT SIXTH AVENUE AND THIRTY-THIRD
STREET STATION OF ELEVATED RAILWAY, NEW YORK CITY

A DUPLEX ESCALATOR OF THE CLEAT TYPE IN A DEPARTMENT STORE
This type of escalator makes use of hard wood cleats in place of steps.

stepping on or off at the bottom or top, it being estimated that more than 10,000 people an hour can be thus moved.

The Cleat Escalator.

In the original type of escalator the steps flatten out into a level platform at

AN ESCALATOR OR MOVING STAIRWAY FOR THE USE OF
EMPLOYEES IN A LARGE WORSTED MILL

top and bottom, easy to step on and off, and divide into regular steps as they climb upward, passengers in a hurry being able to hasten their speed by walking at the same time that they are carried. Another type is that known as the cleat escalator. In this there are no steps, it being composed of hardwood cleats moving in longitudinal ridges and grooves, there being a handrail on either side moving at the same speed. The platform glides through the prongs of a comb at the lower level and journeys upward at a moderate speed. At the upper level it disappears through a similar comb and returns out of sight. The passengers slide off upon the prongs of the comb at the top and land without jar or shock. Both these types of escalators can be made to move up or down by aid of a swinging switch, or two of them can be placed side by side, one moving upward and the other downward.

A CLEAT TYPE ESCALATOR
SHOWING THE HARDWOOD CLEATS
USED IN PLACE OF STEPS

The Moving Platform.

A device acting on the same principle is the moving platform, with the difference that this

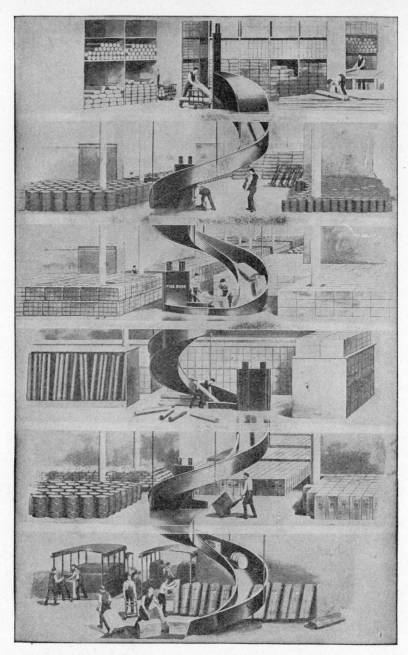

A GRAVITY CONVEYOR OF THE SINGLE SPIRAL OPEN TYPE
For the quick and safe conveyance of heavy goods from upper to lower levels.

may be of indefinite length and act as a sort of railway for carrying passengers from place to place. The passenger steps from a sideway at rest to one in moderate motion, and from this to a second one moving more rapidly, and in this way can be carried horizontally at a fair rate of speed. On reaching his station he has but to step back on the slower platform and from this to the moveless sideway. The pioneer example of this contrivance was installed on a long pier leading into Lake Michigan at the Chicago Exposition of 1893, and plans for putting it into practical use in various cities have been entertained. None of these, however, have yet been put into effect. Certain drawbacks, possibly that of cost of installation and operation, has served as a hindrance.

What Happens when Animals Hibernate?

We have all heard of certain animals sleeping through the long winter months and most of us have probably wondered what happens to them when they do this.

This hiding away for a long sleep, or hibernation, as it is called, commences when the food of the animal begins to get scarce, and the length and depth of the sleep depends on the habit and constitution of the animal.

Bats, bears, some animals of the rodent order, such as the porcupine, the dormouse, some squirrels, etc., all the animals belonging to the classes of *Amphibia* and *Reptilia*, such as tortoises, lizards, snakes, frogs, etc., and many species of mollusks and insects, hibernate more or less completely, retiring to suitable places of concealment—the bat to dark caves, the hedgehog to fern-brakes, snakes to holes in trees, etc.

During hibernation there is a great decrease of heat in the bodies of the animals, the temperature sometimes sinking to 40° or even 20° F., or in general to a point a little above that of the surrounding atmosphere. The respiration as well as the pulsation of the heart is exceedingly slow, and the irritability of the animal often so low that in some cases it can be awakened only by strong electric shocks.

With frogs and amphibious reptiles "the dormant state is very common, and if the temperature is kept low by artificial means they may remain dormant for years."

The term "æstivation" has been used to describe a similar condition into which certain animals, such as serpents and crocodiles, in tropical countries pass during the hottest months of the year.

How do Peanuts Get into the Ground?

Peanuts are really the seeds or pods of a plant belonging to the family called the earthnut in Great Britain, the nuts there being used chiefly to fatten swine. The peanut-stand so commonly seen on street corners here is kept well supplied by the extensive cultivation of peanuts in the United States, mainly in the South, and in several tropical countries.

As most people have discovered, the nuts have a much more agreeable taste after being roasted. They also yield an oil which is often used for olive oil, and very good "peanut butter" is now made by grinding them up and mixing them with oil.

The peanut plant, or groundnut as it is also called, has a hairy stem and the leaves usually grow in sets of two pairs each, on the extreme end of each little branch-stem. The pod or nut is situated at the end of a separate stalk, which is longer than the leaf-stems, this stalk having the peculiarity, after flowering, of bending down and pushing the fruit into the earth. After the peanuts have reached their full growth, they are dug up very much in the same way as potatoes, a machine potato digger now being extensively used for this purpose.

MACHINE POTATO DIGGER DIGGING PEANUTS

PICKING PEANUTS BY HAND

How did Your State Get Its Name?

Alabama is named after the Indian word which means "Here we rest;" Alaska comes from the Eskimo word "Alakshak" or "Alayeska" and means "The main land;" Arizona is the result of the Indian word "Arizonac," meaning "small springs" or "few springs;" and Arkansas is sort of a mixture of the Indian "Kansas," which means "smoky water," and the French prefix "arc," meaning "bow" or "bend."

California comes from the Spanish words "Caliente Fornalla," or "hot furnace;" Colorado, also from the Spanish "colored," from the red color of the Colorado River; and Connecticut, in Indian, means "long river."

Delaware was named after Lord De la Warr; Florida originated from the Spanish "Pascua de Flores," which means "Feast of Flowers," because it was discovered on Easter Day; Georgia was called after King George II of England; and Hawaii is a name peculiar to the natives there, although Captain Cook called it part of the "Sandwich Islands" after Lord Sandwich.

Idaho is Indian, meaning "Gem of the Mountains;" Illinois is another mixture of Indian and French, the Indian word "illini" and the French suffix "ois" meaning "tribe of men;" and Indiana and Iowa are both plain Indian, the former standing for "Indians' land," and the latter, "beautiful land."

Kansas and Kentucky are Indian, too, Kansas meaning "smoky water" and Kentucky "at the head of the river," or "the dark and bloody ground;" and Louisiana is named after Louis XIV of France.

Maine and Maryland each come from abroad, Maine being called after the Province of the same name in France, and Maryland after Queen Henrietta Maria of England, consort of Charles I; while Massachusetts, Michigan, Minnesota, Mississippi and Missouri are all from the native Indian language, meaning, in the order in which they are given, "place of great hills," "fish weir," "sky-tinted water," "great father of waters" and "muddy;" and Montana traces back to the Latin word "montanus," meaning "mountainous."

Nebraska is another Indian name, and means "water valley;" while Nevada is Spanish, meaning "snow covered;" New Hampshire and New Jersey are both from across the water, the former after Hampshire County in England, and New Jersey after the Island of Jersey at the time when Sir George Carteret was its governor; New York and both North and South Carolina were also named after monarchs abroad, New York after the Duke of York in England, and the Carolinas after Charles IX of France; while North and South Dakota bring us back to the Indian language again, meaning "allies."

Ohio and Oklahoma are both Indian, too, Ohio meaning "beautiful river," and the latter, "home of the red men"; while Oregon is from the Spanish word "oregano," which stands for the wild marjoram, a plant abundant on the coast; Pennsylvania traces back to the Latin, meaning "Penn's woody land;" the Philippine Islands come from the Spanish words "Islas Filipinas," after King Philip; and Porto Rico is also Spanish, from "Puerto Rico," meaning "rich port."

Rhode Island is called after the Island of Rhodes; Tennessee, Texas and Utah are all Indian, Tennessee meaning "river with the great bend," Texas coming from several different forms of very old Indian language, meaning "friends," and Utah after the tribe by that name, also called the "Utes;" Vermont is from the French, meaning "green mountains," and Virginia is called after Elizabeth, the "Virgin Queen" of England.

Washington gets its name from a good, straight American source—George Washington; West Virginia is so called because it was formerly the western part of Virginia; and Wisconsin and Wyoming are both Indian, the former meaning "gathering of the waters," and the latter, "great plains."

The Story of Coal Mining

An interesting story is told in an English book by Edward Cressy, of the great coal strike in 1912. Many factories and workshops had to close for want of fuel. A workman from one of these, on reaching home, purchased a sack of coal and set it up against the back door. Then he sat in the kitchen, in which there was no fire. From time to time, when he felt chilly he got up, flung the sack of coal across his shoulders and ran around the yard until he became warm. That was his way of saving fuel. He was only doing in his own fashion what all engineers and manufacturers are trying to do in other ways all the year round.

The extent to which all manufacture and transport, all industry there, was paralyzed during the strike, shows the complete dependence of modern life upon fuel. In spite of the fact that in Great Britain nearly 240,000,000 tons of coal are mined annually, a temporary stoppage of supply threw all the ordinary machinery of existence out of action and revealed the magnitude of the debt that the world owes to those who win precious stores of fuel from the depths of the earth.

Probably no industrial operation excites more widespread interest, when accorded publicity, than the mining of coal, and that because of the dangers which attend it. The annual list of victims buried beneath a falling roof, or mangled by runaway cars, causes little comment, but every now and then the world is startled by an appalling catastrophe in which hundreds of men lose their lives. From the early days when growing industry demanded more coal, inventors have been busy devising all sorts of safety appliances for the miner.

The original safety-lamp, with which practically everyone is familiar, is the parent of scores of others, each claiming to offer some special advantage. All sorts of mechanical devices to prevent overwinding—an accident which would fling the cage with its coal or human freight out of the pit mouth—have been invented, and every section of the work has been made as safe as human ingenuity and human skill have been able to make it. But the number of disastrous explosions has not been materially reduced.

Many varieties of coal give off a gas known as marsh-gas or fire-damp. This is inflammable and, when mixed with air, violently explosive. It is the presence of this gas that necessitates the safety-lamp. There are a few kinds of mines which evolve no gas, and in these naked lights are used. But all mines must be ventilated by forcing air through them with a fan, and this air must be in sufficient quantity to keep the percentage of gas below a dangerous standard. Most mines are examined at regular intervals by a "fireman" who can estimate approximately the percentage of gas present by the size of the faintly luminous "cap" which hovers above the flame of his lamp.

Explosions have occurred, however, in cases where it is extremely doubtful whether gas has been present in dangerous quantity, and attention has been drawn to the possible causes. Many varieties of coal produce a quantity of fine dust which settles in the roadways, on roof, and sides, and floor. For many years there has been a controversy as to the relative importance of gas and dust in producing explosions, and the question is still one which gives rise to a lively difference of opinion. But there is no doubt that a mixture of coal-dust and air is explosive, and that even if an explosion is started by gas, the disturbance creates clouds of dust which give rise to secondary explosions and spread the disaster over a wider field than was originally affected.

Courtesy of the Link-Belt Co., Chicago.

HANDLING COAL

Four-ton grab buckets operating on the four bridge-tramways pick up the coal from the hold of lake steamers and deposit it either on the dock or in cars. The four machines can be moved to any part of the dock to which steamers are moored and four ships can be unloaded rapidly at one time. The motive power is electricity.

Courtesy of the J. M. Dodge Co.

STORING COAL

A 480,000-ton anthracite coal storage plant. Coal cars are dumped into hoppers under the tracks and the coal carried to the top of the piles by conveyors. It is reloaded into cars by other conveyors operating at the base of each pile. This system has been of great value in preventing a shortage of coal during strikes.

Consequently a plan has been evolved for the ventilating current to be reversed periodically, in order to remove dust which has settled on the side of timbering and crevices, and the roadways to be watered in order to allay the dust. A plan has also been tried of spreading fine stone-dust in the roadways. This mixes with the coal-dust and renders it less inflammable.

Unfortunately the disastrous effects of an explosion do not end with the explosion itself. The main products of combustion, whether of fire-damp or coal-dust, are carbon monoxide and carbon dioxide. The latter causes suffocation and the former is a dangerous poison. It is the dreaded "after-damp" of the miner. Those who survive an explosion are therefore in danger of suffocation or poisoning, and it becomes imperative to restore the circulation of the air with the least possible delay. For even if the fan has escaped injury, fallen portions of the roof may have choked up some of the roadways, or the explosion may have torn down doorways and provided a short cut for the air. But if the atmosphere is dangerous for men in the pit at the time, it is equally dangerous for others to go down and effect repairs or render first aid.

The work of the rescue party is therefore a labor of desperate heroism and often attended by additional loss of life. It has recently been found possible to reduce the dangers of after-damp by providing rescue parties with respirators fitting over the mouth and nose, and supplied with oxygen from two steel bottles of the compressed gas strapped across the back. An effective apparatus of this kind, such as has been adopted by the United States Government for the use of the Bureau of Mines Rescue Crew, is shown in the accompanying illustration. The bag in front is known as a "breathing bag" and has separate compartments for the inhaling and exhaling, the tube at the right leading to the former and that at the left to the exhaling compartment, which usually contains sticks of caustic soda to absorb the carbon dioxide exhaled by the wearer.

Coal is largely formed from vast masses of vegetable matter deposited through the luxuriant growth of plants in former epochs of the earth's history. In the varieties of coal in common use the combined effects of pressure, heat and chemical action upon the substance have left few traces of its vegetable origin; but in the sandstones, clays and shales accompanying the coal the plants to which it principally owes its origin are presented in a fossil state in great profusion and frequently with their structure so distinctly retained, although replaced by mineral substances, as to enable the microscopist to determine their botanical affinities with existing species. Trees of considerable magnitude have also been brought to light.

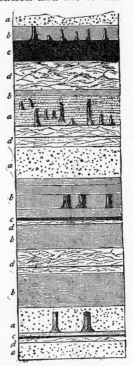

SECTION OF PART OF A
COAL-FIELD, SHOWING
A SUCCESSION OF
BURIED TREES AND
LAND SURFACE

a, sandstones.
b, shales.
c, coal-seams.
d, under-clays or soils.

The animal remains found in the coal-measures indicate that some of the rocks have been deposited in fresh water, probably in lakes, while others are obviously of estuarine origin, or have been deposited at the mouths of rivers alternately occupied by fresh and salt water. The great system of strata in which coal is chiefly found is known as the carboniferous.

There are many varieties of coal, varying considerably in their composition, as anthracite, nearly pure carbon, and burning with little flame, much used for furnaces

MINE SAFETY CREW

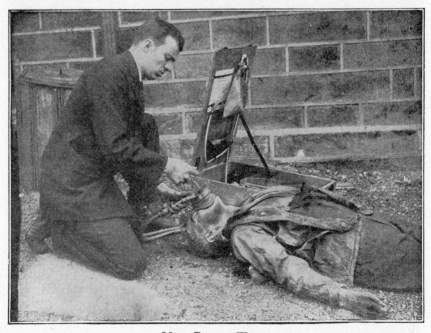

MINE RESCUE WORK

Upper view, Bureau of Mines Rescue Crew in safety helmets, ready to enter a gas-filled mine. Lower view, resuscitating a victim overcome by gas by means of the oxygen reviving apparatus.

BRIQUETTING MACHINE

Enormous quantities of coal are lost at the mines in coal dust. By adding a binding material, such as pitch, and pressing the mixture into *briquettes* or small bricks, an excellent fuel is made.

MINE RESCUE WORK

The mine rescue crew is using the canary-bird test for poisonous gas. The bird succumbs to gas earlier than a man and thus indicates a dangerous condition of the atmosphere. The canary is revived by oxygen and the crew puts on safety helmets before proceeding.

and malt kilns; bituminous, a softer and more free-burning variety; and cannel or "gas-coal," which burns readily like a candle, and is much used in gasmaking. The terms semi-anthracite, semi-bituminous, coking coal, splint coal, etc., are also applied according to peculiarities.

All varieties agree in containing from 60 to over 90 per cent of carbon, the other elements being chiefly oxygen and hydrogen, and frequently a small portion of nitrogen. Lignite or brown coal may contain only 50 per cent of carbon. For manufacturing purposes coals are generally considered to consist of two parts, the volatile or bituminous portion, which yields the gas used for lighting, and the substance, comparatively fixed, usually known as coke, which is obtained by heating the coals in ovens or other close arrangements.

About 260,000,000 tons of coal are annually mined in Britain, the value being over $300,000,000. Large quantities are exported. The British coal-fields, though comparatively extensive (covering about 9,000 square miles), are far surpassed by those of several other countries, as the United States and China, the former having coal-fields estimated to cover about 451,000 square miles; the latter over 200,000 square miles. Britain no longer mines the largest quantity, having been far surpassed by the United States. Other countries in which coal is worked are Belgium, France, Germany, Russia, India, New South Wales and Canada. China has hitherto mined only on a small scale.

The annual production of anthracite coal in Pennsylvania is more than 86,000,000 tons of 2,240 pounds, valued at the mines at $198,000,000. In 1910 there were produced of bituminous coal 388,222,868 tons, valued at $463,654,776; amount of coke manufactured, 37,000,000 tons. This was distributed widely over the country, the greatest producers, after Pennsylvania, being Illinois, West Virginia, Ohio, Alabama and Colorado.

Recently a very large output of coal has been discovered in Alaska, the value of which is as yet undetermined, though it is believed to hold a vast quantity of coal. The value of the western coal-fields also is far from known, and since 1906 very extensive tracts of coal-bearing lands have been withdrawn from settlement, principally in Wyoming, Montana, Colorado, Utah and New Mexico, their beds being largely of lignite. These cover about 50,000,000 acres, and, with those of Alaska, are held by the government as national assets. The mines of Alaska are claimed to be exceedingly rich, both in bituminous and anthracite coal, the beds examined being estimated to contain 15,000,000,000 tons, while there are large districts unexamined. They have not yet been worked, the government keeping them back for public ownership.

How can We Hear through the Walls of a Room?

We are able to hear easily through the walls of many rooms because the material used in those walls are good conductors of sound. We know that some things are better conductors of heat than others, and just in that same way, some things conduct sound better than others. Wood has been shown to be an even better conductor of sound than air. Most of us have stood at the foot of an overhead trolley pole to see if we could hear a car coming, and we know that the reason we did this was because we could hear the wire humming, when we put our ears against the pole, even though we could not hear any sound in the air.

When we are in a room that has wooden walls we can hear sounds in the next room very plainly, not because the wall is thin, but because the wood in the wall is a good conductor of sound. Other walls made of different kinds of material, are not as good conductors of sound. While you may hear through them, you cannot hear as plainly as you can through a wooden wall.

What is a Diesel Engine Like?

The Diesel engine has caused a great deal of comment of late years because of the spectacular uses to which it has been successfully applied. A specially constructed Diesel engine was probably the chief aid in the accomplishment of the first submarine transatlantic voyage by the German submarine "Deutschland."

It is an oil engine which was invented by Rudolph Diesel in 1893.

THE S. S. "GRIPSHOLM"

The S. S. "Gripsholm," new flagship of the Swedish-American Line, is the first motor-driven passenger vessel to be placed in the New York-Europe route. Motive power is furnished by two double-acting six-cylinder Diesel engines of a new design, which are the largest ever built for any purpose. Crude oil is used for combustion. Each engine directly drives a propeller, just as a motor-boat engine does, and combined power of the two main engines and auxiliary engines is 22,000 horsepower. Electricity is generated by the three smaller Diesel engines of 650 H. P. each, while three other similar engines of 950 H. P. are used for the production of compressed air to start the main engines.

The Story in a Silver Teaspoon*

The spoon is older than history. There is, perhaps, no article or utensil of common use today that can trace an earlier origin. The evolution and development of the spoon into the graceful and beautiful forms in use on our tables is fascinating and instructive.

Primitive men of the Stone Age used an implement that might by courtesy be called a spoon. From then on down through the Egyptian, Greek and Roman civilizations it can be clearly traced in varying forms and substances—wood, shell, flint, bone, ivory, bronze and the precious metals, gold and silver.

A witty Frenchman has said that spoons, if not as old as the world, are certainly as old as soup.

In the Bible is the first recorded mention of the use of spoons made of precious metal. This reference is the twenty-fifth chapter of the Book of Exodus, wherein the Lord commanded Moses to make golden spoons for the Tabernacle.

Excavations in Egypt have brought to light early examples of spoons of various materials, and it is certain that the early Greeks and Romans used gold and silver spoons, both at the table and in the Temple. Early specimens of spoons made of wood, ivory, bronze, silver and gold are preserved in the museums of Europe and Egypt.

During the early Christian and medieval eras spoons were in common use. Saxon and Early English examples are to be seen in the English museums today.

The medieval spoon was of silver, horn or wood, etc. On the Continent, silver spoons were made much earlier than in England. In Italy they were in use probably long before 1000 A. D.

During the Tudor and Stuart reigns a fashionable gift at christenings was the apostle, so called because at the end of the handle was the figure of an apostle. Sometimes a thirteenth spoon was added, called the "Master" spoon, because it bore the figure of Christ. A complete set was a very valuable gift, and could only be afforded by the rich.

Folks of limited means used copper, pewter, latten or alchemy spoons; the latter two materials being somewhat like brass, examples of which are sometimes found in this country in the graves of Indians of the sixteenth and seventeenth centuries, showing their intercourse with early English traders.

At this period the stems were hexagonal, ending in an acorn, a bird or a ball, while the bowls were fig shape. Later the stems were baluster shape with a seal top, and at the time of the Commonwealth the stem became flat and perfectly plain. These latter are called "Puritan" spoons.

Naturally, the early New England colonists brought with them the spoons they had used at home, and the early Colonial silversmiths followed closely the designs which they found at hand or which were later imported from England. In fact, within a few years after a certain type had become popular in the mother country, it was adopted in this country as the fashionable style. It is, therefore, easy to date, approximately, an American-made spoon, because it follows so closely in style the dated or hall-marked English spoon.

During the last quarter of the seventeenth century, both in England and America, spoons were generally of a style now known as rat-tail. From the end of the handle, down the back of the bowl to about the middle, ran a ridge shaped like a rat-tail.

---

* Illustrations by courtesy of the International Silver Co.

This is sometimes thought to have been an attempt to strengthen the spoon, but its use must have been purely ornamental, for it adds little strength to these strongly made spoons. Sometimes the rat-tail was shaped like a long V and grooved, while on each side were elaborate scrolls. The bowl was perfectly oval in shape, while the end of the handle was notched or trifid.

This style of spoon was continued, with modifications, through the first third of the eighteenth century. Then the bowl became ovoid, or egg-shaped, and the end of the handle was rounded, without the notch.

The rat-tail was gradually replaced by what is known as the drop, or double drop, frequently terminating in a conventionalized flower or shell, or anthemion, while down the front of the handle ran a rib.

Later, the bowl became more pointed, the drop was replaced by a tongue, and the handle, after 1760, instead of slightly curving to the front at the end, reversed the position. Somewhat later, the handle became pointed, and was engraved with bright, cut ornaments and a cartouch at the end in which were engraved the initials of the owner.

During the first ten years of the nineteenth century a popular style was the so-called coffin-shaped handle, succeeded, probably about 1810, by a handle with a shoulder just above the junction with the bowl, while the end became fiddle-shaped or of a style now known as tipped, shapes produced to this day.

LATTEN SPOONS

One found in an Indian grave at Deerfield, Mass., and the other in an Indian grave at Hadley, Mass. Period of about 1660. Actual size, 6 inches and 6¼ inches.

Until about 1770, spoons were of three sizes: the teaspoon, as small as an after-dinner coffee spoon; the porringer spoon, a little smaller than our present dessert size; and the tablespoon, with a handle somewhat shorter than that of today.

So few silver forks have been found in collections of old silver that it forces the belief that they were generally made of steel, with bone handles. There seems no reason why, if in general use, silver forks should not now be as common as spoons.

In the great silver exhibition recently held in the Museum of Fine Arts, Boston, of more than one thousand pieces, there were only two forks to be found.

Great skill was developed by the early silversmiths of England and America. The purity and gracefulness of design in many cases remain as standards for our best craftsmen today. It is. however erroneous to suppose that all of the ornamentation was done by hand.

Ornaments on the back of spoon bowls and handles were impressed by dies forced together by drop presses or under screw pressure. This is absolutely proven by the exact duplication of the pattern on sets of spoons. Accurate measurements show that these ornaments were not handwork, for there is not the slightest deviation in dimensions.

But, however beautiful the silver of our forbears and however valuable now,

Front   Back

Back   Front

FRONTS AND BACKS OF TWO EARLY AMERICAN SPOONS OF THE
RAT-TAIL TYPE

The spoon in the center is the earliest of that type, made
about 1690. The other dates about 1695.

from a historic standpoint, there are few of us who, if given the choice, would not decide in favor of the product of the twentieth century silversmith, who brings to his creations all of the good of the old masters, and who has the facilities for turning out work more perfect in line and detail and uniformity than was ever dreamed of by the silver worker of old.

have any understanding how silver plate is made; and there is, perhaps, still less knowledge of its interesting history.

The combining of two separate metals—that is, the plating of a base metal with a finer one—was, until the eighteenth century, a lost art of the ancients.

The application of one metal upon another was practiced by the Assyrians, who overlapped iron with bronze; copper implements and ornaments coated with silver have been found at Herculaneum, while many ancient Roman specimens of harness and armor are found to be ornamented with silver on copper. The Aztecs of Mexico and the Incas of Peru used the process of fixing two metals together by the action of heat, before making up. The method was also known to the old Celts, as shown by specimens found in Iceland. It seems, however, to have been a lost art in Europe, probably because up to the thirteenth century the Church had control of the arts and crafts in England, and the finer metal work was used only for church vessels, the household implements being very simple and mostly of wood and cheap metal.

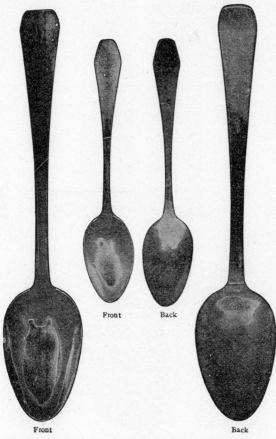

Front   Back

Front   Back

TABLE AND TEASPOON WITH THE SO-CALLED COFFIN-
SHAPED HANDLE

A shape peculiar to America. This type common from 1800 to 1815. Reductions about one-half.

Horace Walpole, writing in 1760, states: "I passed through Sheffield, a business town in a charming situation, with 22,000 inhabitants, and they remit £11,000 a week to London. One man there has discovered the art of plating copper with silver."

The inventor to whom the quotation refers was Thomas Bolsover, a skilled silversmith, who, in the year 1742, it is traditionally reported, while repairing a thin layer of silver on the copper handle of a knife, evolved the idea of combining copper with silver in layers ready for manufacture into any desired form.

Bolsover himself apparently did not appreciate the importance of this invention, and it remained for Joseph Hancock, one of his apprentices, to develop the idea to a commercial success. He vigorously encouraged the trade in Sheffield, Birmingham and other manufacturing centers, and finally constructed a rolling-mill and made his fortune by supplying the plate to the silversmiths.

The earlier specimens of this Sheffield plate, as it came to be known, had the silver on one side of the copper only, but later attempts were made to improve the appearance of finer pieces by covering the underside of the copper with tin.

Crude as this idea and the old methods of manufacture may seem, compared with modern processes, this old plate found a ready sale. It replaced in many households pewter ware which, until the introduction of Sheffield plate, was the best substitute for sterling silver. It became fashionable for everyday use by the nobility and wealthier families, who put aside their solid silverware to be used on state occasions only. The name "plate," which is from the Spanish word *platte*, came to be used generally to designate the imitation of solid silver.

This plate, being such a close imitation of solid silver, was not permitted by the laws of England to bear any stamp whatever prior to 1773, when the town of Sheffield was specially privileged to put upon its product the marks of the makers. These marks, however, were not to bear any resemblance of the lion or leopard's head, these being the hall-marks of England.

It was not until 1785 that this privilege was extended to the town of Birmingham and other manufacturing centers.

It is curious to note that this law against the imitation of silver, which really dated from the fifteenth century, made a special exception to articles made for the Church.

Sometimes this old Sheffield plate, in addition to bearing the maker's name, bore the name of the lord or earl for whom it was made, and today these old pieces are more highly valued by their owners than silver which is intrinsically more valuable.

Much of the charm of old plate was in its beauty of form and design, for the work attracted the best of English artisans. It would appear, too, that they were fairly well paid for their labor, as Pepys, in his "Diary," refers to

Westminster   Frontenac   Brandon

MODERN DESIGNS

a present made him of a pair of flagons which cost £100. "They are said to be worth five shillings, some say ten shillings, an ounce for the fashion."

The first notable improvement over the Sheffield work came toward the middle of the nineteenth century, when electro-silver plating was first practiced and, in 1847, commercially perfected, by Rogers Brothers of Hartford, Conn.

The marvelous force of electricity was brought to bear on the making of silver-plated knives, forks, spoons, etc., as well as hollow-ware articles, such as coffee and tea pots, water pitchers, sugar bowls and platters. Instead of these articles being made of sheets of rolled copper and silver, a silver plate of any desired thickness is applied to the base metal by electricity.

This quick and less expensive method of manufacture rendered silver plate available to all classes, and the Sheffield plate was quickly superseded, the old method of manufacture becoming obsolete.

While the process of manufacture was cheapened, the newer craftsmen wisely held to the art standards of the old masters. With the new process came the perfection of modern construction, and the cost is so much less than in the old days that a perfect table service of authentic design, of quality beyond question and guaranteed in every respect, is within the reach of any well-to-do family. Many of the old family pieces of Sheffield have found their way into the melting pot in exchange for the modern electro-plated silverware.

The making of silver-plated flatware is an interesting process and one that requires a great amount of skill and care. The finished teaspoon, as it lies in the show-case or chest, is the result of over thirty distinct operations, while a plain silver-plated steel knife has passed through thirty-six stages in its evolution from the bit of steel rod, in which shape it begins its journey. Some of the more important steps in the making of a spoon are briefly described below:

The Blank.

The metal underlying the silver plate of the best plated teaspoons is of nickel silver, a trade name for a metal composed of nickel, copper and zinc. This metal is procured in sheet form of varying lengths. From this sheet is cut a blank, which bears little resemblance to a spoon, being about half the length of the finished article and very much wider.

Squeezed.

The blank is then "squeezed," which gives to the part that is to become the handle a little more of the appearance that it will have later.

Rolling.

This "squeezed" blank is then passed through a series of steel rolls, giving length to the handle and width to the bowl, and distributing the metal according to the correct thickness—that is, the bowl will be thin and the shank thick.

Clipping.

The next process is termed "clipping," the spoon being cut out from the blank in the correct outline of the pattern.

Annealing.

The process of rolling the metal has so compressed the latter that it cannot be readily worked. It is necessary, therefore, that the spoon be annealed—that is, the shaped blanks are placed in an oven and brought to a red heat, which renders them malleable.

The Evolution of a Spoon.

From the crude blank of nickel silver to the finished spoon, there are over thirty distinct operations necessary, a few of the more important stages being illustrated. When the spoon emerges from the plating solution (see No. 8), it is perfectly white and looks as if it had been treated with a heavy coat of enamel. It is then scratch-brushed, burnished and, in some patterns, the handle is greyed. After this, the spoon is buffed and finished.

Every operation is performed with the utmost care, and not until the piece is actually finished can this vigilance be relaxed, as it is the final processes that make the plating of pure silver an actual part of the spoon and insure its wearing qualities.

Striking and Bowling.—The pattern is then stamped on the handle and the bowl is shaped.

Trimming, etc.—After the pattern and the bowl have been struck, there is usually a small burr left where the metal has oozed out between the dies. This is removed by trimming. The trademark is then stamped on the back of the handle.

Polishing.—The goods are put through various operations of polishing until they are brought to a high finish.

Plating.—The articles to be plated are suspended in a frame in the silver solution. This frame is connected with the negative pole of a magneto-electro machine, while the silver is suspended in the solution from bars and connected

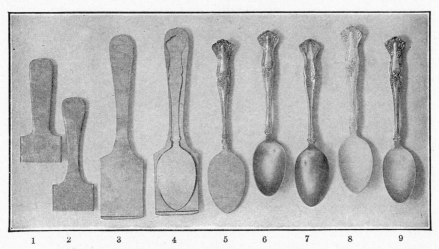

1. The blank. 2. Squeezed. 3. Blank rolled. 4. Spoon cut from blank. 5. Design struck. 6. Bowl raised. 7. Trade-mark stamped. 8. After plating. 9. The finished spoon.

with the positive or opposite pole of the machine, thereby forming a circuit for the electricity through the solution.

A patent automatic scale, designed to weigh the silver while depositing, is balanced to the exact weight of silver to be deposited on the article. The circuit is completed by turning a switch and the plating begins.

As soon as the articles receive the proper weight of silver, the scale beam rises, thus making a separate connection with the electro-magnet, which springs the switch, breaking the electric current and stopping the plating at the same instant, also ringing an alarm bell to notify the workman that the articles have received the proper weight of silver.

Quality.—Standard silver-plated spoons are made in two grades of plate—triple and quintuple. The former, however, is the one generally used and answers all ordinary requirements. The quintuple grade is designed more particularly for hotels, restaurants, clubs and other institutions where the wear is especially severe.

The Evolution of a Knife.

There are thirty-six stages in the evolution of a plain steel knife. At one end of the journey we see the cylindrical bar of steel, black and unlovely; at the other, the silver-plated knife, light, well-balanced and heavily plated with pure silver. In the case of other than plain knives, the work involves also the stamping of the pattern.

Double Burnishing.—The thickness of the silver deposited, however, is not the only requisite to insure quality. The plating must be hard as well as thick. This is accomplished by means of a double-burnishing process after the article is plated and before it receives its final buffed finish.

The first burnishing is on machines and this is followed by hand burnishing. This process produces a hard plate.

No matter how heavy the plate, if it is not properly burnished or hardened after plating, the article will not give satisfaction in long wear. When manufacturers treat their wares to as little burnishing as possible, practically relying upon the buff alone for their finish after plating, the result is most unsatisfactory. The buff finish

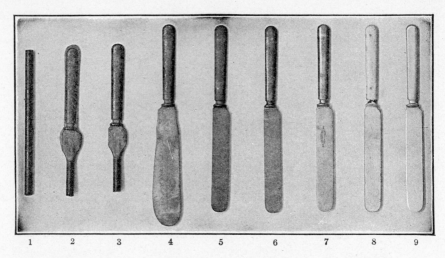

1. Steel cut to length. 2. Handle formed by 1,000-pound blow. 3. Handle margin, or flash, removed. 4. Blade drawn out through a pair of rolls. 5. Blade cut out to shape. 6. Knife roughed with coarse emery. 7. Trade-mark etched. 8. After plating. 9. The finished knife.

looks all right, but it does not harden the silver sufficiently and in consequence the latter does not wear well. When the article comes out of the plating bath the silver deposited is in a comparatively porous and "fluffy" state. The buffing will hit the high spots but the proper process turns the minute edges, closes the pores and makes the silver hard and compact, vastly increasing the wearing quality.

The silver thus deposited, is absolutely pure—finer, in fact, than any articles of sterling silver. Sterling is but .925 fine, requiring an alloy to stiffen it, whereas silver for plating can be used .999 fine.

How do Chimes Strike the Hour?

Chimes are ordinarily produced mechanically by the strokes of hammers against a series of bells, tuned agreeably to a given musical scale.

The hammers are lifted by levers acted upon by metallic pins or wooden pegs stuck in a large barrel, which is made to revolve by clockwork, and is so connected with the striking part of the clock mechanism that it is set in motion by it at certain intervals of time, usually every hour or every quarter of an hour.

The chime mechanism is sometimes so constructed that it may be played like a piano, but with the fist instead of the fingers.

How is Electricity Brought into a House?

The electric transmission of power is effected by employing the source of power to drive a machine called a dynamo, which generates an electric current.

This current is conveyed by a copper conductor, insulated from the earth, to the distant station, where it passes through a machine called an "electromotor," one part of which is thereby made to revolve, and imparts its motion to the machinery which is to be driven.

This is the simplest arrangement, and is that which is commonly employed when the original currents are not of such high tension as to be dangerous to life in the case of accidental shocks. There is, however, a great waste of power in employing low-tension currents when the distance is great; hence it is becoming a common practice to employ high-tension currents for transmission through the long conductor which connects the two stations, and to convert these into low-tension currents before they reach the houses or workshops where they are to be used. This is done sometimes by employing the high-tension currents to drive a local dynamo which generates low-tension currents.

The discovery that a Gramme machine is reversible—that is to say, when two Gramme machines are coupled together and one is operated as a generator, the other will act as a motor—was an important step taken in the transmission of power. Numerous efforts, since then, have been made to utilize electricity for the transmission of power over a long range. For this purpose the alternating current seems eminently adapted, as transformers only are needed to raise the line to high transmission voltage and to lower it again for use.

The possibilities offered by electrical transmission of water power for sections of country favored with waterfalls are numerous and have been extensively developed, which should result in making them great industrial centers. In this direction much has been done in utilizing the immense power of the Niagara Falls by electrical transmission, works having been built for this purpose both in New York and Canada, and several hundred thousand horse-power developed. The application of the power of waterfalls to the generation of electricity is rapidly extending, and promises to become a great source of mechanical power in the future.

What was the Origin of Masonic Signs?

Fable and imagination have traced back the origin of freemasonary to the Roman Empire, to the Pharaohs, the Temple of Solomon, the Tower of Babel, and even to the building of Noah's ark. In reality, it took its rise in the middle ages along with other incorporated crafts.

Skilled masons moved from place to place to assist in building the magnificent sacred structures—cathedrals, abbeys, etc.—which had their origin in these times, and it was essential for them to have some signs by which, on coming to a strange place, they could be recognized as real craftsmen and not impostors.

What is a Dictograph?

The dictograph, to which much publicity is now given, by reason of its use in detective work, is an instrument for magnifying sound. It was invented by K. M. Turner of New York, in 1907.

It consists of a master station in the form of a box less than a foot long and six inches deep, and any number of sub-stations that may be required. Any voice within fifteen feet is taken by the receiving instrument and carried over the wires to any distance within about a thousand miles.

It has now been adopted by a great many business organizations as a convenient means of inter-communication.

The Story of the Radio Telephone and Telegraph

Though means of transmitting messages by electricity have been known now for a great many years, the mechanisms by which they are accomplished are understood only by those who take a general interest in physical science, and the few to whom electrical communication is a profession. So far as theory and details of working are concerned, there are a good many people still in the same shadowy frame of mind as the old Aberdeen postmaster, of whom the story is told. When asked to explain the working of a telegraph instrument he said, "Look at that sheep-dog. Suppose we hold his hind-quarters here and stretch him out until his head reaches Glasgow. Then if we tread on his tail here he will bark in Glasgow. As it is not convenient to stretch a dog, we stretch a wire, and that serves the purpose."

As the name implies, "stretching a wire" between the sending and receiving station is unnecessary in radio telegraphy and telephony, though in order to understand the finer points of theory one needs to stretch the imagination a little. This is necessary in almost any consideration of electricity and magnetism for the reason that they operate across apparently empty space, and the links which connect cause and effect often have to be guessed at.

The invention of the radio telegraph is generally credited to Guglielmo Marconi, who patented the first practical system of telegraphing without wires, in 1897. The earlier experimenters had contributed largely to the knowledge of this science but

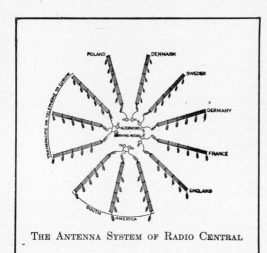

THE ANTENNA SYSTEM OF RADIO CENTRAL

had not succeeded in putting it into workable form. Electromagnetic waves may well be likened to the miniature waves created on the smooth surface of a pond when a stone is thrown into the center. When the stone strikes the water a series of ripples is sent out which extend in ever-widening circles out toward the edge of the pond until their force is lost in the distance. So the waves of radio are radiated out from the sending station at the speed of light, 186,000 miles per second. By means of a sending apparatus consisting of a generator of high frequency alternating currents of electricity, one conductor of which was connected to the earth and the other to a system of wires suspended in the air, known as an antenna or aerial, Marconi was successful in transmitting messages by electromagnetic waves to a receiving station which contained an aerial of similar design to the sending station, and a means of tuning and rectifying the currents received from the sending station, and making them audible by means of telephone receivers.

Successful experiments were conducted in 1899 across the English Channel and since that time the radio telegraph has extended its range until it is now possible to telegraph by radio half way around the globe, and systems are planned by various nations which will give them a complete relay service around the world. Regular commercial radio service is now maintained between practically all the countries of

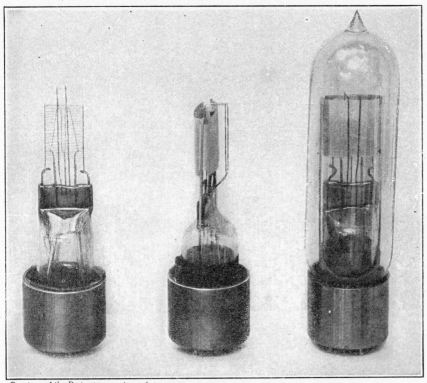

Courtesy of the Radio Corporation of America.

THE THREE ELEMENT VACUUM TUBE WHICH IS CHIEFLY RESPONSIBLE FOR THE RAPID DEVELOPMENT OF RADIO COMMUNICATION. THE FIRST VIEW ON THE LEFT SHOWS THE FILAMENT SURROUNDED BY THE GRID. IN THE CENTER VIEW THE PLATE HAS BEEN ADDED AND ON THE RIGHT IS THE COMPLETE TUBE.

the earth and both press matter and private business are handled with far greater speed and less expense than is possible by cable. Radio on shipboard has saved many lives by calling for aid in emergencies. An important example is that of the sinking of the Titanic in 1912. A law in the United States now requires that all ocean steamers carrying fifty or more passengers on routes of 200 miles or over must be equipped with efficient wireless apparatus and operators. The distance reached must be at least 100 miles. The Canadian law provides that every sea-going and coasting passenger ship of over 400 tons gross, registered in Canada, and every sea-going and coasting freight ship of over 1200 tons gross, shall be equipped with a wireless apparatus. All the larger vessels now publish a daily paper on board, the news in which has been supplied by the same agencies who feed the newspaper on land. Information is flashed to meet or overtake the vessel and caught up by her aerial, as she pursues her way at twenty-five or thirty miles an hour.

In the Studio of Radio Broadcasting Station WJZ

At the left is the announcer with his microphone and switches for cutting in or out the big microphone through which the music is broadcast.

Courtesy of the Radio Corporation of America

In the case of cargo vessels, the owners are able to get into touch with them at any point of their voyage. They can advise the captain where to call for coal or cargo, while he on his part can get into communication with the authorities or his firm's agents at the port of call, and have every necessary or desirable preparation made for his arrival. Should an accident happen, he can call assistance, inform the owners or relieve anxiety and suspense. At no time is he isolated from the world. The fortitude, courage and daring of those "who go down to the sea in ships" has never been called into question, but it has if anything been emphasized by the receipt of messages from an operator at his post, to whom the bonds of duty were as bonds of

Courtesy of the Radio Corporation of America.

FROM RADIO CENTRAL AT ROCKY POINT, LONG ISLAND, MESSAGES CAN BE SENT TO ALL QUARTERS OF THE GLOBE

steel, and who calmly operated the key until the waves entered his cabin and brought him honorable release. The marvelous radio compass now serves to give sailing masters and airplane pilots their location in storm and fog and direct them to safe harbors and landing places.

During the World War radio played an all-important part in every theater of action on land and sea. Ashore, radio equipped airplanes flew above the enemy lines and telegraphed the ranges to their gunners. In the front line trenches instruments attached to low aerials kept headquarters in touch with all developments. At sea radio played an even more important part not only in diverting the ships which carried our troops across from zones infested with enemy submarines, but in locating the submarines when they talked at night by radio and telling our destroyers where to look for them.

The American boy and his elder brother were not slow to take up the new science of radio. Amateur stations grew in number throughout the United States until in every community there was a club whose members became adept in picking the dots and dashes out of the atmosphere and translating them into weather reports, baseball scores, and the news of the day.

Courtesy of the Radio Corporation of America.

THE TOWERS OF RADIO CENTRAL ARE 410 FEET HIGH AND EACH ANTENNA CONSISTS
OF SIXTEEN SILICON BRONZE CABLES, ⅜ OF AN INCH IN DIAMETER AND NEARLY A MILE
AND A HALF LONG.

Suddenly and without any warning these radio fans were startled by hearing scraps of music and conversation when they listened in. Voices were heard in song and sermon, piano and violin solos, jazz orchestras and phonograph concerts began to fill the air. Boys and their elders were startled and fascinated. The wonder of wonders had come to pass and the radio telephone, which had been a subject for experiment since the early days of the radio telegraph, was an accomplished fact.

Realizing the importance of the publicity which had been given to radio through the World War and impelled by the recent perfecting of radio telephone sending and receiving apparatus, the large electrical manufacturing companies began broadcasting by radio. The immediate result was an enormous boom in the sale of receiving instruments. Homes, offices and schools were prompt to install receiving equipment and the broadcasting stations multiplied fast as the possibilities of this new avenue of publicity became apparent to the dealers and manufacturers of apparatus, to artists, players and musicians anxious to gain publicity for themselves, to ministers as an aid in taking church services to those who either could not or would not come to church, to politicians and public servants wishing to send a message to the people at large. By means of loud-speaking devices and amplifiers it is now possible for one man to address all the people of the United States if they were gathered in groups of one million people or less. Loud-speakers are now available which can amplify the human voice to such an extent that it is clearly audible for over seven miles, and it is perfectly possible for the President at Washington to address the entire nation at one time through broadcasting stations located throughout the country.

Radio telephony is carried on by much the same type of apparatus as that used in the radio telegraph with the exception of the fact that the broadcasting stations employ a microphone transmitter instead of a telegraph key to control the electromagnetic waves. On these waves the voice vibrations are impressed by the transmitter and they come in at the receiving end clear and distinct, though the origin may be hundreds and even thousands of miles away. The range of radio telephony is not yet as great as that of radio telegraphy but the distances are increasing every day and it will not be long until we can talk around the world. Passengers on steamers can keep in touch with their friends and business associates on both sides of the ocean, and day by day the news is transmitted both by telegraph and telephone so that one can keep up with affairs throughout the entire voyage. Concerts broadcast by stations in the United States are frequently heard in England.

It is perfectly possible for anyone to take up the receiver of the wire telephone in his home, call central and be connected to a radio station which will in turn connect him with a ship on the high seas by radio telephone. Combined radio and wire telephone systems are in operation in which long radio links across the water are included, frequently without the knowledge of the speaker, who talks without difficulty over this combination line.

Many inventions have been added to the art of radio during recent years. By far the most important of these was the adaptation by Dr. J. A. Fleming, an English inventor, of the principle of the emission of electrons (minute particles or negative charges of electricity) from a heated

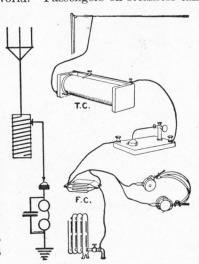

Fig. 1.—A Simple Receiving Set Consisting of a Single-Slide Tuning Coil, Crystal Detector, Telephones and a Telephone Condenser.

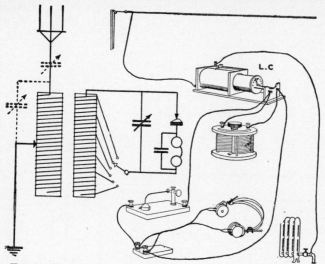

FIG. 2.—USING A LOOSE COUPLER IN A CRYSTAL DETECTOR SET.

filament in a vacuum tube, to apparatus for receiving radio signals. Fleming's tube or valve consisted of a glass bulb, from which the air had been exhausted, containing a filament similar to that in an incandescent light bulb, surrounded by a thin piece of metal called the plate. An American, Dr. Lee De Forest, improved this by the addition of a coil of wire, called the grid, between the filament and plate, and produced the three-element tube in universal use today. Its functions in radio are (1) as a detector to rectify alternating current, changing it to pulsating direct current; (2) as an amplifier to magnify weak signals received in the aerial and build them up to the point at which they are audible; (3) as a generator of high-frequency current for both sending and receiving; (4) as a modulator to control or mould the high-frequency oscillations generated by the sending tubes; (5) as a rectifier of alternating current for charging storage batteries. This device changes the alternating current used in radio transmission to direct current, and acts as a detector and amplifier by means of which the incoming signals are used to control much stronger current generated at the receiving station and so make the signals strong enough to be heard in the telephones or to operate loud-speakers.

The apparatus necessary to receive radio telegraph or telephone signals, including broadcast concerts, may be either very simple and inexpensive or extremely elaborate at a corresponding increase in cost, depending on the distance to be covered. If the sending station is not more than from fifteen to twenty-five miles away, the only apparatus needed to hear the signals is a set consisting of a single-wire antenna, properly insulated, a good connection to ground, such as a cold water pipe, a tuning coil, a crystal detector, and a

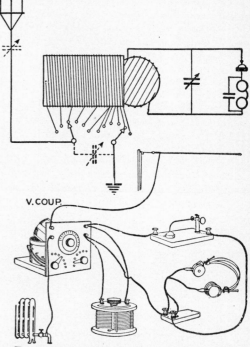

FIG. 3.—CIRCUIT FOR A VARIOCOUPLER IN A CRYSTAL DETECTOR HOOKUP.

good pair of telephones. Such a set is shown in Figure 1. If, however, more than one sending station of approximately equal power and employing nearly the same wave length is within the range of the receiving set, tuning apparatus capable of a finer adjustment is necessary to avoid hearing both stations at the same time. The substitution of a loose-coupler for the tuning coil is one way to accomplish this result. (See Figure 2.) In this instrument the outer coil (which is similar to a single-slider tuning coil) forms the primary, which is tuned to the wave length of the sending station by means of the slider which can be moved over the turns of wire until a sufficient number are included in the circuit to bring the wave length of

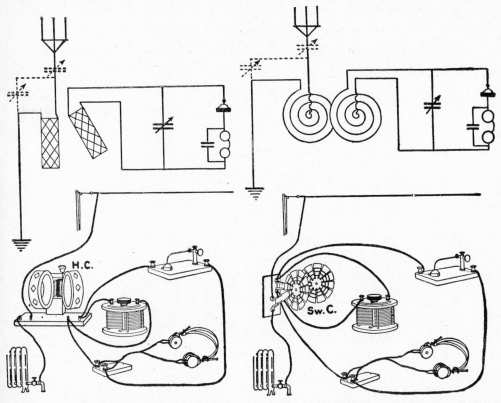

Fig. 4.—Honeycomb Coils in a Crystal
Detector Hookup.

Fig. 5.—Spider Web Coils in a Crystal
Detector Set.

the receiving set up to that of the sending set. The secondary consists of another coil which slides inside the primary. This coil is tuned to the wave length of the primary by means of taps taken at intervals from the winding. When the signal has been tuned in by the slider on the primary and the secondary tap switch, the tuning is made sharper by sliding the secondary out of the primary until the interfering station is no longer heard. Similar results are more easily secured by the use of a variocoupler. (See Figure 3.) In this instrument, the outer or primary coil is tuned by taps taken from the winding to switches, the secondary consists of a ball or tube which may be revolved within the primary to loosen or tighten the coupling. The secondary is tuned by the variable condenser shown in the illustration. Other instruments frequently used in tuning are honeycomb coils and spider-web coils, as

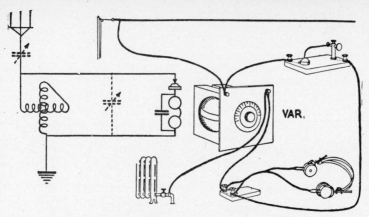

FIG. 6.—A VARIOMETER TUNED CRYSTAL DETECTOR SET.

shown in Figures 4 and 5. In these coils the number of turns in the primary and secondary cannot be varied and the tuning must be done by means of primary and secondary variable condensers. The amount of coupling is varied by the distance between the coils. The variometer is another instrument much employed in radio circuits. (See Figure 6.) In this instrument an outer coil containing a fixed number of turns of wire is connected in series with another coil which revolves inside. The relative position of the coils governs the inductance or tuning effect of the instrument.

If it is desired that signals should be received from greater distances, amplification of the minute current picked up by the antenna is necessary in order to make it powerful enough to actuate the telephones or loud-speaker. Such amplification can be accomplished by the use of vacuum tubes. In receiving sets the functions of these tubes are as a detector, or rectifier, of alternating current, and as an amplifier to build up the current received and magnify the variations, thereby increasing the volume of sound heard in the telephones. It is possible to substitute a vacuum tube for the crystal detector in any of the circuits previously shown with greatly improved results, both in volume of sound and distance covered. (See Figure 7.) Two sources of local current supply are needed to operate a vacuum tube, a low voltage to heat the filament, and a higher voltage in the plate circuit to actuate the flow of electrons on which the tube depends for operation. If batteries are used as current sources, the low-voltage filament supply is called the "A" battery, and the plate supply is called the "B" battery.

The circuit in Figure 7 is a simple vacuum tube hookup. Due to the rectifying action of the tube, current of two frequencies flows in the plate circuit, a high, or radio frequency, of which no use is made,

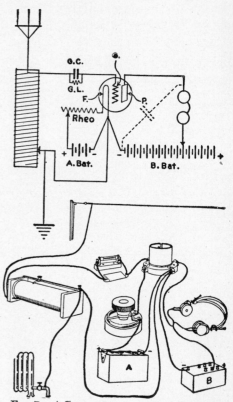

FIG. 7.—A SIMPLE VACUUM TUBE DETECTOR SET WITH SINGLE SLIDER TUNING COIL.

and a low, or audio-frequency current, which actuates the telephones. By the discovery of Major Armstrong of the "feed-back circuit" the unemployed radio-frequency current can be returned to the grid circuit by means of what is called a "tickler coil," as shown in Figure 8, passed through the tube again and again until the maximum capacity of the tube is reached. This results in a great increase in the sensitiveness of the tube as a detector and also in the volume of the output. Circuits of this type are also frequently called "regenerative circuits." Many other forms, besides the one shown, are employed, but all depend on the principle of feeding back the radio-frequency energy from the plate to the grid circuit.

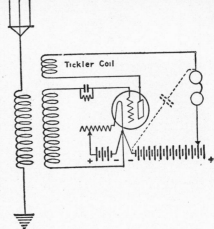

FIG. 8.—A REGENERATIVE CIRCUIT USING A LOOSE COUPLER WITH A TICKLER COIL.

If an audio-frequency transformer is substituted for the telephones and the current from its secondary coil led through another tube acting as an amplifier, a further great increase in volume results. Such a hook-up is shown in Figure 9. Two stages, or steps, of audio-frequency amplification are usually sufficient for all practical purposes. If greater amplification is necessary for receiving from greater distances, radio-frequency amplification is resorted to. This consists in employing one or more tubes to amplify the current received from the antenna before it reaches the detector tube. Such a circuit is shown in Figure 10. A circuit of this type employing three stages of radio-frequency amplification, a detector and two stages of audio-frequency amplification will bring in signals from very great distances with remarkable strength and clearness.

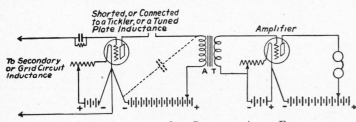

FIG. 9.—A DETECTOR AND ONE STAGE OF AUDIO-FREQUENCY AMPLIFICATION.

Wonderfully efficient as the radio telegraph and telephone are, there is one enemy which has seemed unconquerable. That is the curious phenomenon known as static. The summer months and tropic climate are especially friendly to static, but it is hoped that by means of choke coils, wave traps, and other devices it may be possible in the near future to defeat this arch enemy of radio communication.

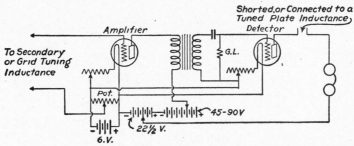

FIG. 10.—ONE STAGE OF RADIO-FREQUENCY AMPLIFICATION WITH A DETECTOR TUBE.

Pictures by Wire and Wireless

Photo Jennings Laboratories
PICTURE BY WIRELESS

Photo A. T. and T. Co.

PICTURE BY WIRE

The most marvelous recent inventions are those connected with sending photographs, manuscript, autographs, etc., long distances by wire and by wireless.

In sending a picture by wire it is prepared as a film transparency in the form of a cylinder. The film picture is inserted in the machine by rolling it up and slipping it into the drum. During operation a very small and intense beam of light shines through the film upon a photo-electric cell within. In the receiving machine a sensitive film is put on a rotating cylinder and turns like the cylinder record on a phonograph. On this film falls a point of intense white light varied constantly. To synchronize the motions of the two cylinders two separate currents are sent over the wires, one called the picture channel and the other the synchronizing channel.

The method of sending pictures by radio is not dissimilar. As the message or picture on the sending cylinder rotates, the different strengths of the light when thrown on the black and white portions of the message cause fluctuations in the cell. Consequently, the values of the electric impulses flowing through the cell to the broadcasting antennæ differ according to the black and white portions. Moving slowly sideways as it rotates, the whole message passes in front of the light sensitive cells in strips or "slices."

The message is "sliced" or "taken to pieces" in this way and radio signals are broadcast to represent each black or white space in every "slice" of the document. The light values are converted into electrical values.

When the radio signals are carried into the receiving set from the antenna they cause the Moore lamp, with its 500,000 flashes a second capacity, to light and go out in an order which represents the black and white spaces. Meanwhile, the cylinder around which the light sensitive film was wrapped is rotating in front of the blinking lamp and the film being exposed to impressions which produce a duplicate of the document on the glass cylinder at the sending station.

While the film is rotating, it is also moving slowly to the left, so that its entire surface passes in front of the "light pencil" and becomes covered with fine lines. As the strength of the radio signals change, a changing amount of light is thrown on each portion of the film. Each black space on the original document is reproduced on the film and each white space is reproduced also.

(272)

The Story of the Advance of Electricity*

It is often remarked that the history of electrical development is the history of modern industrial development. This is true, except that the terms should be reversed. Electric lighting was not invented to equip skyscrapers and the huge apartment buildings of today. In point of fact, the invention of these structures was possible only because electric light already existed. Electric motive power was not devised to supply the great manufacturing establishments of the present. On the contrary, such institutions were erected precisely because such a thing as the electric motor was available. The history of modern industry is thus seen emphatically to be the history of electricity.

The First Commercial Central Station.

The first central station for the commercial distribution of electricity was set going on the 4th of September, 1882, by Thomas Edison himself, at 257 Pearl Street, New York City. Newspapers of the following day had much to say. Wonder was expressed over the "blazing horseshoe that glowed within a pear-shaped globe." Another told of "the dim flicker of gas supplanted by a steady glare, bright and mellow." A third observed, "As soon as it is dark enough to need artificial light, you turn the thumb-screw and the light is there; no nauseous smell, no flicker, no glare."

Among the five or six buildings supplied with the new lighting were the *Herald* offices and the Drexel Building, at the time one of New York City's show places. The illumination of the latter was held to be a truly momentous achievement owing to its great size. The equipment, in other words, reached the grand total of 106 lamps. In comparison, it is interesting to mention the lighting equipment of the new Municipal Building, in New York City, numbering something over 15,000 lamps.

The Old Pearl Street Plant.

This primitive central station in Pearl Street was a converted warehouse of brick construction, four stories high, and it was separated in two parts by a fire wall. One of these parts was used for the storing of underground supplies, while the other was occupied by the generating machinery, for the support of which a special foundation of steel and concrete was provided. The necessary steam boilers were accommodated in the basement, while the second floor was occupied by six generators of 125 horse-power each, nicknamed "Jumbos."

Simple as sounds this original Edison equipment, it nevertheless represented years of research and experimenting on the part of Edison and those associated with him.

Edison and the Electric Light.

In 1878 Thomas A. Edison, at his experimental laboratory at Menlo Park, New Jersey, where he had already invented the carbon telephone transmitter and many other things, undertook the task of devising a general system for the generation. distribution and utilization of electricity for lighting and power purposes.

The first marked accomplishment in operative detail was a lamp with a platinum wire burner of high resistance, protected by a high vacuum in an all-glass globe

---

* Illustrations by courtesy of New York Edison Co., unless otherwise indicated.

Photo by Brown Bros. "THE GREAT WHITE WAY"

Times Square, New York, at night, with Broadway on the left, a curving ribbon of white light. Here every night in winter thousands upon thousands of people throng to theaters and cafés.

and with the leading-in wires sealed into the glass by fusion. Such a lamp necessarily had a small illuminating power compared with that of the arc light, which was the only electric light then in commercial use.

The next step in the development of Mr. Edison's electric-lighting system was taken on October 21, 1879, when he discovered that if a carbonized cotton thread were substituted as a burner for the platinum wire of his earlier lamp, the slender and apparently frail carbon was mechanically strong, and also durable under the action of the electric current. The announcement of the invention of the carbon filament lamp was first made to the public in December, 1879.

With the experience gained by an experimental system at Menlo Park, Mr. Edison began, in the spring of 1881, at the Edison Machine Works, Goerck Street,

STEAM DYNAMO IN EDISON'S OLD STATION

New York City, the construction of the first successful direct-connected steam dynamo. The development of an adequate underground conduit proved also most serious. The district selected for lighting was the area—nearly a square mile in extent—included between Wall, Nassau, Spruce, and Ferry Streets, Peck Slip and the East River in New York City. In those days such electrical transmission as existed—this of course related largely to telegraphy—was accomplished by means of a veritable forest of poles and wires augmented by the distribution equipments of fire alarm, telephone, burglar alarm and stock ticker companies. So used had people become to this sort of thing that even the most competent electrical authorities of the time doubted extremely whether Edison's scheme of an underground system could be made either a scientific or a commercial success, owing to the danger of great loss through leakage. However, the Edison conduits once in use, both the public and even the telephone, telegraph and ticker companies acknowledged their feasibility. Such, in fact, was the success of the new method that the city compelled at length the removal of all telegraph poles.

In the Trenches.

The systematic laying out of street mains in the first company district was begun in the summer of 1881. It must not be thought, of course, that these old-time conduits resembled strikingly those of the present day.   The method then used was to dig a trench in which were laid the pipes measuring twenty feet in length. Through these the conductors were drawn, two half-round copper wires kept in place first by heavy cardboard and afterward by rope.   The conductors having been drawn in, a preparation of asphaltum and linseed oil was forced into the piping to serve as insulation.   The spending of three and four arduous nights a week in these trenches by Mr. Edison and his associates suggests the rigor of the later European warfare.   This work, together with that incident to the operation of the new station, often proved too much even for Edison's phenomenal endurance.   At such times he slept on a cot close beside the running engines, while the rest of the crew crawled in on the lower row of field-magnet coils of the dynamos, a place warm

THE DYNAMO ROOM OF THE FIRST EDISON ELECTRIC LIGHTING STATION IN NEW YORK

enough, though a trifle bumpy.   One of the inventor's early assistants tells of going to sleep standing up, leaning against a door frame—this, after forty-eight hours of uninterrupted work.

September 4th saw a full 400 lamps turned on from the Pearl Street station. From that day on the station supplied current continuously until 1895, with but two brief interruptions.   One of these happened in 1883 and lasted three hours. The other resulted from the serious fire of January 2, 1890, and lasted less than half a day.   The record in the second case would appear astounding, as no less a handicap occurred than the burning down of the station itself.   The situation was saved, however, by the presence of an auxiliary plant that had already been opened on Liberty Street.

Edison as a Central Station Pioneer.

The layman, while appreciating the tremendous advance in generating machinery since the early eighties, is surprised to learn that the great Edison system of today is conducted upon principles that Edison developed and put into practice at that

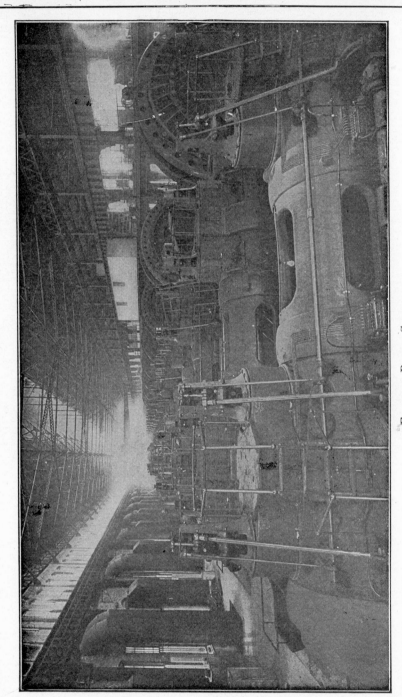

Courtesy of Indiana Steel Co.

ELECTRIC POWER STATION

The seventeen great gas engines are operated by gas from the blast furnaces which was formerly allowed to escape. Each engine drives a 2,500-kilowatt dynamo.

time.   Edison's, in truth, was the master mind, the forming spirit of all the advances made in the seventies and eighties.   Exceedingly much, on the other hand, is due the energy of his fellow workers, many of whom figure conspicuously in the country's electrical affairs at present.

In this manner Edison and his assistants became established in New York City. Current at first was supplied free to customers for approximately five months, which speaks quite as much for Edison's Scotch "canniness" as for his inventive genius. Well before the period was over the new illuminant had justified itself, until today it shows itself an element indispensable in every phase of the country's activity.

Early Growth.

Within two years from the opening of the station the demand for service had so increased that over one hundred applications were filed in excess of what could

ELECTRIC DELIVERY WAGONS LOADING EDISON LAMPS

be accepted, because the plant was taxed already to its utmost capacity.   Allusion has already been made to the auxiliary plant at Liberty Street, a station of 2,000 lights' capacity which was instituted in 1886.   By 1887, not only a second but a third district had been mapped out, the whole extending from Eighteenth to Forty-fifth Street.   All the underground system in the two new districts was laid according to Edison's new three-wire patent; and it was presently announced that customers would be supplied with power as well as with light.

Six months after the disastrous fire of 1890, in which the Pearl Street station was burned, the site was chosen for the Edison Duane Street building on which operations were so hastened that machines were installed and current turned on the first of May the following year.

The Waterside Stations.

For some time the need of a central generating plant had been apparent to all familiar with the company's facilities and prospects.   Already during the summer of 1898 an engineering commission had visited all the chief electrical stations of Europe and consulted the best-known experts of the industry, and in 1902 the first waterside station in New York was opened upon a site bordering the East River between

Thirty-eighth and Thirty-ninth Streets.   The new operating room contained sixteen vertical engines with a capacity each of over 5,000 horse-power.   From these current was generated by 3,500 kilowatt generators and sent out to the various distributing centers.

As a very natural consequence of such development, the company by 1902 had 420 miles of underground system supplying installation amounting to 1,928,090 fifty-watt equivalents.

Electricity a Living Factor.

To talk about electrical development in terms of power consumed tells but one side of the story.   More impressive even than figures are the immense number

ELECTRIC SEWING MACHINES IN THE MANHATTAN TRADE SCHOOL

of uses to which electricity is put.   Electric lighting, introduced in 1882, has become practically the standard for illumination, not only here, but for the entire civilized world.

In the Printing Trade.

Electric power was introduced, timidly, by way of a few fans in 1884 and following this, in 1888, motor drive for printing presses was undertaken.   At the present moment in New York City there is hardly a printing establishment worthy the name that is not electrically operated throughout.   Among the largest customers of the central station in New York City are the great daily newspapers, among them the *Times*, the *World*, the *Sun*, the *Evening Post*, and the *American*.

Construction.

Not only are passengers conveyed up and down by electric elevators in skyscrapers, but the buildings themselves are erected by means of electricity.   Recent examples of such construction are the Woolworth and Equitable buildings in New

Photo by Brown Bros.

A FAIRYLAND OF LIGHT

The canyon of lower Broadway, south from the Woolworth Building—a glorious miracle of light.

York City; in this last instance a thousand horse-power was used in digging the foundations alone.

Not only are New York City's subways operated by electricity; they were also built by electricity, a statement which applies to the new subways as well as the parts of the first system. In digging for the new Broadway subway, an electric company supplied 25,000 horse-power. The mammoth new aqueduct system by which water is carried from the Catskills to the Battery is another example of electricity as a source of power for large construction work. Still more picturesque is the use of electricity in building the under-river tubes. Indeed, it is doubtful whether this particular form of operation could have been carried on without the aid of electricity.

Loft Manufacturing.

Aside from these special instances of electricity in construction, one must think of electricity as responsible for nearly all the manufacturing, large and small, that goes on in the ever-increasing number of loft-buildings throughout all large cities. For example, New York City serves as the center of the garment-making industry for the entire country, there being fully a quarter of a million garment-trade workers in the Greater City. Along Fifth and Fourth Avenues are found the large establishments, electrically equipped throughout for cutting, stitching and pressing, while even in the smallest shops on the East Side foot-power machines have become almost a thing of the past.

Electric Heating.

The commercial use of electric heating is one of the more recent electrical developments. For the most part, this also applies to the garment trade and its closely allied clothing industries. In the modernly equipped factories one finds electric flat irons, velvet steamers and coffee urns. In the printing trade, electrically heated linotype melting pots are being introduced successfully, while glue-pots and sealing-wax melters can be seen in binderies and banking institutions. Absence of fire risk accounts for the introduction of electric heating units of different kinds into the motion-picture film manufacturing industry, a rapidly growing province. The same element of safety where inflammable substances are employed has produced the electric japan oven and similar apparatus.

Electricity and Safety.

The importance of electricity in factory work cannot be over-estimated. A shop fully equipped with electric machinery is the best possible kind of shop for employee as well as for the owner. Motor-driven machines are the safest possible kind, while absence of overhead shafting and dangerous belts mean health as well as security. In the electric shop, motor-driven blowers carry fumes and dust away from the worker and bring fresh air in. Electrically driven machinery is now regarded as the standard machinery. In the various vocational schools in New York City at present both boys and girls are taught to operate electrically driven machines, it being assumed that those will be what the pupils will be called upon to operate when they leave the school for the shop.

Electricity in Medicine.

Another domain of electric enterprise of the greatest value for the country at large is the increasing use of electricity in medicine. The most conspicuous element in this is the wide-spread acceptance of the X-ray as a necessary tool of the medical profession. Newspapers and magazines were full of the remarkable X-ray achievements of surgeons in charge of the various European war hospitals.   Those, of course, were spectacular instances, but it should not be forgotten that every day, in our great hospitals, the X-ray is proving itself almost indispensable in the examination of the sick and injured.   Besides utilizing X-rays in the diagnosis of disease, the rays themselves are employed in treatment of cancer and skin diseases.   The oculist, the dentist, indeed medical specialists of all kinds, are coming to recognize the immense aid that electricity can give in its various forms and applications.

Electric Vehicles.

The electric truck has already demonstrated itself as a safer and less expensive rival of the gasoline delivery truck in many kinds of service.   In the boroughs of

THE GREAT PRESS ROOM OF "THE NEW YORK TIMES" IS ALL ELECTRICALLY OPERATED

Manhattan and the Bronx alone, in New York City, there were more than 2,000 such trucks in operation in 1916.   Counting both pleasure and business vehicles, the borough of Manhattan boasted about 2,500 storage-battery driven wagons in active use.   It is rather interesting to note that Chicago operates many more electric pleasure cars than New York, while New York does far more of its business by means of the electric vehicle.   Recently, there was established in New York an electric co-operative garage, the joint enterprise of the electric passenger car manufacturers and an electric company.   It was believed that by providing proper and adequate facilities for garaging electric pleasure vehicles the use of passenger-electrics in New York City would be greatly increased.

Electricity and the Home.

In emphasizing the important part which electricity plays in the business of a great metropolis, the home should not be forgotten.   It is now possible, by means

ELECTRIC TRAIN CHART AND SWITCH CONTROL

SUBWAY CONSTRUCTION

In the upper view the electric chart on the wall facing the switch operator indicates the location of every train in the New York subway system at all times. The lower view shows typical subway construction for third rail train and surface cars. The material used is reinforced concrete.

ONE TYPE OF ELECTRIC CONSTRUCTION ON RAILROADS

The system shown here is used upon the New York, New Haven and Hartford Railroad. It consists of pairs of wire cables supported by bridges placed about 300 feet apart. Rigid triangles of iron pipe are secured to these cables and the trolley wire attached to the triangles. The trolley wire is kept rigid and free from slack in this manner.

of electric appliances, practically to eliminate all drudgery from housework. The use of many of these domestic machines is familiar to all: vacuum cleaners, washing machines, fans, and the more usual electric cooking devices. Within the next decade, one looks to see a remarkable advance in this direction. One anticipates the more extensive use of electric refrigeration and other electric labor-saving devices, to the great improvement of city homes, making them pleasanter and more healthy as toilsome operations are done away with. And it must not be forgotten that the city home, like the country home, is the backbone of the well-being of the community. Electricity can have no greater mission than improving, strengthening and upbuilding good homes.

Decreased Cost of Electricity.

Closely akin to this is another electrical development most pleasing to consider. Years ago, electricity was considered the luxury of the rich. Now electric light is coming to be shed on rich and poor alike. Little by little the shops, factories and dwellings of more humble inhabitants are provided with electricity, so that cleanliness, safety and comfort are by no means confined even to the well-to-do or the more comfortable homes.

One great factor in this change has been the decreasing cost of electricity. Within the last decade, the cost of almost all necessities of life has ascended with leaps and bounds, so that a dollar now, expended in ordinary household goods, will purchase hardly more than what thirty cents would in 1890. But all this while, the cost of electricity has steadily decreased. With centralized generating plants, improved machinery and better lamps, one dollar today will buy eighteen times as much electric light as it would in 1884. With such facts before us, it is fairly easy to predict the still further electrical development of all important centers. There will be more and better light in homes; there will be more and better light in offices and factories, thus greatly lessening the chances for injury or eye-strain. In all industry, great and small, laborious hand processes will be replaced by safely operated electric machinery, while wider use of electric labor-saving appliances will extend into the home.

Hospitals, by aid of electricity, will be able to increase still more their splendid work for the relief of suffering, while cleaner and safer ways of living will serve as a preventive of disease. One can easily say that with increasing electrical development the country will come to be still greater, a country where electricity shall provide for the safety and well-being of all its people.

How is Die-Sinking Done?

Die-sinking is the art of preparing dies for stamping coins, buttons, medallions, jewelry, fittings, etc. The steel for the manufacture of dies is carefully selected, forged at a high heat into the rough die, softened by careful annealing, and then handed over to the engraver. After the engraver has worked out the design in intaglio the die is put through the operation of hardening, after which, being cleaned and polished, it is called a "matrix." This is not, however, generally employed in multiplying impressions, but is used for making a "punch" or steel impression for relief. For this purpose another block of steel of the same quality is selected, and, being carefully annealed or softened, is compressed by proper machinery upon the matrix until it receives the impression. When this process is complete the impression is retouched by the engraver, and hardened and collared like the matrix. Any number of dies may now be made from this punch by impressing upon it plugs of soft steel.

The Story in the Making of a Magazine*

The printing of a few thousand copies of one of the great American magazines would not be a difficult feat for any large first-class printing plant. The putting of the pages into type and running them through the modern job presses could easily be accomplished. But when, instead of a few thousand copies, millions of copies of the magazine are printed, and these millions are produced unfailingly week after

ONE OF THE SCORES OF PRESSES ON WHICH THE INSIDE PAGES OF "THE SATURDAY EVENING POST" ARE PRINTED

week, month after month, in a quality of printing rivaling the production of but a few thousand copies, then, indeed, is it marvelous how results are attained.

Obviously one of the first necessities towards such quantity production is extra speed. This is secured to a certain degree by feeding the paper into presses from rolls instead of sheet by sheet. But as the quality of the print must be retained, there is a limit in this speeding beyond which it is not safe to go. Some other method of increasing the production without lowering the quality of the printed sheet must be resorted to—and this is duplication. By the process of electrotyping, plates of metal duplicating exactly the printing surface of the type and engravings in the original page, can be made. By providing as many presses as may be needed, and by supplying each press with duplicates, or electrotype plates as they are called, the

* Illustrations by courtesy of The Curtis Publishing Co.

problem of vast quantity requirements has been solved, so far as the actual printing is concerned.

But there are other factors to be considered. For example, the printed sheets, as they come from the press, must be folded to the size of the magazine. This is done in two ways. Machines which take the sheets, one by one, from the completed pile, and fold them to the required size, are used on some publications, while on others a folding machine and a binding attachment are included as integral parts of the press itself. The paper, as it comes from the printing section of the press, is mechanically folded, cut apart, the previously-printed cover sheet wrapped around it, and the whole stapled together with wire stitches. Thus the white paper, which enters the press from the roll in one long ribbon, is delivered at the other end of the press

ONE OF THE SEVERAL BATTERIES OF PRESSES NECESSARY TO PRINT "THE LADIES' HOME JOURNAL"

printed, folded and bound up into complete magazines at the rate of sixty each minute. Issues of a magazine of thirty-two, forty-eight, or even more pages, are produced in this manner.

Many magazines, however, have more pages than this. Then it is necessary to print on separate presses the various sections, or signatures as they are called, which, when combined, will make up a complete magazine. If only a few thousand were printed, these signatures could be collected together by hand, and then fed into the wire-stitching machine, also by hand. This method of collecting the sections and binding them together was the one used until editions became so large that mechanical methods became necessary.

Now, however, the various sections which go to make up the magazine are piled in certain troughs of a binding machine, which, with seeming human intelligence, clasps one copy of each section in turn, and combing them with a copy of the cover

A GROUP OF FOLDING MACHINES WHICH AUTOMATICALLY GRASP THE FLAT SHEET AND FOLD IT UP TO THE SIZE OF THE MAGAZINE

sheet, conducts them all, properly collated, into the wire-stitching device, from which they are ejected into orderly piles. Some magazines are bound together in a different manner, however, and are not stitched with wire, but have the inside pages and the cover glued together, and an ingenious binding machine has been perfected which does this automatically.

Another marvel of the periodical of our day is the printing of some of the pages in the full colors of the original paintings. To get this result, it is necessary to print the sheet in four colors and to have each printing in exactly the correct spot on the sheet (a variation of only a hundredth of an inch being detrimental). The process would normally be quite slow—too slow, in fact, for the tremendous quantities necessary for the large editions of the modern magazine. Both of these objections have been overcome, however, by arranging four small cylinders, each printing its designated color—yellow, red, blue or black—so that as the sheet of paper travels around a larger cylinder it is brought into contact with the four printing cylinders in rapid succession.

Many magazines print two colors for covers and inside pages, instead of full four-color printings. Presses of a nature somewhat similar to those explained above are used.

So much for the principal mechanical problems and their solutions, in producing millions of magazines of a high quality each week. But there must be some force that keeps this maze of machinery constantly at work, so that all the parts properly co-ordinate. A slip-up at one spot might cause such a delay as would result if, for instance, hundreds of thousands of the inside pages were printed and ready for binding, but lacked the printed covers. To prevent any such calamity in the work rooms, there is usually prepared a daily schedule which plots out what operation, on each issue of the magazine, is to be completed that day; and if by chance any operation is not up to the schedule, immediate steps are taken to speed up the work until the production has been brought back to where it should be.

And this schedule reaches out into the shipping and mailing departments, so arranging it that the first copies off the press are speeded to the far sections of the country. In this way all the copies as they come from the presses are dispatched, so that the man in San Francisco and the man in Philadelphia find the magazine on the news-stand on the same day.

How did the Ringing of the Curfew Originate?

The word "curfew" is derived from the French "couvre-feu," meaning "cover fire."

The ringing of the curfew originated in England by William the Conqueror, who directed that at the ringing of the bell at eight o'clock all fires and lights should be extinguished. The law was repealed by Henry I in 1100, but the bell continued to be rung in many districts to modern times and probably may still be heard.

The name was also given formerly to a domestic utensil for covering up a fire.

In the United States an ordinance establishing a curfew, with the purpose of keeping young people off the streets, has existed in Salem, Mass., since Puritan days.

Similar ordinances have of late been adopted in other cities, in general providing that children under fifteen shall not frequent the streets after nine o'clock in summer and eight in winter.

The Story of America's First Horseless Carriage

Mr. Elwood Haynes tells an interesting story of his first "horseless carriage:"

In 1890 I became interested in the natural gas field at Greentown, Ind. My work took me through the country a great deal, and I drove a horse, of course. The great trouble with the horse was his lack of endurance, and this became more apparent day after day.

One afternoon, or night, rather, while driving home after a hard day's work, I thought to myself that it would be a fine thing if I didn't have to depend on the horse for locomotion. From then on my mind dwelt a great deal upon the subject of a self-propelled vehicle that could be used on any country road or city street.

I planned to use the gasoline engine. Even the lightest engines made at that time were very heavy per unit of power, and rather crude in construction.

My work was confined to Greentown, Ind., in 1890 and 1891. In the fall of 1892 I moved to Kokomo, and the following summer I had my plans sufficiently matured to begin the actual construction of a machine. I ordered a one-horse-power marine upright, two-cycle gasoline engine from the Sintz Gas Engine Company of Grand Rapids, Mich.

This motor barely gave one brake horse-power and weighed 180 pounds. (It is interesting to note in this connection, that an aeroplane motor of the same weight readily gives forty horse-power.) Upon its arrival from Grand Rapids, in the fall of 1893, lacking a more suitable place, the motor was brought direct to my home and set up in the kitchen.

When the gasoline and battery connection were installed, the motor, after considerable cranking, was started and ran with such speed and vibration that it pulled itself from its attachments to the floor. Luckily, however, one of the battery wires was wound about the motor shaft and thus disconnected the current. In order to provide against vibration I was obliged to make the frame of the machine much heavier than I first intended.

The machine was built up in the form of a small truck. The framework in which the motor was placed consisted of a double "hollow square" of steel tubing, joined at the rear corners by steel castings and by malleable castings in front. The hind axle constituted the rear member of the frame and the front axle was swiveled at its center to the front end of the "hollow square," in which the motor and counter-shaft were placed.

The total weight of the machine when completed was about 820 pounds. July 4, 1894, when ready for test, it was hauled into the country about three miles, behind a horse carriage, and started on a nearly level turnpike.

It moved off at once at a speed of about seven miles per hour, and was driven about one and one-half miles farther into the country. It was then turned about, and ran all the way into the city without making a single stop.

I was convinced upon this return trip that there was a future for the "horseless carriage," although I did not at that time expect it to be so brilliant and imposing.

AMERICA'S FIRST CAR, BUILT BY ELWOOD HAYNES

Courtesy of Haynes Auto Co.

The Story in a Sausage[*]

Away back in the dark ages, even before the Christian era, a Chinese husband-man, so we are told, made a wonderful discovery—that pork was good to eat. No one had ever considered the possibility of eating pork, for in those days pigs were pets, and just as every family today has its dog "Rover," so then, every family had its pig "Scraps."

One day the house of Char-Lee was burned to the ground. The cause of the fire is unknown. Char-Lee was filled with remorse and, as he walked about among the ruins of his home, he felt that the gods of Good Luck had indeed turned their backs on him. As he was thus bewailing his misfortunes, he stumbled over a charred timber and fell flat on the ground. In lifting himself to his feet, he burned the fingers of his right hand, and, as does a child, he immediately proceeded to suck those fingers.

Imagine his amazement to find clinging to his fingers a substance most luscious to the taste, and most gratifying to the palate! He looked to see what it could be, and—behold, he saw that it was the remains of "Scraps," who had been lost in the burning house and roasted as perhaps never has a pig been roasted since.

Eager to further enjoy this new delicacy, Char-Lee proceeded to feast himself, and it was then he found that pork not only pleases and gratifies—but satisfies. Desiring to share his new delights with his friends and neighbors, he called them together and they had a wonderful feast. From that day to this we have eaten roasted pork.

It was many, many years later that a Roman farmer, living on a beautiful little farm at the mouth of the Tiber, formed the habit of putting fresh pork in a covered pan and burying the whole deep in the cool sands by the water's edge. But one day he put the pan too near the edge and at high tide the salt water from the ocean came up, filled the pan, and so smoothed the surface of the sands that he was unable to find the place where he had buried the container.

After several fortnights he accidentally found his meat again. He examined it carefully and was surprised to find that it had seemingly kept in perfect condition, the only trouble being that the water had gotten into his pan and his meat was all wet. So he carried it to his house, and, putting a long skewer through the piece, he hung it high above the fire in his open hearth, to dry it off before he should wish to roast it.

Later in the day he set out with two companions for a two-days' hunting expedition in the woods. As the party returned, laden with the spoils of the hunt, his cook was preparing a meal for them. As he walked into the house, he thought of his piece of pork. You can readily imagine his astonishment when he found that the smoke from the smouldering embers, while he was away, had turned the meat a deep cherry hue, and that the fire, built up to prepare the home-coming feast, had broiled the piece to a nicety. It savored of an aroma so rare that it was given preference over even the choice pheasants which had been prepared.

This was the first time a cured and smoked piece of pork had ever been eaten, but could you have seen how delighted these men were with the result of this accidental preparation, you would have known from their enthusiasm that cured, smoked pork would one day have a very great popularity.

Later, a farmer and his family decided that they would like to eat meat even during the summer months when the activity of haying season made it impossible to prepare it in the usual way, and so, in March, or during some other convenient cool

[*] Courtesy of George A. Hormel & Co.

period, he would kill the pig which had been fattening all winter, and dissect the carcass into hams, shoulders, bacon sides and mess pork.

These parts were cured by different methods; one very popular way was to put the hams and shoulders on about an inch of salt in the bottom of a barrel, keeping these parts around the edge so as to leave room for the mess pork and bacon sides in the center. Each part would be carefully rubbed with salt before it was packed away, and slits were cut from the surface of the hams to the bone, so that one might force salt in them, thus keeping the meat from turning sour. The top of the meat was sprinkled with sugar and saltpetre. A small barrel head was laid on the top of the

CHESTER WHITE SOWS*
Lard Type Hogs

meat and a heavy stone placed on the head so as to hold the meat firmly in place. At the end of a week just enough water was added to cover the barrel head.

Another way was to make a very strong salt brine. To this brine would be added a little sugar and saltpetre, and, after packing the meat the same as in the other case, enough of this brine would be added to entirely cover the meat. By not letting the brine get old, or by keeping plenty of salt on it, the meat could be kept in this way for several months, but would be available for use at any time.

Hams and shoulders were always smoked at the end of about two months. When getting ready to smoke some pieces, the farmer would first soak them twenty-four hours in clear, cold water. By tying a string through the shank of a ham and running this string up through a hole in the bottom of an inverted barrel, he could secure it by tying to a small stick on the outside of the hole. Under the barrel he would build a small fire, sometimes of corncobs, sometimes of hardwood and sawdust. It was the task of the small boy of the family to start this fire in the morning and maintain

*Courtesy of The Field, New York City.

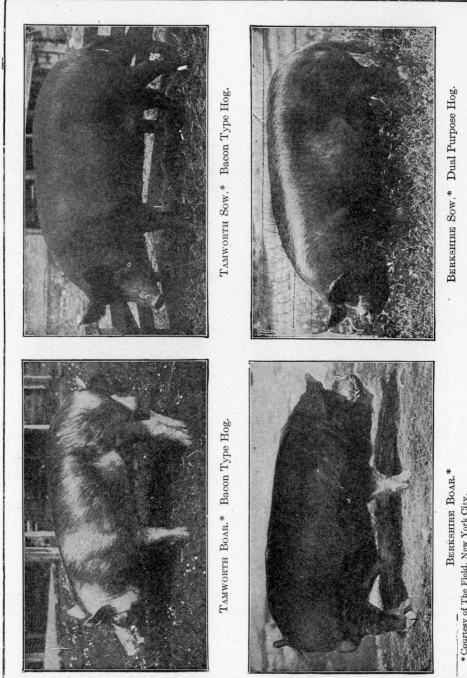

TAMWORTH SOW.*   Bacon Type Hog.

BERKSHIRE SOW.*   Dual Purpose Hog.

TAMWORTH BOAR.*   Bacon Type Hog.

BERKSHIRE BOAR.*

* Courtesy of The Field, New York City.

it all day, the idea being to keep a fire which was not too hot but which would give off plenty of smoke.

At the end of three days the meat was considered thoroughly smoked, although some men liked it smoked much longer. After it had cooled off from the smoking it was hung in a cool, dry place or packed in a barrel of oats, so as to keep it from getting a damp mold and spoiling.

When a farmer had killed a hog, he would render out certain of the fats in an iron caldron. He would take certain parts of the meat and make his home-made sausages, but further than that, by-products were practically unknown.

The foregoing might be considered a short synopsis of the pork-packing industry up to the point which we will call the Modern Era.

This period had a small start back in the early days when a small dealer would kill a few hogs, sell the sausage and lard and cure and smoke the parts, carrying them as far into the summer months as he could, selling them out to his trade. Various methods were resorted to in order to keep mold and insects from spoiling the product. Perhaps the most generally used of these methods was to sew the piece of meat in a canvas sack and paint it with barytes. This gave them an airtight container for the meat and enabled them to keep smoked meats all during the summer months.

The advent of refrigeration, however, really marked the beginning of the modern packing era. When men learned the control of temperature it became possible for slaughter houses to assume such proportions as to warrant scientific research for the best possible methods of carrying on the business.

The story of the development of these methods would be almost endless, but a trip through an up-to-date packing plant of the present day will show what time has brought about.

As the hogs come in from the farmers and shippers they are received by the live stock department, where they are carefully sorted and graded, and then run into holding pens, to carry over until they shall be driven to slaughter. These pens must hold thousands of hogs, for although the stock is held two or three days at the most before it is slaughtered, we must remember that the more important of the packing houses kill thousands of hogs each day, so these pens must be more or less gigantic affairs. The more modern of them are constructed of concrete and brick, and are a picture of cleanliness and sanitation. They are well protected by substantially built roofs and side walls so that the animals are not exposed to the weather at any time of the year.

Veterinarians in the employ of the government examine all the hogs that come into these pens, and any that seem to be at all sickly, or for any reason unfit for food, are held out.

On the killing floor a small army of men is engaged in the business of cleaning and dressing the carcass of the hog. Each man has his particular part of the work to do, and to this end the hogs are conveyed around the room past the various workmen by means of an endless chain and trolley, so that each butcher's work is put right before him and he does not have to make any unnecessary moves. The whole department works like one vast machine, and each man is a very definite and necessary cog in the whole scheme of procedure.

Perhaps the most wonderful thing about this department is the perfection that they are able to reach in cleaning the carcasses. The hogs are first run through a great machine which takes all but a few stray hairs from them. This machine contains a number of rotating beaters and high-pressure streams of water.

As soon as they come out of the machine, the men on the rail finish the job of cleaning the carcass and each animal is then run through a high-pressure washing machine so that it is absolutely clean before a single incision is made in it.

The workmen all stand on high benches, up from the floor, and under the hogs

REFRIGERATING MACHINERY

These great pumps are used for circulating the brine through the cooling system of one of the great packing houses in Buenos Ayres, Argentine

Reproduced by permission of The Philadelphia Museums.

THE HALF-WAY HOUSE

Cattle from the Western plains gathered in the Union Stockyards awaiting slaughter and subsequent shipment. The great Union Stockyards in Chicago are the largest live-stock market in the world. Beef is slaughtered and cleansed very much in the same manner as the pork described in "The Story in a Sausage."

Copyright by Underwood & Underwood, N. Y.

we find troughs to keep any scraps from getting under the workmen's feet. The floors at all times are kept as clean as can be, and the meat is taken away quickly so that there is no chance of contamination of the finished product with the hogs which are just coming from the slaughter house.

Trained men, some of them veterinarians, in the employ of the government, make a thorough inspection of the glands and other organs of the hog. They are so particular that even bruises must be trimmed out before the animals are allowed to pass and go on with the bulk which are fit for food. It is surprising to learn how many carcasses, or parts, are condemned because of one thing or another, for the least sign of sickness or unfitness of any kind calls forth a government "Condemned Tag" and holds the animal out to one side to be used for fertilizer or some other inedible purpose.

Passing through the hog chill rooms, on the way from the killing floor, one is impressed with the great number of hogs hanging there in a temperature near the freezing point. This temperature is maintained both winter and summer, so that the hogs may be thoroughly chilled and the animal heat entirely eliminated as quickly as possible after the killing, so that there will be no chance of the meat souring or any unwholesome condition arising.

After about forty-eight hours in these chill rooms, the hogs are run onto the cutting floor, where they are made into the various commercial cuts which are seen in the meat markets at home. They start out with the whole side of a hog and work it through, until they have what the packers call the "Commercial Cuts"—that is to say, the hams, loins, spare ribs, the bacon sides, and so on.

The cutting room is a light, airy room with a high ceiling, and everything in it seems a perfect example of cleanliness, and men all work with white aprons, jackets and caps.

The next stop is in the by-products building. As the writer entered, his guide told him the old bromide about "everything about a packing house being saved except the squeal, and even that having been known to appear on a phonographic record." He thought to have some fun by asking the guide about the smell, but the laugh was on him, for the guide showed him how the air containing any odor was simply run through a condenser into a great volume of water, which absorbed it. The gases which had made the odor in the first place were then taken out in the form of solids, simply by evaporating the water away. The big evaporators which take care of this work are extremely interesting pieces of machinery to see.

There is a surprisingly large amount of expensive machinery in the hair plant. Hog hair would probably not appeal to the average person as being a thing of particular value, but it is processed so as to make the finished product worth as much as the meat itself.

Certain parts of the hog carcasses which would not be palatable enough to go into human consumption are made up into stock foods. These are sold under a guaranteed analysis. Highly-paid chemists are busy all the time checking up the analysis of these foods, for they must contain certain amounts of protein and crude fiber, which is said to be very beneficial to stock in general.

Another department manufactures what is called a balanced ration, consisting of a certain amount of grain and a certain amount of this stock food, or "digester tankage," as it is called. This balanced ration is said to be the most nutritious food and the quickest fattener which can be given to animals. It is made up as a result of protracted experiments and much scientific research, both by state institutions and by private individuals.

There is always a certain amount of grease which is not edible, but which is suitable for soap stocks, and the tank products which are not fit for food are made into commercial fertilizers, which are gotten up under chemical formulas, and are made up particularly for different kinds of grains, grasses, flowers and the like.

COLD STORAGE OF MEAT, BUENOS AYRES, ARGENTINE

Interior of one of the great South American cold storage plants. Much of the meat consumed in Europe is shipped from this point.

Reproduced by permission of The Philadelphia Museums.

Courtesy of Armour & Co.

PACKING BACON

The girls are packing sliced bacon into glass jars, taking the slices from a moving belt which passes in front of them. The rooms are light, thoroughly ventilated, and cleaned at the end of each day. The girls' hands are manicured at frequent intervals by manicurists employed by the company.

The next place is the lard department. Here great closed tanks cook the fats, under high steam pressure, and make them into snow-white lard. There are great open caldrons, steam jacketed, where an even and uniform temperature is maintained. Only the pure leaf lard, which is supposed to be the choicest fat of the hog, is cooked in these kettles. In the lard packing room there is much automatic machinery, with which the various sized packages of lard are weighed out. Machines hermetically seal the tins, and men pack them in crates and carefully weigh them over two scales.

The average person does not have even an idea of what the modern curing cellar is like. The brines and curing mixtures are prepared by trained men who do no other work but this. Everything goes exactly according to formula, and the different ingredients are weighed out to the ounce. The guide insisted that a bare ten per cent of all the hams or bacon sides produced in the plant are finally allowed to bear the company's trade-mark. The men who finally select these goods are the oldest and most trusted employees of the firm. They weigh out a certain amount of this meat for each tierce, or vat, to be packed, and then an exact number of gallons of pickle is put in with the meat so that each pound of meat will have just a certain amount of pickle to cure it. This is said to insure a uniform product so that one trade-marked ham is exactly like another.

Even the length of time which these are left in cure must not vary a day. In the great curing room thousands of vats and tierces are piled, and the usual tierces hold about three hundred pounds of meat, while the vats hold nearly fifteen hundred pounds.

In the dry-salt curing cellars are kept enormous stocks of the cheaper kinds of meat. These, instead of being cured in brine, are rubbed in salt and piled away. These piles are perhaps three or four feet high, and are so neat and true that they appear to have been the work of a master mason. A single one of these dry-salt curing rooms holds over three million pounds.

Sliced bacon, fancy sausage and other specialties are usually packed in a separate room, into attractive cartons for the retail trade.

The standard of cleanliness in the sausage kitchen has to be unusually high. Wherever white tile is not possible, white paint is used in profusion. The shining metal tables and trucks, on which the product is handled, give a new confidence in sausage. The girls and men employed all wear clean white aprons, jackets and caps, and no effort is spared in keeping everything and everybody in the place in an ideal condition.

The meat is run through enormous automatic grinders and choppers, and through mixers that approach a dairy churn in size. After it has been properly mixed and thoroughly taken care of, it is put into automatic machinery, run by air pressure, which stuffs it into the ham sacks and casings, in which we see the sausage in the markets. The cooking is done in great vats and in enormous electric ovens.

When we stop to think of the proportion of our food which is a packing-house product, we can be glad indeed that conditions such as those described above are becoming available more and more every day.

Why do We Call them "Dog-Days"?

When we talk about "dog-days" now, we mean the period of the year between July 3d and August 11th, twenty days before and after the rising of the "dog-star."

The name was applied by the ancients to a period of about forty days, the hottest season of the year, at the time of the rising of Sirius, the dog-star.

The time of the rising is now, owing to the precession of the equinoxes, different from what it was then (July 1st). It is now about July 23d.

ELECTRIC COINING PRESS, U. S. MINT, PHILADELPHIA
Woman feeding planchets to brass tubes, from the bottom of which they are carried to the steel dies which form the coins.

How is a Five Dollar Gold Piece Made?

The process of converting the precious metals into coins is an interesting one.

The rolling machines through which the ingots are passed are adjustable, the space between the rollers being governed by the operator. About two hundred ingots are run through per hour on each pair of rollers.

When the rolling is completed the strip of metal is about six feet long. As it is impossible to roll perfectly true, it is necessary to "draw" these strips, after being softened by annealing. The drawing benches resemble long tables, with a bench on either side, at one end of which is an iron box secured to the table. In this are fastened two perpendicular steel cylinders. These are at the same distance apart that the thickness of the strip is required to be. It is drawn between the cylinders, which reduces the whole to an equal thickness.

These strips are now taken to the cutting machines, each of which will cut 225 planchets per minute. The press used consists of a vertical steel punch. From a strip worth $1,100 about $800 of planchets will be cut. These are then removed to the adjusting room, where they are adjusted. After inspection they are weighed on very accurate scales. If a planchet is too heavy, but near the weight, it is filed off at the edges; if too heavy for filing, it is thrown aside with the light ones to be remelted.

The planchets, after being adjusted, are taken to the coining and milling rooms, and are passed through the milling machine. They are fed to this machine through an upright tube, and as they descend are caught upon the edge of a revolving wheel and carried about a quarter of a revolution, during which the edge is compressed and forced up. By this apparatus 560 nickels can be milled in a minute; for large pieces the average is 120.

The massive but delicate coining presses coin from 80 to 100 pieces a minute. These presses do their work in a perfect manner. After being stamped the coins are taken to the coiner's room. The light and heavy coins are kept separate in coining, and when delivered to the treasurer they are mixed in such proportions as to give him full weight in every delivery. By law, the deviation from the standard weight, in delivering to him, must not exceed three pennyweights in one thousand double eagles.

The coinage of the United States mints since the organization of the government has amounted to nearly 6,000,000,000 pieces, valued at over $4,000,000,000.

How does a Bird Fly?

The wing of a bird is an elastic, flexible organ, with a thick anterior and a thin posterior margin; hence the wing does not act like a solid board, but is thrown into a succession of curves. When a bird rises from the ground it leaps up with head stuck out and expanded tail, so that the body is in the position of a boy's kite when thrown up. The wings are strongly flapped, striking forward and downward, and the bird quickly ascends. It has been shown that the wing describes a figure 8 in its action, the margin being brought down so that the tip of the wing gives the last blow after the part next the trunk has ceased to strike; hence, standing in front of a bird, the wing would be divided into two, the upper surface of one-half and the lower surface of the other being visible at the same time. These portions are reversed when the wing is drawn back and towards the body, before beginning another stroke; but it will be observed that during retraction the wing is still sloped, so that the resemblance to a kite is maintained. There are many varieties of flight among birds; of these the most remarkable is the sailing motion, in which the wings are but slightly moved. Probably the original impetus is maintained by the kite-like slope of the wing, and advantage may be taken of currents by a rotation of the wing at the shoulder, a movement invisible at any distance.

The Story of the Big Redwood Trees*

The "Big Trees" of California are the most magnificent specimens of tree growth that have ever been found. In addition, they are the oldest known living things; they connect the present with the past in a chain of living rings in the tree that betray their great age to the modern scientist. Estimates of the age of the "Big Trees" vary from the Christian Era through a period dating back beyond the coming of the Christian Saviour about 4,000 years.

The "Big Trees" of California are known as the "Sequoias," and they are divided into two different although closely related species. The few enormous trees of great age which are now preserved in groves are known as the *Sequoia Gigantia*. These big trees grow at an altitude between 4,000 and 7,000 feet, and, whether individual or in groves, they are found in protected valleys, canyons, etc.

What is known as the Redwoods, or scientifically listed as *Sequoia Sempervirens*, grow in heavy stands and really are a younger growth of the "Big Trees." The redwoods grow in the fog belt in the counties bordering the coast from Monterey Bay north to the Oregon line. These trees range in age from 500 to 2,000 years, and are generally supposed by the scientists to be a reproduction growth that began their earthly existence shortly after the glacial period. The *Sequoia Gigantia* reproduce from cones, while the redwoods reproduce from suckers that grow from the stump. The redwoods bear non-fertile cones. Both species of the sequoias are evergreen.

These trees, including both species, range in height from 100 to 400 feet and in circumference from 15 to 90 feet. When full grown the "Big Trees" are proportionate and symmetrical in girth and height and the beauty of the tree is enhanced by flutings that traverse the bark from the base to the apex. The root system is a remarkable feature of the "Big Trees," for they have a very poor footing for trees of their great size and weight. The roots radiate a short distance below the surface of the ground and there is no stabilizer in the shape of a tap root such as in other woods. The bark ranges in thickness from four to thirty inches, although in rare instances it has been found fifty inches thick. The bark is light, soft and of a bright cinnamon color. The lumber from the redwood tree is light, and ranges in color from medium to light cherry, while the lumber from the "Big Trees," or *Sequoia Gigantia*, has a decided pink cast.

John Muir, the eminent California naturalist, evolved the theory from the topographical position of the enormously big trees, which grow only in the vicinity of Yosemite Park, that they escaped the glacial action because they were located in protected places in the mountains.

Commercial redwood—and there are twenty-one mills cutting redwood—is one of the most valuable woods on the Pacific coast. It carries with it into lumber two traits of the tree itself—fire retardance and rot resistance. These two qualities are the real secrets of the "Big Trees." There is no fungus growth on the redwoods neither are the redwoods attacked by boring worms or other insects so common to other species of wood.

Some of the giant redwood logs must be split in the woods with powder before they can be handled on the saw carriage, and the average yield per acre is in the neighborhood of 150,000 feet. At the present rate of cutting, about 400,000,000 feet a year, there is more than one hundred years' supply of redwood still standing.

The redwoods thrive in moisture—it is taken into the roots, the foliage and the bark. This accounts for the remarkable rot-resisting quality. The railroads prefer

° Courtesy of the California Redwood Association.

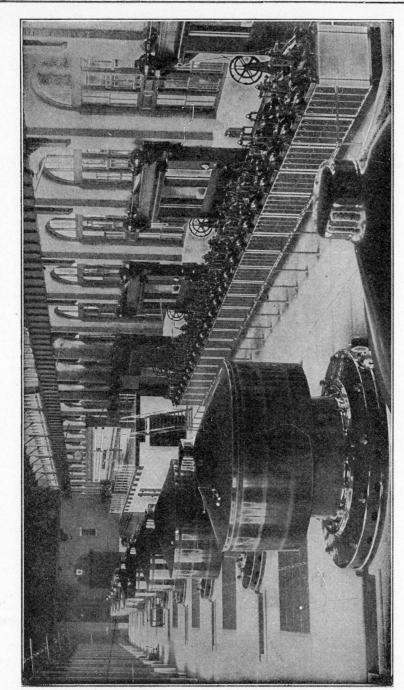

having a screw thread, and is made to revolve rapidly by a belt which passes over it. The end to be pointed passes over a series of coarse, medium and fine revolving files or cutters. The pin now drops into a pan, ready to be finished after being inspected.

In the finishing room, the pins are put into a revolving or tumbling barrel and are rolled in sawdust, which absorbs all the oil, leaving them clean and bright. They are now dropped through a blower, where the sawdust is separated from the pins. The whitening is done by boiling the pins in a large copper kettle, which also contains layers of grained tin and a solution of argol or bitartrate of potash. After boiling for five or six hours, they have a thin coating of tin, which gives them their silvery appearance. Again they are cleaned, this time being washed in clean water, then tumbled in strong soap water, and finally tumbled in hot sawdust to dry them. The pins are separated from the sawdust as before. From there the pins go to the sticking department, where they are stuck on papers as you buy them. The sticking machine is of a simple construction, but is wonderful in operation, and requires no attention by the operator, except to keep it supplied with pins and papers.

The pins are put into a vibrating hopper, which slopes slightly towards the sticking machine. The conductor from the hopper to the machine is made of two strips of steel, down which the pins, held by their heads, slide. They are taken from the conductor by a screw thread and fed to the carrier, which takes thirty pins at a time and places them in front of a set of thirty punches. They are then forced along

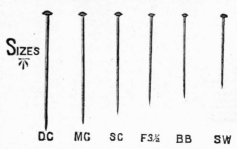

SIZES DC MG SC F3½ BB SW

thirty grooves in the steel clamps, which crimp the paper, and on through the crimp. Thus a whole row of pins is stuck at once. The paper is now advanced the proper distance, and another row is stuck. When the center of the paper is reached, after six rows have been stuck, the machine automatically spaces the paper so as to skip the space used for the brand name. Then six more rows are stuck, and the operator removes the completed paper and inserts another without stopping the machine. These papers are inspected to make certain that no poorly made pins have gotten by the former inspection, are rolled and packed, usually in boxes of twelve papers each.

Pins today are made in many sizes from the 3½-inch stout blanket pins down to the fine, slender, bronze pins used by entomologists, 4,500 of which pins make an ounce. Toilet pins are usually made in six sizes as shown in the illustrations. Besides the common or toilet pins, there are today numerous special bank and desk pins which are made to meet special requirements.

Pin production in the United States has reached a high stage of development. The number of pins made in 1914 reached the tremendous total of 25,000,000,000. These figures are almost too great for comprehension. If all the pin wire used for these 25,000,000,000 pins were in one piece it would go around the earth fifteen times.

Safety pins, hooks and eyes, and hairpins, are generally made by pin concerns. Each of these different articles require very ingenious machines. Many of them are almost human in their operation.

The popular name of the prominence seen in the front of the throat in a man is called the "Adam's apple" because of the story in the Old Testament, telling of the eating of the forbidden fruit of the tree of knowledge by Adam, a piece being supposed to have lodged in his throat where the bulge appears.

An Alpine Glacier

The Mer de Glace

The upper view shows the method of crossing a glacier.   Each of the climbers is
carrying an alpenstock, or staff with ice ax at one end and spike at the other.   The
lower view is the famous sea of ice in Switzerland.

MOUNT RAINIER, WASHINGTON

One of the largest glacial systems in the world radiating from a single peak is situated on this mountain in western Washington.

How are Glaciers Formed?

Away up in the high valleys formed among the peaks of the tallest mountain ranges of both the Rocky Mountains and the mountains of Alaska, as well as those in Switzerland and European countries, the snow freezes into great solid masses because of the intense cold, and is forced by its own pressure into vast fields and mountains of ice. This ice is not like that produced by the freezing of water, but resembles more a very hard, solid form of snow, being composed of thin layers filled with air bubbles and more brittle and less transparent than the ice we are accustomed to see. Glaciers exist in all zones in which mountains rise above the snow-line, that is, the height where it is so cold that there is always snow.

We all know that if we press two pieces of ordinary ice together each piece will melt at the place where it touches the other and just in that same way the pressure of the ice above them causes glaciers to be continually moving downward, frequently reaching the borders of cultivation even. As they descend they also experience a gradual diminution from the action of the sun and rain, and from the heat of the earth. Investigation has shown that they move very much like a river, the middle and upper parts faster than the sides and bottom, similar to the way in which a mass of thick mortar or a quantity of pitch flows down an inclined trough. The rate at which a glacier moves generally varies from eighteen to twenty-four inches in a day.

The Glacier National Park is the latest addition to the series of great natural attractions which the United States Government has been acquiring for years. It lies in Northern Montana, between the Canadian border and the line of the Great Northern Railroad, and contains about a million acres of natural wonders, ranging from verdant valleys and wooded heights to glacial peaks. There are numerous glaciers and mountain lakes and the locality presents many examples of sublime scenery. The City of Tacoma, Washington, is situated in the valley below Mt. Rainier and commands a wonderful view of that mountain, on which there is situated one of the largest glacial systems in the world radiating from any single peak.

One of the most famous glaciers of the Alps is the Mer de Glace, belonging to Mont Blanc, in the valley of Chamouni, about fifty-seven hundred feet above the level of the sea. Those of the Andes and the Southern Alps of New Zealand are conspicuous, and they abound in Norway, Iceland and Spitzbergen, but it is more especially in the chain of Monte Rosa that the phenomena of glaciers are exhibited in their greatest wonder, as also in their most interesting phases from a scientific point of view.

How Large are Molecules?

When a great scientist named Sir William Thomson was asked about the size of a molecule, he replied: "If a drop of water were magnified to the size of the earth, the molecules would each occupy spaces greater than those filled by small shot and smaller than those occupied by cricket balls." That gives us about as clear an idea as it is possible to get of the size of molecules. And yet molecules are made up of even smaller particles, called atoms. An atom is the smallest division of anything that we know about now.

A molecule of water is made up of three atoms. Evaporation of water consists of the movement of these atoms in such a way as to make the liquid water change into a gas. Freezing water into ice is caused by making the molecules, and, in turn, the atoms, stick to each other. It takes a great deal of power to separate the molecules in water, and for this reason water was long regarded as something which could not be divided up, or, in other words, a basic element, such as the oxygen in the air.

FISHING

HALIBUT FISHING

BAITING UP

COMING ABOARD

ICED UP

Six pictures by courtesy of Gloucester (Mass.) Board of Trade.

ARTHUR JAMES

ALICE

NIAGARA

MARY DE COSTE

TARTAR

MODERN FISHING VESSELS

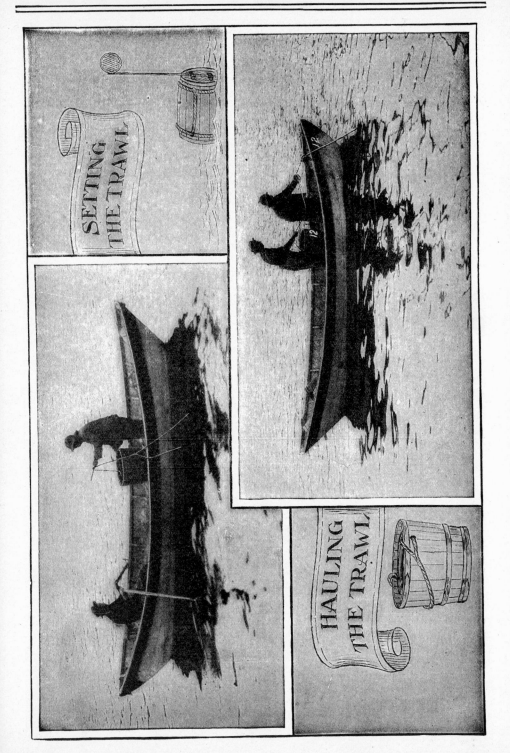

DRAWING THE NET

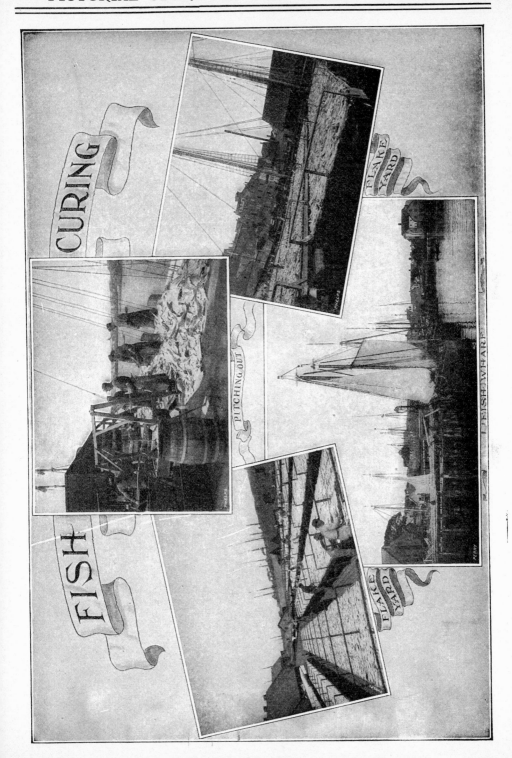

Preparing Salt Fish for Market

SKINNING

DRY FISH SHED

PICKING

BONE PULLING

The Story in a Box of California Oranges

For several hundred years oranges have grown in this country. For about the last forty years men have made a business of growing them.

Oranges and lemons are called citrus fruits on account of their content of citric acid.

The two predominating varieties in California are the Washington Navel and the Valencia orange.

The California Navel orange is in the markets of the country from December 1st until about June 1st, when the California Valencia type takes its place and remains until the latter part of November.

It is a fact, therefore, that oranges are now picked fresh every day the year round in this country, and that the California oranges you buy in the summer are not fruit that has been held in storage, but are as fresh as any fresh fruit that the retailers offer.

Most California oranges and lemons are picked from the trees by gloved hands, so that the finger nails of the pickers will not injure the skin, for even a tiny scratch on the skin of an orange or lemon is sufficient to open the way for germs of decay.

Mr. G. Harold Powell, formerly connected with the United States government, was the discoverer of this source of great loss to the citrus industry. The use of gloves in the picking is thought to save the growers approximately $1,000,000 yearly.

When the oranges have been picked they are sent in boxes to a packing house where they are put through an automatic washing machine which thoroughly scrubs all dust and dirt from the skin; they then pass through a dryer and thence along a belt to men and women who roll the oranges over for examination and distribute them to other belts according to their color and the condition of the skin with regard to blemishes of all kinds. The oranges then pass over automatic sizers—that is, V-shaped rollers revolving horizontally. The oranges continue along these rollers until the space between the rollers has widened to the point where each particular size drops into a labeled bin. The sizes are designated by numbers, such as 150, 176, 250, etc., these figures signifying the number of oranges that may be packed in a regulation size box in which the jobbers and retailers buy the fruit. In other words, size 150 is a larger orange than 250.

The quality of an orange is judged in the packing house merely by the color and the condition of the skin. Size has something to do with it, but this is only one consideration. Many of the smaller oranges are just as good to eat and sometimes very much better than the larger sizes, and the condition of the skin, unless it happens to be broken in any way so that germs of decay can enter, ordinarily has no depreciable effect upon the flavor. The public, of course, finally judges an orange by its sweetness and tenderness, and a large, well-colored, smooth fruit is likely to reach the market in better condition than the rougher fruit which has a marred skin.

Oranges are usually divided in grades into four classes called, in the order of their quality, Extra Choice, Choice, Standards and Culls.

Lemons are handled throughout the processes in practically the same manner as oranges.

After the fruit has passed the graders and the several sizes are separated, it

Photo by Brown Bros.

WHERE THE GOLDEN ORANGE GROWS.

The far-reaching orange groves surrounding Riverside are one of the most beautiful of all beautiful sights in Southern California, and the fragrance of the blossoms is subtlest witchery.

goes to the packers, who pick up each orange or lemon and place a tissue wrapper around it, and press it firmly into the shipping box until the fruit "stands up high" above the top of the box. The cover is then nailed on and the box is placed in the freight car which is waiting at a convenient door. The average car carries 400 boxes of oranges or lemons.

The fruit is shipped in refrigerator cars, and is usually about eight days in making the trip from Southern California to the Eastern markets.

The California Fruit Growers' Exchange ships on an average of sixty-five per cent of the California production of citrus fruits. This is a strictly non-profit, co-operative organization of 8,000 growers, the largest body of agriculturists operating on the non-profit co-operative plan in the world, and probably the most successful. At least, the cost to market the citrus crop under this system is lower than the marketing cost of any other agricultural crop in the world, which accounts in part for the fact that oranges and lemons are sold throughout the United States at retail prices which place this fruit within the reach of all.

What Kind of Steel Knives do not Stain nor Rust?

Shortly after the first of the year, in 1916, the U. S. Consul at Sheffield, England, reported that a new steel had been introduced there for use in making table cutlery. It was said to be untarnishable and unstainable even when used with the strongest acid foods, as well as non-rusting. The new product, which is called "Firth's Stainless" steel, can be thoroughly cleansed by ordinary washing with soap and water, and cutlery made from it will retain its original polish after use. The properties claimed for it are of the steel itself and not the result of any treatment; consequently knives made from the new product can easily be sharpened in the regular way without fear of resulting damage.

While the initial cost of cutlery made from "Firth's Steel" will probably be about double the usual cost, for not only is the price of the steel considerably more than that of other steels used for the same purpose, but it also costs more to work up, it is nevertheless expected to prove a welcome discovery to restaurant and hotel keepers as well as other large users of table cutlery because of the immense saving in labor occasioned by its use.

Why is it Necessary to Keep Unusually Quiet when Fishing?

The experienced fisherman who smiles at the amateur's restless fidgeting and complaining has discovered by careful observation that the fish who swims around in such an exasperating manner just a foot or so away from the temptingly baited hook has had an advance tip that something out of the ordinary is going on up above him. For sound, whether it be the noise of an oarlock or a companion's casual remark, can be heard more than four times as easily by the fish in the water beneath than it can up above in the air. Sound travels very quickly through the air, traversing ten hundred and ninety feet in a second, but it reaches forty-seven hundred feet away under water in the same time.

When the crowd on the other side of the baseball grounds yells across the field it seems as though we have heard their cheers as soon as they have been given, and so we have for all practical purposes, although in reality half a second has elapsed while the sound has been coming across the field. The time taken by sound in traveling is more apparent when the volume is sufficient to carry it a long distance. The sound of an explosion of a large quantity of dynamite and ammunition in Jersey City was not heard in Philadelphia, ninety miles away, for over seven minutes after it occurred.

CLIFF DWELLINGS, WALPI, ARIZONA

Photo by Brown Bros.

HOMES OF THE LONG-AGO

Famous reproduction of the Cliff-dwellers' Ruins, near Colorado Springs, Col. The cliff-dwellers of early America, built their habitations in the canyons of the Colorado and Rio Grande, where the action of the elements had worn away a layer of soft rock, leaving layers of hard rock above and below as roof and floor for the dwelling.

What were the First Apartment Houses in this Country?

A great many years ago, long before the white men came to America, there was a race of Indians called "cliff-dwellers," because they built their dwelling places far up on the sides of steep cliffs. They probably made their homes so hard to reach in order that they might be safe from visits of their enemies. While many of their homes were small single-family houses, there were also a number of large two and three-story dwellings with many rooms in which different families lived.

Some of these cliff dwellings may still be seen in the valleys of the Rio Grande and the Rio Colorado and its tributaries. Close examination shows that many of them were very skilfully built, every advantage being taken of the natural rock formations, and the stones being dressed and laid in clay mortar, very much as the bricklayer does his work on an up-to-date apartment house today. The outsides of the buildings somewhat resembled the cement houses which have been put up in later days, a coat of clay being spread on the outside walls and carefully smoothed off. Oftentimes the inner walls were plastered too.

Many relics of the inhabitants have been found in these cliff dwellings, although we cannot tell how they lived, for the region is now rainless and therefore destitute of food plants. Conditions must have been different then and the ground less barren.

Why do We Call 32° Above Zero "Freezing"?

We know that freezing is the transformation of a liquid into solid under the influence of cold. Each liquid always solidifies at some fixed temperature, which is called its freezing point, and the solid melts again at the same temperature. Thus the freezing point and the melting point, or point of fusion, are the same, and the point is always the same for the same substance.

Consequently the freezing point of water, or the melting point of ice (32° F.), is taken for one of the fixed points in thermometry. The freezing point of mercury is 39° below zero, of sulphuric ether 46° below zero, of alcohol 203° below zero F.

How is Fresco Painting Done?

In producing fresco paintings, a finished drawing on paper, called a cartoon, exactly the size of the intended picture, is first made, to serve as a model.

The artist then has a limited portion of the wall covered over with a fine sort of plaster, and upon this he traces from his cartoon the part of the design suited for the space. As it is necessary to the success and permanency of his work that the colors should be applied while the plaster is yet damp, no more of the surface is plastered at one time than what the artist can finish in one day. A portion of the picture once commenced, needs to be completely finished before leaving it, as fresco does not admit of retouching after the plaster has become dry. On completing a day's work, any unpainted part of the plaster is removed, cutting it neatly along the outline of a figure or other definite form, so that the joining of the plaster for the next day's work may be concealed.

The art is very ancient, remains of it being found in India, Egypt, Mexico, etc. Examples of Roman frescoes are found in Pompeii and other places. After the beginning of the fifteenth century fresco painting became the favorite process of the greatest Italian masters, and many of their noblest pictorial efforts are frescoes on the walls of palaces and churches.

Some ancient wall paintings are executed in what is called "Fresco Secco," which is distinguished from true fresco by being executed on dry plaster, which is moistened with lime water before the colors are applied.

Fresco painting has in recent years again been revived, and works of this kind have been executed in the British Houses of Parliament and other public and private buildings, more especially in Germany.

The Story of a Piece of Chewing Gum*

The original "chewing gum" was spruce gum, the exudation of the cut branches of the spruce or fir tree. Later, pure white paraffin wax, variously flavored, took its place, but only in its turn to give way to the "chicle" now almost exclusively employed.

Though its employment in the manufacture of chewing gum is of comparatively recent date, chicle was used by the Indians prior to the days of Columbus as a means of quenching their thirst. It was first commercially imported as a substitute for rubber, but its peculiar suitability for chewing gum has resulted in the entire product being consumed by that industry. In 1885 the United States imported 929,959 pounds of chicle. The growth of the chewing gum industry is shown by the importation of nearly 5,500,000 pounds for the year ending with June 30, 1910.

The trees are "tapped" during the rainy season. The sap, or juice, as it exudes has the appearance of milk, but gradually changes to a yellow color and is about the thickness of treacle. The tree drains rapidly, the full supply of "milk" being generally obtained within a few hours, but an interval of several years usually elapses before it will yield a fresh supply. The milk differs from the juice obtained from the sugar maple, for example, in that it is not the life sap of the tree, and the flow varies greatly, some trees which show full life yielding much less than apparently poorer specimens. "Crude chicle" is obtained by simple boiling and evaporation of the milk, accompanied by frequent kneading. The product, as pressed in rough molds, is of a light gray color.

The bulk of the crude chicle manufactured is shipped in blocks to Canada, where it is further evaporated and carefully refined prior to importation into the United States. When the chicle arrives at one of the chewing-gum factories it is immediately turned over to the grinding department. It comes from Mexico in cakes, varying in size from twelve- to eighteen-inch cubes; these are a putty color, but in composition chicle is porous and brittle, particularly after it is thoroughly dried. In the cubical form it is said to contain from twenty-five to thirty per cent moisture. After it is ground and dried it is practically free of moisture, but one of the most difficult problems which the manufacturer faces is to thoroughly dry chicle before he proceeds to treat it for its introduction as the base of chewing gum.

The cubes are broken by a large steam hammer into irregular-shaped pieces weighing from a few ounces to a pound. These chunks are then run through grinding machines, which reduce the chicle to a coarse meal. Sometimes this breaking and grinding is done in Mexico, but the duty on ground dried chicle is five cents per upon cube chicle.

Chicle meal is dried upon frames in a special drying room, which is kept at a temperature of 80° F. An electric blower exhausts all of the moisture from the air. The pure meal is then transformed into a thick syrup under intense heat and passed through a filtering machine, one of the latest and most expensive pieces of machinery employed in the entire manufacture of chewing gum. This machine has practically solved the perplexing problem of separating impurities and foreign substances from chicle. Before the filter was invented it was almost impossible for the manufacturer of chewing gum to produce gum entirely free from particles of grit.

During the process of filtration the chicle is also sterilized, and comes from the machine as pure as distilled water.

It is next passed to the cooking department and placed in huge steam-jacketed kettles, which revolve continually and thus keep the chicle from scorching. While

---

* Illustrations by courtesy of the Common Sense Gum Co. Story by courtesy of the American Chicle Co. and the Common Sense Gum Co.

A BATTERY OF SUGAR-COATING MACHINES

A CORNER OF THE SCORING ROOM

THE LABORATORY

WRAPPING AND PACKING DEPARTMENT

it is being cooked in these large kettles sugar is added, and as soon as the gum is done it is placed in a kneading machine. It is now about the consistency of bread or cake dough, and after being kneaded and cooled, flavor is added.

Peppermint, spearmint and other oils used are triply distilled and absolutely free of all impurities. The orange oil comes from Messina and is always the product of the very latest orange crop.

From the kneading machine it reaches a sizing table, to which are attached heavy rollers for reducing the mass of gum to a strip about a quarter of an inch in thickness and twelve inches wide.

At this stage it will be seen the gum begins to take on a ribbon shape. As it comes from the first series of rollers, it is cut into short lengths sprinkled with powdered sugar, and these short lengths are passed in sticks about two feet high on to a second series of rollers. Under the second rollers each short length of gum is once more reduced in thickness and extended in length.

The surfaces of the second rollers contain knives running lengthwise and around. These knives partially cut the gum to its final size. The thin sheets are then sent to another drying room. They remain in this room from twelve to forty-eight hours, according to the season of the year, and are then ready for the wrapping machines.

Machines have also been invented which stamp out little nuggets of gum. To be finished these pieces are sent to a long room containing a line of twelve large white kettles, each on a separate base. It is these machines which coat the nuggets with snowy sugar. The kettles revolve until a sufficient coating of the liquid sugar has adhered.

The chewing gum wrapping machine is considered by machinery builders to be one of the most ingenious automatic manufacturing machines in use. It is about the size of an ordinary typewriter desk and is operated by one girl. She receives the thin sheet of partially cut gum from the last drying room. The machine operator drops the slabs of gum into a feeding chute. Each slab is here automatically wrapped in wax and silver-foil papers. These papers are fed from rolls, as printing paper is fed to a newspaper press.

As the slabs are wrapped they slide into a pocket. When five of them are finished, two steel fingers remove them and put on the final outside wrapper. The complete, wrapped packages of five slabs slide along a little runway into boxes.

The same girl who feeds the gum into the wrapping machine closes the lids of the boxes and places them on a packing table by her side. When the packing table is filled with boxes a boy removes it to the shipping room, where it is crated and forwarded to the wholesale dealers.

Where did the Ferris Wheel get Its Name?

The Ferris wheel was named after its builder, George W. Ferris, an able engineer, now dead.

The original Ferris wheel was exhibited at the Chicago World's Fair. It was a remarkable engineering feature.

Its diameter was 270 feet and its circumference 825 feet. Its highest point was 280 feet. The axle was a steel bar, 45 feet long and 32 inches thick. Fastened to each of the twin wheels was a steel hub 16 feet in diameter. The two towers at the axis supporting the wheel were 140 feet high, and the motive power was secured from a 1,000 horse-power steam engine under the wheel.

The thirty-six cars on the wheel each comfortably seated forty persons. The wheel and passengers weighed 12,000 tons.

By the Ferris wheel the almost indefinite application of the tension spoke to wheels of large dimensions has been vindicated, the expense being far smaller than that of the stiff spoke.

STEEL RAIL MILL

Interior view of the Bethlehem Steel Company's rail mill finishing department, showing the machinery for straightening and drilling rails.

What is Done to Keep Railroad Rails from Breaking?

The breaking of rails has been the cause of much attention on the part of railroad and steel engineering experts ever since the tendency toward the construction of heavy locomotives and greater train loads became evident.

The report of the Interstate Commerce Commission for 1915 gave broken rails as the cause of 3,345 accidents, in which 205 people were killed and 7,341 were injured, with a property loss of $3,967,188. A steel man is authority for the statement that one cold winter day in 1913, a single locomotive, making excessive speed, broke about a hundred rails in the distance of a mile on one of the leading railroad systems.

Both steel and railroad men were, therefore, much interested in the announcement made by the New York Central Railroad, in August, 1916, to the effect that the road's staff of specialists had discovered the cause and remedy for the hidden flaws in steel rails. It was said that no rails produced under the specifications provided by them had yet developed any fissures.

The process by which those rails were prevented from developing fissures consisted mainly of rolling them from reheated blooms, and although that method is said to have been used in a number of rail mills for many years, no mention had previously been recorded of the prevention of breakage in that way. The experiments are, therefore, sure to be watched with a great deal of interest, and it is probable that fewer accidents will occur from broken rails in the near future.

The technical man will be interested in an outline printed in the *Iron Age*, which said: "Induced interior transverse fissures in basic open-hearth rails are due in part to an occasional hot rail being cooled so rapidly by the rolls or so chilled by the gusts of air before recalescence on the hot beds as to cause a log of some of the transformations of the metal in the interior of the rail head. Induced interior transverse fissures can only develop in the track from the effects of preceding causes, either of which is no longer a mystery."

The report of the railroad experts also laid stress on the theory that "gagging" rails—subjecting them to blows for the purpose of straightening them—was also likely to cause faults by injuring the metal.

How does a " Master Clock " Control Others by Electricity?

With the aid of electric currents, one clock can be made to control other clocks, so as to make them keep accurate time.

By means of this method one high-class clock, usually in an astronomical observatory, compels a number of other clocks at considerable distances to keep time with it.

The clocks thus controlled ought to be so regulated that if left to themselves they would always gain a little, but not more than a few minutes per day.

The pendulum of the controlling clock, in swinging to either side, makes a brief contact, which completes the circuit of a galvanic battery, and thus sends a current to the controlled clock. The currents pass through a coil in the bob of the pendulum of the controlled clock, and the action between these currents and a pair of fixed magnets urges the pendulum to one side and to the other alternately. The effect is that, though the controlled clock may permanently continue to be a fraction of a second in advance of the controlling clock, it can never be so much as half a second in advance.

An electrically controlled clock usually contains a small magnetic needle, which shows from which direction the currents are coming. The arrangements are usually such that at every sixtieth second no current is sent, and the needle stands still. Any small error is thus at once detected.

The Story of the Calculating Machine

How did Men Learn to Count?

Historians tell us that man was able to count long before he was able to write. Of course, he could not count very far, but it was enough for his needs at that time. He had no money and very few possessions of any kind, so that he did not have much occasion to use arithmetic.

It was fairly simple for prehistoric men to distinguish one from two, and to distinguish a few from a great number, but it was more difficult for him to learn to think of a definite number of objects between these extremes. Those who have studied the evolution of figures say that man found it hard to think of a number of objects without using a mark or a finger or something to stand for each object. That is how the first method of counting came into use.

Because man had ten fingers and thumbs, he learned to count in tens. When he had counted ten, he could make a mark to remind him of the fact, and then count them over again. Some of the early races learned to designate units from tens and tens from hundreds by working their fingers in various ways. Other peoples also made use of their toes in counting, so that they could count up to twenty without getting bothered.

Cantor, the historian, tells of a South African tribe which employed an unusual system of finger counting. Three men sat together facing a fourth who did the counting. Each of the three held up his fingers for the fourth man to count. The first man's ten fingers and thumbs represented units; the second man represented tens, and the third hundreds. By this means, it was possible to count up to 999.

Who Invented the First Adding Machine?

Early cuneiform inscriptions, made about 2200 B. C., show that the Babylonians had developed a fairly extensive system of figuring. This was in the days of the patriarch Abraham. When men's minds were overtaxed with the strain of counting into the hundreds and thousands, the Babylonians invented the first adding machine, a "pebble board," a ruled surface on which pebbles were shifted about to represent different values.

The next adding and calculating machine was an evolution from the digits of the human hand and is known as the abacus in China, and the soroban in Japan.

The abacus may be defined as an arrangement of movable beads which slip along fixed rods, indicating by their arrangement some definite numerical quantity. Its most familiar form is in a boxlike arrangement, divided longitudinally by a narrow ridge of two compartments, one of which is roughly some three times larger than the other. Cylindrical rods placed at equal intervals apart pass through the framework and are fixed firmly into the sides. On these rods the counters are beaded. Each counter slides along the rod easily and on each rod there are six tamas or beads. Five of these slide on the longest segment of the rod and the remaining one on the shorter. Addition, subtraction, multiplication, division, and even square and cube root can be performed on the abacus, and in the hands of a skilled operator considerable speed can be obtained.

The Oriental tradesman does not deign to perplex himself by a process of mental arithmetic; he seizes his abacus, prepares it by a tilt, makes a few rapid, clicking movements and his calculations are completed. We always look with some slight

FINGER COUNTING WAS COMMON AMONG EARLIER PEOPLES, AND WAS BROUGHT TO A
FAIR DEGREE OF EFFICIENCY BY SOUTH AFRICANS
Courtesy of the Burroughs Adding Machine Company.

THE "ABACUS" WAS ONE OF THE EARLIEST AIDS TO CALCULATION

It is still used extensively in China, and occasionally will be found in Chinese laundries in the United States.

Courtesy of the Burroughs Adding Machine Company.

contempt upon this method of calculation, but a little experience and investigation would tend to transform this contempt into admiration, for it may be safely asserted that even the simplest of all arithmetical operations, the abacus, possesses distinctive advantages over the mental or figuring process.   In competition in simple addition between a "lightning calculator" and an ordinary Japanese small tradesman, the Japanese would easily win the contest.

Blaise Pascal, the wonderful Frenchman, who discovered the theorem in conic sections, or Pascal's hexogram, was not only one of the foremost mathematicians of his day but also excelled in mechanics; when he was nineteen years old he produced the first machine for the carrying of tens and the first arithmetical machine, as we know it, was invented by him about 1641.   This was the first calculating machine made with dials.   The same principle, that of using discs with figures on their peripheries, is employed in present-day calculating machines.   Among these are numbering machines of all kinds, speedometers, cyclometers and counters used on printing presses.

A MODERN BOOKKEEPING MACHINE, USED FOR LEDGER POSTING AND STATEMENT MAKING

It has seventeen "banks" or rows of keys, is electrically operated, and automatically adds, subtracts, and computes balances.
Courtesy of the Burroughs Adding Machine Company.

Who Discovered the Slide Rule Principle?

It was early in the seventeenth century that Napier, a native of Naples, invented the first actual mechanical means of calculating. He arranged strips of bone, on which were figures, so that they could be brought into various fixed combinations. The instrument was called "Napier's rod" or Napier's bones." It was the beginning of the slide rule, which has been found of invaluable aid to accountants and engineers.

One trouble with all these contrivances was that, although they aided man to figure, they offered no means of making a record of the work.   The man who used these machines had no way of checking his work to know if it was right unless he did it all over again.

The first machine to perform multiplication by means of successive additions was invented by Leibnitz in the year 1671 and completed in 1694.   It employed the principle of the "stepped reckoner."   This model was kept first at Göttingen and afterward at Hanover, but it did not act efficiently, as the gears were not cut with sufficient accuracy.   This was long before the days of accurate machine tools.

The first satisfactory calculating machine of this nature was that of C. X. Thomas, which was brought out about 1820.   It is usually called the Thomas de Colmar Arithmometer.   This Thomas type of machine, which is commonly known as the beveled gear type, is still in use today in modern business.

The " Difference Engine."

In the year 1822 a very ambitious project was conceived by Charles Babbage. He commenced to construct an automatic calculating machine, which he called a "difference engine." The work was continued during the following twenty years, the English government contributing about $85,000 to defray its cost. Babbage himself spent a further sum of about $30,000. At the end of that time the construction of the engine, though nearly finished, was unfortunately abandoned, owing to some misunderstanding with the government. A portion of this engine is exhibited in South Kensington Museum, London, along with other examples of Babbage's work. If the engine had been finished it would have contained seven columns of wheels, twenty wheels in each column, and also a contrivance for stereotyping the tables calculated by it. It was intended to perform the most extended calculations required in astronomy and navigation, and to stamp a record of its work into plates of copper or other material.

Babbage began to design his "analytical engine" in 1833 and he put together a small portion of it shortly before his death in 1871. This engine was to be capable of evaluating any algebraic formula. The formula it is desired to evaluate would be communicated to the engine by two sets of perforated cards similar to those used in the Jacquard loom. These cards would cause the engine automatically to operate on the numerical data placed in it, in such a way as to produce the correct result. Notwithstanding its simple action, its structure is complicated by a large amount of adding mechanism. A complete set of adding wheels with carrying gear being required for the tabular number, and every order of difference except the highest order.

After Babbage, there was much experimenting done by inventors to produce a real adding and listing machine. Also inspired by Babbage's work Scheutz of Stockholm made a "difference engine," which was exhibited in England in 1864,

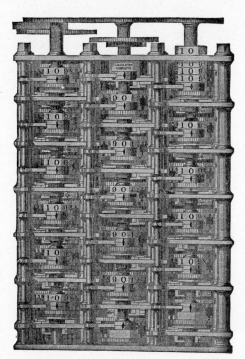

CHARLES BABBAGE'S "ENGINE OF DIFFERENCES" WAS THE FIRST ADDING MACHINE INVENTED WHICH WAS DESIGNED TO PRINT A RECORD OF ITS WORK, BUT IT WAS NOT A SUCCESS

Courtesy of the Burroughs Adding Machine Company.

and subsequently acquired for Dudley Observatory, Albany, N. Y. Scheutz's engine had mechanism for calculating with four orders of differences of sixteen figures each.

As far as we know the first patent in this country issued by the patent office for a calculating machine was to O. L. Castle of Alton, Illinois, in 1850. It was for a ten-key adding machine which did not print and only added in one column.

Work on Some of the Present-Day Models.

Frank S. Baldwin, a construction engineer, living in the United States, began to work on calculating machines in 1870. In 1874 he received a patent for a small hand adding machine. In 1875 a patent was granted him on a calculating machine. This machine was along entirely original lines. Mr. Baldwin did not even know of the existence of the Thomas machine at that time. The machine had a number of important advantages over the Thomas system. Scientists were very much interested in the invention at the time, and the John Scott medal for meritorious inventions was conferred upon Mr. Baldwin by the Franklin Institute. The only other invention being honored in that year (1875) was the George Westinghouse air brake.

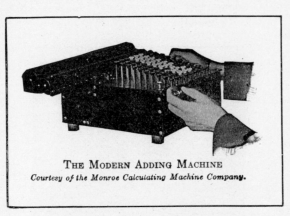

THE MODERN ADDING MACHINE
Courtesy of the Monroe Calculating Machine Company.

This calculating machine, however, seemed to be too much in advance of the times, and Mr. Baldwin was unable to interest capital in it. He was very successful in his business as construction engineer and continued to spend all his spare time and money in experimental work. He brought out a number of models at later dates with important improvements.

In the early eighties one of Mr. Baldwin's 1875 models found its way to Europe into the hands of one Ohdner, a Swede. He took out patents in all European countries on a machine that did not vary in any important particular from Mr. Baldwin's machine, and several large manufacturing companies in Europe took it up. It is now appearing under ten to fifteen different names in Europe, the most important being "Brunsviga" and Triumphator in Germany. There is no essential difference between the machines they are turning out today and Mr. Baldwin's original machine. More than 50,000 machines of this type have been sold throughout the world.

In 1883 a young man who started to work in a bank in Auburn, N. Y., discovered that nine-tenths of his work was mechanical addition. He also found that the human brain is but an imperfect tool, incapable of sustained effort without accident. His health gave way under the strain, and he quit the bank to begin work in a machine shop in St. Louis.

This was William S. Burroughs. He was of mechanical turn of mind, with an intense hobby for painful

ONE OF THE FIRST SUCCESSFUL ADDING
AND LISTING MACHINES
Courtesy of the Burroughs Adding Machine Company.

accuracy. By lamplight at home he worked out pencil outlines of a machine which would write figures and at the same time add them. It required the most painstaking work for him to make a machine to do what he had in mind. His early associates say of Burroughs that no ordinary materials were good enough for his creation. His drawings were on metal plates that would not stretch nor shrink by the fraction of a hair. He worked with hardened tools ground to a point, and when he struck a center or drew a line, he did it under a microscope.

In 1884 Burroughs took his plans to a St. Louis dry goods merchant, who thought so well of the idea that he raised $700 toward forming a company.   The young man took up his work in the machine shop conducted by Joseph Boyer.

It was in January, 1885, that he applied for his patent, which was not issued until 1887.

His mechanism throughout operated on the pivotal principle.   This means a minimum of friction, therefore the least wear on the machine and the least exertion on the part of the operator.   The principle elements in the machine remain practically unchanged today, a fact which testifies to the excellence of the inventor's work.

Experimenting on the machine swallowed a great deal of capital, and the stockholders of the company he had formed became impatient.   Burroughs objected

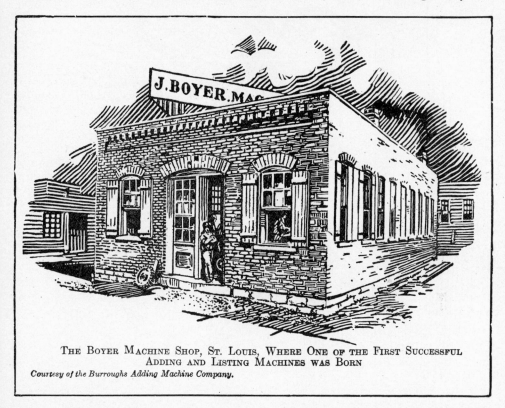

THE BOYER MACHINE SHOP, ST. LOUIS, WHERE ONE OF THE FIRST SUCCESSFUL
ADDING AND LISTING MACHINES WAS BORN
Courtesy of the Burroughs Adding Machine Company.

strenuously, for he did not wish to market the machine until he was convinced that it was perfect, but he finally agreed to manufacture fifty machines.

In his public demonstrations, he could do wonders with the machine.   The public was skeptical, however, and some averred that he was a "lightning calculator" who did sums in his head and printed them on the machine.   The first machines worked all right for the inventor, but inexperienced operators obtained surprising results through punching the keys and jerking the crank.

To meet this trouble and make the machines "fool proof," he invented the "automatic control" in 1890.   This was a governor. called the "dash pot"—a small cylinder partially filled with oil, and in which was a plunger.   This, in connection with an ingenious management of springs, absorbed the shocks and governed the machine so that no matter what was done to it, it would operate only at a certain speed. It is this same shock-absorbing device which is used to catch the recoil on the immense siege guns used in modern warfare.

Other improvements were made, and in 1891 the first hundred machines that were really marketable were manufactured. While still flushed with his success, Burroughs thought of the first fifty machines which had proved such a disappoint-

"THERE'S AN END TO MY TROUBLES," SAID WILLIAM SEWARD BURROUGHS AS HE THREW INTO THE STREET THE FIRST FIFTY ADDING MACHINES HE HAD MADE

He wished nothing to remain to remind him of this early failure.

Courtesy of the Burroughs Adding Machine Company.

ment. These machines still remained in a dusty storeroom to mock him. Determined to get them out of his sight and memory, he seized them and threw them one by one from a window to the pavement below.

When he had disposed of the last one, he called Mr. Boyer to see the ruin. "There," he exclaimed, "I have ended the last of my troubles."

The first machines were called "Registering Accountants," and "Arithmometers." Burroughs lived to see the fulfilment of his dreams and the machine commercial success.   He died September 14, 1898, at his country home in Citronelle, Alabama, a victim of tuberculosis.

There were at that time 8,000 banks in the country, and it was Burroughs' idea that as soon as these were supplied the market for adding machines would be exhausted.   Today, there are more than 200,000 adding machines of that one make in use.

The need for an all-around office assistant that could multiply, divide, subtract as easily as it could add, was an idea nourished in the mind and thought of a young student of the University of Michigan.

After graduation, Jay R. Monroe turned his attention to clerical and commercial

THE LATEST MODEL CALCULATING MACHINE

Courtesy of the Monroe Calculating Machine Company.

lines.   He became acquainted with all the different types of adding and so-called calculating machines.   He saw their limitations and restrictions.   He saw the need for versatility—for more simplicity in operation—for getting away from arbitrary rules—for release from the sapping mental tax.

So in 1911 Monroe met Mr. Baldwin.   Mr. Monroe realized the possibilities of Mr. Baldwin's idea.   Together they set about designing the machine to make it as nearly perfect as possible in adaptation to the needs of modern business.

They produced a machine in which the best of the European features are said to be combined with the operating ease and simplicity of American-made machines.

Provision is made for the correction of errors, and operation is in two directions, forward for addition and multiplication, and backward for subtraction and division. The latest model is a desk machine, occupying less than one square foot of space and weighing about twenty-six pounds.

One of the latest developments of the adding machine is a type that will post

THE "DUODECILLION"—THE LARGEST CAPACITY ADDING MACHINE IN THE WORLD—HAS FORTY ROWS OF KEYS AND WILL ADD TO WITHIN A UNIT OF TEN DUODECILLIONS

To appreciate this prodigious figure, imagine that a marvelous high-speed flying machine were invented that would go to the sun and back in a day. If you made this 186,000,000-mile trip every day, it would take you just 14,729,700,000,000,000,000,000,000 years to travel a duodecillion miles.

Courtesy of the Burroughs Adding Machine Company.

ledgers and statements. This machine is said to be the final step in relieving bookkeeping of its drudgery.

How Big is the Largest Adding Machine in the World?

The largest adding machine ever made was produced in 1915 and has a capacity of forty columns, or within one unit of ten duodecillions. This is a number too prodigious for the mind of man to grasp. This machine was exhibited at the Panama Expositions in 1915.

To get an idea of the capacity of this machine, suppose that your income is $1,000,000 a second. At this rate for twenty-four hours a day, with no stops for eating or sleeping, it would take you 352,331,022,041,828,731,333,333,333, years to accumulate a duodecillion dollars. All the hairs on the heads of all human beings, which are supposed to be numberless, are only a small fraction of a duodecillion.

This machine has a practical use in adding several sums simultaneously, and takes the place of from ten to a dozen smaller machines.

Adding machines are made that figure in English pence, shillings and pounds; in Japanese yen, and in the monetary system of most civilized countries. They will change inches into feet, pounds into bushels, and do other "stunts" that would make the average schoolboy envious when it comes to arithmetic.

The most complicated problems of multiplication, division and fractions may be handled with ease on these machines. They have taken a great part in the day's work of modern business, and it would be hard to imagine how the world's finance and industry could be handled without them. Adding and calculating machines have become almost as necessary in modern business as the telephone and the typewriter.

How are Adding Machines Used?

Adding machines may be found at work in all kinds of business places from corner groceries to department stores and manufacturing plants. In the various offices and plants of the Western Electric Company, which are scattered through the country, more than 1,600 machines are in use. Other big users are railroads, banks, mail-order houses, and city, state and government offices.

The Bank of France, the Bank of England, and other of the world's largest financial institutions do the burden of their figure work on adding machines made in the United States. The German post-office uses more than

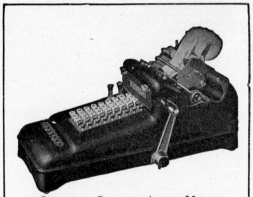

ONE OF THE SMALLEST ADDING MACHINES IS ADAPTED FOR USE BY RETAIL MERCHANTS AND OTHERS WHO DO NOT ADD FIGURES OF MORE THAN FIVE DIGITS

Courtesy of the Burroughs Adding Machine Company.

1,200 machines. There are individual American banks, like the Corn Exchange National Bank of New York, that employ as many as 150 adding machines in their work.

Some surprising uses are found for adding machines. One is used in a Japanese boarding house in California; another is used by a retired Dayton millionaire to count the coupons he clips; the Rockefeller Sanitary Commission uses a machine in fighting the hook-worm; the United States government uses thousands in making census tabulations and in other ways. Others are used by newsboys, egg farmers, housewives, undertakers, dentists, judges in automobile races, and by persons in a thousand different lines of business. Without adding machines the public would be obliged to wait for days for the results of most elections.

In this way, the idea of a tired bank clerk came to change the figuring methods of the world.

The words "Almighty Dollar" have been generally adopted since Irving first used them in his "Creole Village," and the use of "lynching" to represent mob law and the action of mobs has become common since a Virginia farmer by that name instituted the first vigilance committee in America.

Where does Ermine Come From?

The ermine fur, with which we are all familiar, is furnished by the stoat, a small animal of the weasel tribe. It is found over both temperate Europe and North America, but is common only in the north.

Because of that change which occurs in the color of its fur at different seasons—by far most marked in the Arctic regions—it is not generally known that the ermine and stoat are the same. In winter, in cold countries or severe seasons, the fur changes from a reddish-brown to a yellowish-white, or almost pure white, under which shade the animal is recognized as the ermine. In both states the tip of the tail is black.

ERMINE (*Mustela Erminea*)

Like many other species of this genus, the ermine has the faculty of ejecting a fluid of a musky odor.

Its fur is short, soft and silky; the best skins being brought from Russia, Sweden and Norway and Hudson Bay territories. Its fur was formerly one of the insignia of royalty, and is still used by judges. When used as linings of cloaks the black tuft from the tail is sewed to the skin at irregular distances.

What is the Principle of " Foreign Exchange "?

Exchange, in commerce, is a transaction by which the debts of people residing at a distance are canceled by a draft or bill of exchange, without transfer of any actual money.

A merchant in New York who owes for $1,000 worth of goods in London, gives a bill or order for that amount which can be negotiated through banking agencies or otherwise against similar debts owing by other parties in London who have payments to make in New York. This obviates the expense and risk of transmitting money.

The process of liquidating obligations between different nations is carried on in the same way by an exchange of foreign bills. When all the accounts of one country correspond in value with those of another, the exchange between the countries will be at par, that is, the sum for which the bill is drawn in the one country will be the exact value of it in the other.

Exchange is said to be at par when, for instance, a bill drawn in New York for the payment of $1,000 in London can be purchased there for $1,000. If it can be purchased for less, exchange is under par and is against London. If the purchaser is obliged to give more, exchange is above par and in favor of London.

Although the thousand circumstances which incessantly affect the state of debt and credit prevent the ordinary course of exchange from being almost ever precisely at par, its fluctuations are confined within narrow limits, and if direct exchange is unfavorable between two countries this can often be obviated by the interposition of bills drawn on other countries where an opposite state of matters prevails.

What do We Mean by " The Old Moon in the New Moon's Arms"?

"Earth-shine," in astronomy, is the name given to the faint light visible on the part of the moon not illuminated by the sun, due to the illumination of that portion by the light which the earth reflects on her. It is most conspicuous when the illuminated part of the disc is at its smallest, as soon after new moon. This phenomenon is popularly described as "the old moon in the new moon's arms."

The Story in a Bowling Alley

From the "stone age" onward the probabilities are that man has always had some kind of bowling game.

Bowling, as we know today, is an indoor adaptation of, and an improvement upon, the old Dutch game of "nine-pins." This game was brought from Holland by those colonists who settled Manhattan Island in 1623.

Washington Irving, in his story, "Rip Van Winkle," refers to the old Dutch fairy tale, that the rolling thunder on the mountain tops of the Catskill was the noise made by the rolling balls as the elfs and gnomes engaged in their favorite pastimes of bowling.

That little section of New York City known as Bowling Green is the original spot which, in 1732, Peter Bayard, Peter Jay and John Chambers leased for eleven years and enclosed for a bowling green.

With the influx of German immigrants, who brought with them a game similar to the Dutch game, additional popularity was given to the sport.

The game was originally played on the bare ground. The Germans used a board

LOOP THE LOOP RETURN

about a foot wide on which to roll the ball, and then improved on this by using cohesive mineral substances solidly packed together. At an early date, the Dutch had covered the alley with a roof, and later enclosed it in a rough shed, to protect it and make play possible in any kind of weather. But, great as these improvements were over the crudeness of previous centuries, they are not worthy of comparison with a modern bowling academy.

In the best hard-wood section of the United States, one of the large bowling equipment manufacturers owns about thirty thousand acres of maple. From this raw material is gathered the chief stock that goes into bowling alleys and the pins.

The company has its own logging crews that cut the timber and pile it on flat cars, whence it is transported over a private railroad until it arrives at the company sawmills. Here the raw material enters upon the manufacturing process.

The rough stock-strips for the alley "bed," "leveling strips," "return chute," "post" and "kick-backs" are sawed out of certain of the logs. They are then shipped to a factory where they are seasoned, being kiln dried. The stock is next cut to the required sizes.

* Illustrations by courtesy of The Brunswick-Balke-Collender Co.

The bed stock is cut into strips, planed on all sides, and tongued and grooved on the widest sides. When finished, the strips measure 3 x 1 inch. Part of the bed stock, however, is hard pine, shipped from the Southern states in the rough boards. This is finished similar to the maple strips.

The "kick-backs" are the two partitions, shaped somewhat like a ship's rudder, which form the two pit sides. Each consists of two facings of the best maple with a core of hard but resilient wood in the middle. They are built in this way to make the pins that fly side-wise spring back on the bed and knock down other standing pins, and also to withstand the exceedingly rough usage to which they are subject by the flying pins and rolling balls.

The cushion forms the rear end of the pit. The frame is stoutly constructed, and the face thickly upholstered with scrap leather and a heavy but pliable covering. It swings on hinges which suspend it from the cross bar, running from each of the kick-backs across the pit end at the top. The cushion diminishes the force of the rolling balls and flying pins, permitting them to fall gently into the pit.

The "gutters" are the concave boards that extend the complete length of the alley, from the foul line to the pit, on both sides of the bed. The purpose is to take care of the misdirected balls that roll off the bed before reaching the pit.

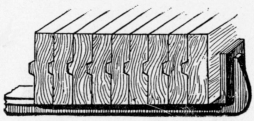

CROSS-SECTION OF BOWLING BED SHOWING STEEL CLAMP

The "return chute," or "loop-the-loop return," is the railway along which the balls travel in their return from the pit to the bowler. It is usually placed on the right-hand side of the alley, or between a pair of alleys.

At the pit end, the chute is solidly constructed with a concave flanged surface placed on the top of the kick-back. It conforms to the downward curve of the latter, but the rail work begins at the top of the incline and extends back to the newel post at the bowler's end of the alley. The flanges easily accommodate the balls when placed on the chute by the pin boy.

The newel post is not made of a solid block, but is built up, being veneered on the inside, as well as on the outside, to make it impervious to atmospheric changes. The top contains a sponge cup to moisten the fingers of the bowler.

The rails form a semicircle at the post, with the ends of the arc pointing down the alley. A tightly stretched leather strap extends horizontally from the upper end of the arc back to the post, where it is fastened with a swivel screw. Half way up, from the points of the arc, a second rail, i. e., the "receiver," is built, with sufficient space between it and the strap to allow the passage of the largest size ball. With the momentum gained by rolling down the incline of the kick-back, the ball rolls back on the inside of the curve until it strikes the strap, where its course is stopped, and it drops on the receiver, ready again for use by the bowler.

In beginning the construction of an alley, the mechanic lays the leveling strips on which the bed is to rest. These are set at right angles to the direction in which the bed is to lie, and must be spirit-leveled for accuracy, and firmly fastened to the foundation. A strip of cork carpet is then laid the full width of the alley and extending the entire length of the bed. This is to reduce to a minimum the sound of the balls dropping on and rolling down the bed.

On the leveling strips at the extreme side of where the bed is to lie, a 3 x 1-inch maple strip is laid, widest side downward, with its finished one-inch edge nearest to the gutter. One end of this strip marks the extreme end of the approach. The other end of the strip is continued by adding other strips the full length of the bed. When these have been carefully squared to the exact direction the alley is to run, they are fastened to the leveling strips.

The next strip, also of maple, is tongued into the lower one, but its continuous length extends only about five feet beyond the foul line, or about eighteen feet from the approach end.

A bowling bed cannot be laid as an ordinary floor. It is built upon its side and when finished resembles a wooden wall about seventy-five feet long four inches high and three inches wide.

The approach end of the bed, approximately eighteen feet long, is constructed of maple, with each alternate strip of the 3 x 1-inch bed stock about eighteen inches shorter. The pit end of the bed is similarly constructed for a distance of about six feet. The space between is filled in with the pine strips of the same dimensions, and the alternate long and short strips at the inner ends of the approach and pit ends form mortices into which the pine dovetails.

The wear on the bed occurs where the bowler walks and drops the ball and

PIT END SECTION OF BOWLING ALLEYS

where the ball strikes the pins; hence the hard maple. The interior is filled with pine, which is softer, because it retains a higher polish and prevents the rolling ball from bumping; thus throwing it from its proper course.

The bed is thus built up for its continuous length, strip by strip, the tongue of one strip fitting into the groove of the other, and both nailed firmly together, until the proper width (while being built, the height) is attained. When the bed is finished, the strips are clamped with steel clamps, the turned-up ends of which firmly grip the sides of the bed, thus preventing warping or spreading. While the bed is still in this upright position, a one-inch slot is cut across where the foul line is to rest, and holes are bored through the bed. A black composition strip, i. e., the "foul-line," is inserted in the slot and bolted through the holes to the bottom of the bed.

At the pit end, circular slots are cut and holes bored for the purpose of counter-sinking and fastening the "pin spots." The latter are of the same substance as the foul-line and all are sunk flush with the surface of the bed.

This—clamping and fastening—explains the necessity for building the bed on its side.

It is now ready to be placed into position. It is merely toppled over, face side upward, clamped side underneath. So exact has it been built, according to specifications and alignment, and the mass is so heavy, that the dead weight makes it lie where it falls and only the slightest adjustment is necessary.

The height of the leveling strips, plus the height of the bed, lift its surface about six inches from the foundation floor. At the pins end of the bed, this forms one of the sides and the bottom of the pit. The bottom is floored with maple and covered with a specially prepared pit mat, durable, yet soft, so as not to damage the balls and pins falling upon it. The back and sides of the pit are formed by the kick-backs, braces and cushion.

After the kick-backs are placed in position, the gutters are laid, and then the return chute railway is laid, between and slightly above them. At the approach end of the bed the newel post is firmly fastened to the foundation, and the floor that is laid above the latter and flush with the surface of the bed serves to brace the post, making it immovable. The curved end of the chute and the receiver are then added.

BACKUS AUTOMATIC PIN SETTERS

The bed is then planed its entire length, sandpapered, shellaced and polished. The remainder of the woodwork is finished in its natural color except the gutters, which are stained mahogany and shellaced. They are thus stained, not only for artistic effect, but to clearly define the outer edges of the bed—a matter of great importance to the bowler when trying to knock down the two outer pins in the third row.

In making the pins, the best selected logs are sawed into blocks about 2 x 1 feet. These are placed in a lathe and gouged out, forming the pin in the rough. They are next turned down to size and selected for quality and weight, after which they are kiln dried and receive a final turning to perfect their formation, then smoothed and finished.

The Backus pinsetter is almost human in its operation. The old way was to hire boys to set up the pins on the spots and return the ball via the return chute. The pin-setter relieves the boy of the major and most time-consuming part of this work. A frame holding the machine is set up over the spots. It is placed so high that it does not interfere with either the flying pins or the rolling balls.

As the pins are knocked off into the gutters, or the pit, the pin boy picks them up and lays them flat on their sides into the pockets at the top of the machine. When a "frame" is rolled those pins standing on the alley remain there and the machine is lowered by a balance weight controlled by a lever. As it descends the pins are automatically set on end, and when they rest on the spots on the alley the machine releases them and springs up to its original position.

Wooden balls for bowling were never satisfactory. They wore out too easily and never retained perfect rotundity. Fortunes were spent in experimenting with other materials until at last the famous "mineralite" ball was perfected.

Its composition is a trade secret, but its chief ingredient is rubber.

First the composition is rolled into sheets. These are then molded and later vulcanized, being subject to terrific pressure. The balls are then smoothed and polished.

As it is impossible to make a perfectly round ball and have the weight equally distributed, the ball can not roll true; an ingenious device overcomes the difficulty. The ball is set in a basin of mercury, where it floats. Naturally, the heavier side of the ball swings to the bottom. On the top, diametrically opposite to the center of weight, a chalk mark is placed on the ball and it is then lifted out of the mercury.

Diametrically opposite to the chalk mark a small hole is punched into the ball to indicate the weightiest point. Directly beneath this is stamped the trademark of the firm.

Having ascertained the proper distance apart the finger holes are to be bored, the ball is weighed to determine the excess of its proposed weight when finished.

The holes are then machine bored at the respective points, sufficiently deep to reduce the weight to exact specifications.

How are Artificial Precious Stones Made?

The art of manufacturing gems synthetically, that is, by the combination of chemical elements present in the real stone, has reached a high degree of success.

The diamond, which is an allotropic form of carbon, has hitherto resisted attempts to reproduce it of sufficient size to have a commercial value. By dissolving carbon in molten iron and suddenly cooling the molten mass by a stream of water, whereupon the outer part contracts with great force and compresses the interior so that the carbon separates out, Moissan, the French chemist, succeeded in isolating small crystals, none, however, as large as one-twenty-fifth of an inch in diameter.

Experiments in the manufacture of the ruby have met with such success that the synthetic ruby is produced of a size and of a perfection that would place a prohibitive value on the natural stone. The ruby, chemically considered, is crystallized alumina, or oxide of aluminum, with a small percentage of oxide of chromium.

Sapphire is of the same material, differing from the ruby only in color. The ruby owes its fine red color to the presence of oxide of chromium; the sapphire its deep blue to either a lower oxide of chromium or to an oxide of titanium.

Crystallized alumina in the different colors receives different trade names, as Oriental emerald for the green; Oriental topaz for the yellow; Oriental amethyst for the purple; while the water-clear, colorless crystal is known as white sapphire.

The process of manufacture of rubies is carried on with the oxyhydrogen blowpipe, to whose intense heat the powdered alumina with its coloring oxides is subjected. Rubies have been thus produced weighing twelve to fifteen carats when cut. The average weight of the native Burmese ruby is about one-eighth of a carat. The sapphire and the so-called Oriental stones are prepared in the same manner, with the addition of proper coloring matter.

The emerald and opal have not emerged from the experimental stage, although Becquerel, a French chemist, is reported to have produced opals from solutions of silicates with high-tension electric currents.

To be distinguished from synthetic gems are reconstructed stones, which (as yet only done with the ruby) are pieces of the natural stone fused together. They are very brittle.

The pearl is not produced synthetically, but many imitations exist. The Japanese produce them by fastening a piece of mother-of-pearl in the shells of the pearl-oyster and allowing it to remain there for a number of years.

The turquoise, a phosphate of aluminum colored with copper, is not synthetically produced, although various experiments with its manufacture have been made.

Reproduced by permission of The Philadelphia Museum.   MAZZANTINI BULL-FIGHT

The last act in a bull fight, City of Mexico. The bull, tired out by the attacks of the *picadores* or pikemen, and *banderilleros* or dart men, whose *banderillas* or darts are seen planted in the bull's shoulders, faces the *matador*, armed with the *estoque* or sword, and carrying the *muleta* or red flag in his left hand, and about to deliver the death stroke.

What is a Mexican Bull-Fight Like?

Bull-fights are among the favorite diversions of the Spaniards. They are usually held in an amphitheater having circular seats rising one above another, and are attended by vast crowds who eagerly pay for admission.

The combatants, who make bull-fighting their profession, march into the arena in procession. They are of various kinds—the *picadores*, combatants on horseback, in the old Spanish knightly garb; the *chulos* and *banderilleros*, combatants on foot, in gay dresses, with colored cloaks or banners; and finally, the *matador* (the killer).

As soon as the signal is given the bull is let into the arena. The *picadores*, who have stationed themselves near him, commence the attack with their lances, and the bull is thus goaded to fury. Sometimes a horse is wounded or killed (only old, worthless animals are thus employed), and the rider is obliged to run for his life. The *chulos* assist the horsemen by drawing the attention of the bull with their cloaks; and in case of danger they save themselves by leaping over the wooden fence which surrounds the arena. The *banderilleros* then come into play. They try to fasten on the bull their *banderillas*—barbed darts ornamented with colored paper, and often having squibs or crackers attached. If they succeed, the squibs are discharged and the bull races madly about the arena.

The *matador* or *espada* now comes in gravely with a naked sword and a red flag to decoy the bull with, and aims a fatal blow at the animal. The slaughtered bull is dragged away, and another is let out from the stall. Several bulls are so disposed of in a single day.

What is the Difference between "Alternating" and "Direct" Current?

Strong currents of electricity are generated in the electric central stations and supplied to our homes, street lamps and so forth, in one of the two forms, either "alternating" or "direct." While many of us know which kind is furnished to our homes, everyone does not always understand the difference between the two.

The central station contains a number of powerful dynamo machines, driven usually by steam power. The positive and negative terminals of the dynamo are put in connection with the positive and negative main conductors which are to supply the district, and from these mains smaller conductors branch off to the houses or lamps. All these conductors are of copper, that metal when pure having seven times the conductivity of iron.

Different methods are in use for keeping the supply of electricity steady in spite of the varying demands made upon it. In some systems of distribution, instead of the two main conductors being one positive and the other negative, each is positive and negative alternately, the reversals taking place some hundreds of times per second. The currents are then said to be "alternating." When such reversals do not take place, the currents are said to be "direct."

What was the "Court of Love"?

The "Court of Love" existed in what we call the chivalric period of the middle ages.

It was composed of knights, poets and ladies, who discussed and gave decisions on subtle questions of love and gallantry. The first of these courts was probably established in Provence about the twelfth century. They reached their highest splendor in France, under Charles VI, through the influence of his consort, Isabella of Bavaria, whose court was established in 1380. An attempted revival was made under Louis XIV by Cardinal Richelieu.

The Story of the Addressograph*

If you were asked to enumerate the different kinds of clerical work performed in the modern business office, you would probably fail to mention the writing of names. Yet the writing and rewriting of names is as essential in most offices as the addition of figures or the dictation of correspondence.

In fact, names represent the backbone of nearly every business or organization. There is the list of names of those people you sell to; the names of those people you want to sell to; the names of those people you buy from; the names of those people who owe you money; the names of those people to whom you owe money and the names of those people who work for you. Then, lodges, clubs, churches and other organizations must maintain lists of names of their members; and so the different kinds of lists go on *ad infinitum*.

Now, in most offices, these names must be written and rewritten over and over again—often many times each month—on envelopes, price-lists, statements, checks, pay forms, ledger sheets, order forms, tags, labels, etc. And in many offices the writing of names is still a slow, tedious, drudging task—as the workers in those offices will testify.

The Birth of Mechanical Addressing.

But in one office this monotonous task of writing and rewriting the same names over and over again became such a hardship that the man who had to do it, thinking twenty-five years ahead of his time, had a vision of performing such work mechanically. That vision was the forerunner of the Addressograph.

In the early 90's, Mr. Joseph S. Duncan was manager of a little flour and grist mill in Iowa. The requirements of his business necessitated the daily addressing of 100 quotation cards. Those were the days of pen and ink and the imperfectly developed typewriter. Mr. Duncan's office was small. He was the sole worker in that office—and as the typewriter was still a curiosity in that section of the country, Mr. Duncan was obliged to depend upon pen and ink in addressing his daily price cards. This routine task wasted a great deal of his valuable time each day. In an effort to finish the work quickly, so that he could devote his attention to more important matters, Mr. Duncan found that he was frequently sacrificing accuracy for speed. Result—his concern often suffered considerable loss of profit because his quotation cards did not reach the people for whom they were intended. Finally, becoming disgusted with inefficient and inaccurate pen and ink addressing methods, Mr. Duncan made a trip to Chicago for the purpose of purchasing a machine for addressing his price cards. But, on visiting the leading stationery and office equipment stores, he was told there was no such machine. He returned to his office resigned to the task of addressing his 100 daily quotation cards by pen and ink. But the drudgery and monotony of this work would not down in his mind. The mistakes and omissions made in addressing these price cards became no less frequent. Finally, because Mr. Duncan could no longer be reconciled to the drudgery, inaccuracy and expense of hand addressing, he determined to build for himself a machine that would lift from his shoulders this monotonous task.

Builds First Addressograph.

Mr. Duncan invented and built his first addressing machine in 1892. He called it the "Addressograph"—a coined word meaning "to write addresses." Although

---

* Illustrations by courtesy of the Addressograph Co.

Mr. Duncan appreciated the saving of time and money and increase in accuracy which his little invention would surely create in the writing of names and addresses, he did not at first realize the great place his remarkable invention was destined to take in the commercial world as a "business energizer" and simplifier of routine work.

Like the first steam engine, telephone or automobile, the first addressograph was crudely simple and of course presented an uncouth mechanical appearance. Mr. Duncan experimented by gluing the rubber portion of a number of hand stamps to a wooden drum. This drum was placed on an operating shaft in the addressograph, so that after the printing of one name and address, the drum revolved so that the next name and address came into printing position. The type impressions thus obtained were fairly readable. But Mr. Duncan soon realized that the idea of gluing the type permanently to a wooden drum was unpractical. Only a few addresses could be placed around the drum and the method of gluing them permanently into place made it practically impossible to make corrections when changes in address occurred, or to add new names as occasion demanded.

THE FIRST ADDRESSOGRAPH

Greater flexibility was needed. So Mr. Duncan designed and built what is now known as the first chain addressograph. Individual rubber type characters were pushed into metal type holders with a pair of tweezers. These type holders were then ingeniously linked together in the form of an endless chain. These chains were placed over a revolving metal drum, and as each separate name and address came to the printing point of the addressograph, the operator pushed down on a vertical stamper rod which pushed the envelope, or whatever form was to be addressed, against the rubber type which was inked just before reaching the printing point. Here, at last, was a practical addressing machine which enabled the user to accurately print names and addresses—typewriter style—ten times faster than was possible by any other method, and, quite as important, to make changes and additions to the list.

The Beginning of a Great Industry.

By this time, Mr. Duncan had moved his base of operations from Iowa to Chicago. So well was his first practical model of the addressograph received by Chicago business men that he sold the first half-dozen manufactured within a short time. Enthused with his success, Mr. Duncan decided to enter into the manufacture and sale of addressographs on as extensive a basis as the demand for his invention warranted. But to do this it was necessary for him to secure more capital. Consequently, he interested Mr. J. B. Hall—a Chicago business man—in his project, and in January, 1896, Mr. Duncan and Mr. Hall formed a partnership and called it the "Addressograph Company."

Mr. Hall's first step was to find out what the leading business men of his time thought of the addressograph. So he made a trip to New York City—taking with him one of the little hand-operated chain addressographs. Here, Mr. Hall called upon Henry Clews, J. Pierpont Morgan and other prominent business men. He also visited the offices of the large public service and insurance companies. In every case, Mr. Hall was courteously received; but after demonstrating the addressograph was told that while it was interesting and a step in the right direction, it was still in too primitive a state to prove of any great value in addressing a large list of names.

Answering Demand for Greater Speed.

Naturally, Mr. Hall's first thought on his return to Chicago was to induce Mr. Duncan to build a larger model, capable of greater speed and greater output. Acting upon Mr. Hall's suggestion, Mr. Duncan, in a short time, perfected a larger chain addressograph, operated by foot-lever and embodying several important improvements. As the Addressograph Company was maintaining at that time only a small sales office, a contract was let to the Blackman Machine Company, of Chicago, to build fifteen of these new foot-lever chain addressographs. And it was this new model which caused the addressograph to take its place in the business world as one of the leading office appliances. Many of these new chain addressographs were

RUBBER CHAIN ADDRESSOGRAPH OPERATED BY FOOT LEVER AND MOUNTED IN WOOD CABINET

sold. Having formerly been engaged in the public service field, Mr. Hall was quick to realize the advantages which mechanical addressing offered to gas, electric light, water and telephone companies. As a result, the majority of the first addressograph sales were made to these lines of business.

With the constantly increasing use of the addressograph, suggestions for improvement and further development were freely offered by addressograph customers and just as liberally entertained by Mr. Duncan. As a result of these suggestions, another important advance took place in addressograph development. A customer, after writing words of praise about his addressograph, suggested that if some means could be arrived at to avoid the necessity of setting and resetting the individual pieces of rubber type, a great saving in time and money could be accomplished in making changes and additions to a list of names.

Invents Embossed Metal Address Plate.

After considerable thought, Mr. Duncan hit upon the plan of embossing, typewriter style, characters upon a metal plate. To do this, it was necessary for him to invent and perfect the Graphotype—a machine which writes names and addresses on metal plates almost as quickly as the same data can be written on paper with the typewriter. The first embossed metal plates were linked together in the form of an endless chain, similar to the rubber type plates. A new addressograph was perfected for printing impressions from these embossed metal plates. It was called the No. 2 Chain Addressograph.

The Addressograph Company now had two models to sell. But, owing to the fact that the rubber chain addressograph permitted users to make changes and additions in their own offices, a greater number of machines of this model were sold than of the metal chain addressograph; because, with the latter model, it was necessary for the customer to send to Chicago to have his new metal links embossed with the graphotype for the changes and additions of his list.

By this time, the Addressograph Company had established itself in its own factory in Chicago. Branch offices had also been opened in New York, Philadelphia, Boston and other principal points, and out of these offices was traveling a small but enthusiastic group of salesmen. Many firms, large and small, throughout the country were using and recommending the chain addressograph. And, crude as that model seems now, it was proving a wonderful time and labor saver in the offices in which it was used—and paying back its cost many times each year because of the fact that it accurately printed names and addresses *ten times faster* than was possible to write such data by pen or typewriter.

A Card Index that Addresses Itself.

As the use of the addressograph increased, Mr. Duncan and Mr. Hall realized the need of a more efficient way of making changes and additions to the list of names. It was important that individual names be located and removed from the list more quickly than was possible with the chain addressograph. Demand for improvement along this line was stimulated by the loose-leaf and card index wave which was just then beginning to sweep the country. And Mr. Duncan, taking the card index idea as a basis, designed what he called the Model "A" or Rubber Card Index Addressograph. Instead of the separate plates being linked together in the form of a chain, they were inserted into a tin holder—called the frame —which closely resembled in appearance a 3 x 5 paper file card. In addition to carry-

RUBBER CARD INDEX ADDRESS PLATE

ing a printing plate, this frame also carried a paper card bearing a proof of its respective printing plate. In this complete form, these address plates were filed in steel filing drawers like ordinary paper cards. About every fifteenth address plate in a drawer was equipped with a vertical, subdividing tab—numerical, alphabetical or geographical as the case might require. Each filing drawer carried a printed label showing the contents of the drawer—and by means of these complete card index features it proved a simple matter to locate and remove individual names when making revisions to the list; and, in addition, these features afforded all of the advantages of a perfect reference file, as the paper proof card could be provided with a printed form for retaining memoranda.

Of course, a new addressograph was necessary to handle this card index improvement. And in the Model "A" Addressograph, we find the basic principle of the addressograph of today. A drawerful of plates is emptied into the magazine. The empty filing drawer is placed beneath the addressograph so that after addressing the address plates fall back into the original drawer in their original card index order.

Electric Motor Increases Speed.

Not only was it necessary to meet the demand for card index conveniences, but it was also important to equip the Model "A" Addressograph with an electric motor for increasing its speed of operation and insuring a greater output. As was to be expected, the card index and electrically

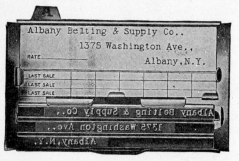

METAL CARD INDEX ADDRESS PLATE

operated features caused thousands of concerns, large and small, to adopt the addressograph. Large mercantile houses, addressing thousands of names—who had formerly held aloof from the addressograph because of its limited advantages for making changes and additions—now placed their orders with instructions to rush delivery. With business houses all over the country rapidly changing from bound books to loose-leaf card index records, the demand for chain addressograph models diminished and more and more orders were received for the rubber card index addressographs. Business men, generally, were now taking a real interest in mechanical addressing and the saving which the addressograph made possible in their offices. This interest was increased materially with the growth of mail-order businesses and the constantly increasing use of direct-by-mail advertising by business concerns, large and small. Firms having mailing lists were increasing them. Those firms which had not previously used direct-by-mail advertising were now coming to realize the many advantages of that modern selling short-cut and were compiling large lists of names. The rubber card index addressograph had by now proved itself a wonderful time and labor saver in addressing and maintaining lists of names of average size. But, with the advent of large lists, the high cost of rubber type presented a serious objection to many firms regarding the installation of the addressograph. Furthermore, large lists of names were subject to many changes and additions—and in this connection, setting up the address plates in rubber type proved quite slow and expensive. So, to bring the addressograph abreast of modern conditions, Mr. Duncan combined the card index filing idea with the embossed metal plate which he

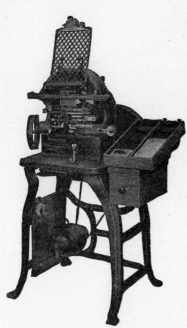

ELECTRIC GRAPHOTYPE WHICH EMBOSSES TYPEWRITER STYLE CHARACTERS ON METAL ADDRESS PLATES

had previously worked out for use with the chain addressograph. With the coming of the metal card index addressograph and the modern graphotype for making the metal address plates, the addressing machine business was "revolutionized," as Mr. Duncan put it. With the graphotype, address plates for changes and additions could be made at almost typewriter speed. The card index address plate required less filing space than was true of the rubber card index address plate, printed cleaner impressions and from every standpoint was superior to the rubber type system. In order that customers could make their changes and additions right in their office, the graphotype was further developed and furnished in two models, one operated by motor, the other by hand.

HAND GRAPHOTYPE WHICH EMBOSSES TYPEWRITER STYLE CHARACTERS ON METAL ADDRESS PLATES

Attachments Increase Utility of Addressograph.

The first addressographs were intended for printing names and addresses consecutively on envelopes and post cards. And so much time was saved on this one application that customers soon began applying it to other kinds of work in their

AUTOMATIC LISTING ATTACHMENT

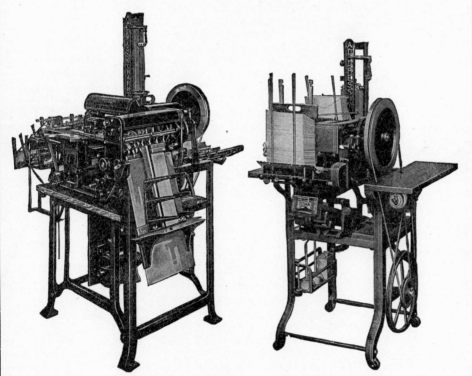

HIGH SPEED AUTOMATIC FEED ADDRESSO-
GRAPH. CAPACITY, 7,500 ADDRESSED ENVELOPES
PER HOUR

AUTOMATIC ENVELOPE FEED AD-
DRESSOGRAPH. SPEED, 5,000 ADDRESSED
ENVELOPES AN HOUR

offices. To do this effectively, it was necessary for Mr. Duncan to work out additional parts called "attachments" which permitted the addressing, listing and imprinting of names and other data on office forms of every nature. To illustrate: the dating attachment enabled users to apply the addressograph to their statement work. With this attachment—which can quickly be thrown in or out of operation —the current date is printed at the head of a statement simultaneously with the printing of the name and address. Further, to use the addressograph effectively for statement work, it was necessary to devise a skipping attachment—manipulated by the operator's knee—permitting him to skip the printing of impressions from address plates of those customers who had paid their accounts. By working out the listing attachment, Mr. Duncan made it possible for users to list names in one or more vertical columns on pay sheets, drivers' route sheets, dividend and trial balance sheets. This attachment automatically feeds the paper and spaces the proper distances between the printing of each address. Then came the electric bell signal and automatic selector attachments. Users of classified lists of names were enabled by these attachments to place tabs in sockets at the top and back of the address plates to indicate the different classifications on the list, such as "Buying Seasons," "Kinds of Products Wanted," "Territories," "Expired Dates," etc., and by means of these attachments, automatically select for addressing certain address plates, skipping the addressing of others.

As the various uses for the adressograph increased, so the demand for different special attachments increased, until today, the addressograph addresses, lists and imprints names, addresses and other data upon every office form. The history of the addressograph has been one of constant development. With the growth of large lists, the demand for greater speed in addressing was answered by automatic feed addressographs. The Automatic No. 1 Addressograph was designed to automatically feed and address envelopes and cards at the rate of 4,000 to 5,000 an hour. In the Automatic No. 3 Addressograph we find the highest development of the system. This machine automatically feeds and addresses public service bills, insurance premium notices and receipts, cards, envelopes, circulars, etc., at the great speed of 6,000 to 8,000 an hour. The wrapper addressograph answered the demand of publishers for great speed and 100 per cent accuracy. This model of the addressograph automatically feeds wrappers from a roll and in addition to printing the name and address exact typewriter style, also prints the name of the publication and postal permit from electrotypes, indicates mail routes on the back of the wrappers, separates into a separate drawer the address plates of those people whose subscriptions have expired, and cuts the wrapper to the proper size—all at the speed of 7,500 per hour.

Small Users not Overlooked.

But, while Mr. Duncan and his associates have given every attention to the needs of users of large lists of names, he has not overlooked the lodge secretaries and other users of small lists of names. In the hand addressograph, which sells for as low as $27, he has worked out three practical models having an average speed of from 750 to 1,500 names and addresses an hour. Thousands of these little machines are in daily use and, like the larger models of the addressograph, are driving drudgery out of the office—freeing thousands of hands from the monotonous, laborious task of writing names and addresses by pen and ink—in short, elevating the position of the office worker far above that of a mere automaton and making it possible for him to earn more money and enjoy a happier existence by doing brain work instead of manual labor.

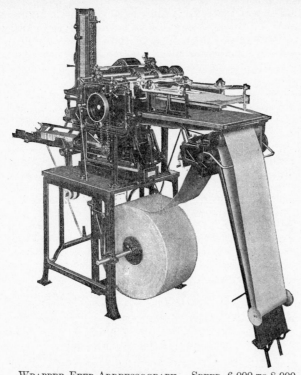

WRAPPER FEED ADDRESSOGRAPH. SPEED, 6,000 TO 8,000
ADDRESSED WRAPPERS PER HOUR

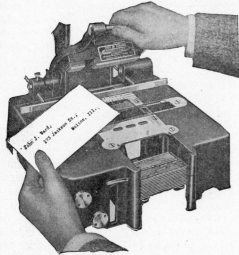

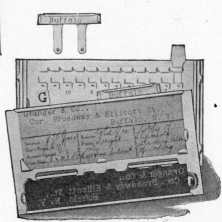

HAND ADDRESSOGRAPH (PRINTS THROUGH
A RIBBON). SPEED, 1,000 TO 1,500 TYPEWRITTEN
ADDRESSES AN HOUR

SHOWING HOW TABS ARE INSERTED
IN BACK OF ADDRESS PLATE FOR PUR-
POSES OF INDEXING AND CLASSIFYING
LISTS

The Addressograph—Its Place in Business.

Twenty-five years' use of the addressograph in over 300 different lines of business—manufacturers, wholesalers and dealers, insurance companies, public service companies, government departments, associations, clubs, churches, lodges, hotels and schools, laundries, commission merchants, publishers, railroad and steamship companies—in truth, every business, large and small, where a list of names is frequently addressed—have proved the utter folly of slow, tiring hands attempting to compete with swift, untiring wheels. Wherever names are written, there you will usually find the addressograph in use, saving time and money, guaranteeing 100 per cent accuracy and insuring maximum efficiency. There are many different models —some operated by hand or foot-lever, others by electric motor; some are entirely automatic. So, no matter how many names and addresses are written—fifty or a million—the addressograph, like the telephone or typewriter, has come to be recognized as a modern business necessity.

What is " Dry Farming "?

Dry farming is a method which has been recently developed and which is coming into even wider use. The United States Department of Agriculture, through its experiment stations, has made a careful study of the conditions, possibilities and limitations of the practice, and the following is a brief abstract of the results:

In defining the term dry farming it is explained that the practice includes (1) deep plowing before the rainy season sets in, in order to provide in the soil a capacious water storage reservoir and an ample space for root development; (2) light, deep, even seeding or planting in a well-prepared, moist soil; (3) frequent, thorough, level cultivation before as well as after sowing or planting; (4) the use of seed bred and selected for the conditions prevailing; (5) the use of machinery of large capacity; (6) the adoption of methods for the concentration of crops.

Crops must be selected or developed that will fit the environment, and there is ample field for investigation in the improvement and development of crops suitable to dry lands. Wheat stands at the head among cereal crops. The durum or macaroni wheats do especially well; but other varieties are also grown, as are oats, rye, barley and spelt. The millets are among the best paying dry-farming crops. There are few legumes that have shown value on dry lands, but peas, beans and alfalfa are the most promising of development. Vegetables and both shade and fruit trees are being grown in districts where dry farming is practiced.

Fall seeding of cereals, wherever the conditions will permit, is preferable to spring seeding, and it is important to retain the snow upon the land, especially in sections where it forms the chief part of the total precipitation. The snowfall may be retained by leaving the ground rough after the late fall plowing, by throwing up borders across the field at right angles with the prevailing winds, or by planting hedge rows or shrubbery across the field at short intervals. Usually less seed should be planted per acre under dry-farming conditions than is used in humid sections. The less precipitation, the smaller should be the amount of seed planted.

What is a " Drying Machine " Like?

This is a machine used in bleaching, dyeing and laundry establishments, consisting of two concentric drums or cylinders, one within the other, open at the top, and having the inner cylinder perforated at its side with numerous small holes. The goods to be dried are placed within the inner cylinder, and the machine is then made to rotate with great velocity, when, by the action of centrifugal force, the water escapes through the holes in the side.

Copyright by Brown Bros.

NEW YORK STOCK EXCHANGE

This is the only photograph ever made of the interior of the New York Stock Exchange, the financial heart of the country. Each stock listed is allotted to one of the posts seen on the floor, which, during a panic, become the scene of the wildest excitement. The exchange is connected by private telegraph wires and "ticker" wires with every important financial center.

How does the New York Stock Exchange Operate?

The New York Stock Exchange is typical of most American stock exchanges, the leading ones of which are located in Boston, Pittsburgh, Philadelphia, Chicago, Baltimore, Cleveland, Cincinnati, New Orleans, Salt Lake City, Denver, San Francisco and St. Louis. American stock exchanges differ somewhat in their operation from the foreign stock exchanges, the principal ones of which are those of London, Paris, Berlin, Amsterdam, Antwerp, Brussels, Vienna and Petrograd.

A stock exchange is really an organization of professional brokers, which conducts speculation and investment in securities, the paper representatives of transportation, industrial, mining, commercial and other properties. On the American stock exchanges one broker may specialize in the shares of the Union Pacific Railroad, for instance, another in those of the United States Steel Corporation, and so on. Some brokers deal particularly in "odd lots"—blocks of less than one hundred shares—and some members, called "room traders," speculate entirely for their own account and do no commission business for customers. The commission charged for buying or selling is twelve and a half cents a share, so that on the usual order of one hundred shares, the broker receives twelve dollars and a half.

The business of buying and selling shares is done in a large room known as the "floor." Scattered over the floor are a large number of high posts. Each post bears the name of the stock or stocks which may be traded in at that post. This provision is to bring buyers and sellers in any security together as quickly as possible. A broker desiring to buy shares of a certain stock will go to the part allotted to that stock and call out its name with the number of shares wished and the price he will pay. This is his bid. Other brokers may offer the stock to him at a slightly higher price, or his bid may be accepted at once. As soon as a price is agreed on, each broker —the buyer and the seller—makes a memorandum of the transaction, which is reported to the offices at once by telephone. Meanwhile the broker also hands another memorandum of the transaction to an errand boy, who takes the memorandum at once to the telegraph operator, who in turn sends it out onto the little instrument called the "ticker."

Transactions on the New York Stock Exchange may be made in three different ways: "Cash," "regular" or on a "limited option" to buyer and seller as to the time of delivery or acceptance. "Cash" means that stock bought in this manner is taken up and paid for the same day; "regular" transactions mean that the stock bought in this way must be taken up and paid for by a quarter past two o'clock of the following afternoon.

Upon the outbreak of the European war, panic ensued among holders of securities, and the stock exchanges of the world were closed to prevent the selling of stocks at prices which would have brought ruin to banks and other financial houses. Practically none of them were opened until December, 1914, and then only under severe restrictions which were held in force until confidence had returned.

How did the Term "Cowboys" Originate?

The term "cowboys" was first used during the American Revolution. It was applied to a band of Tories who infested the neutral ground of Westchester County, New York, stealing cattle from both parties and doing other mischief.

It has been used of recent years to designate the skilled horsemen who have charge of the cattle on the great ranges of the West. Many of them enlisted in the Rough Rider regiment of the Spanish war and proved daring soldiers.

The Story in a Chemical Fire Extinguisher*

A little smoke, a flash, and a waste basket, a curtain or something else is in flames. A few years ago an excited person would fail to extinguish the blaze with water or with any other first aid at hand and would call for the fire department. When that arrived the fire frequently would be beyond control.

Modern methods have wrought great changes. Nowadays, in case of fire, any man, woman or child can reach for a fire extinguisher and after a few strokes of the pump the fire is out.

This change did not come all at once. The fire extinguisher has been developing ever since man learned to fear fire. Devices for extinguishing fire are almost coeval with that element itself. In the second century before Christ, the Egyptians had pumps worked by levers to put out their fires. The Roman, Pliny, refers to fire extinguishers but gives no account of their construction. Apollodorus, architect of the Emperor Trajan, speaks of leathern bags with pipes attached. Water was projected by squeezing the bags. Medieval Europe used various forms of water pumps, and it was not until the opening of the nineteenth century that chemicals were used to combat fire.

There are two classes of chemical fire extinguishers: the soda and acid tank or three-gallon type, and the one-quart pump type. The latter came when the efficiency of carbon tetrachloride as an extinguishing agent became known. All the extinguishers of this type use a liquid which has carbon tetrachloride as a base. The liquid is a combination of organic materials with an aromatic odor and high specific gravity. When subjected to a temperature of 200° F. or over, it changes to a heavy, cohering, non-poisonous gas blanket which surrounds the burning material and cuts off the air suppy necessary for the life of the fire.

The first one-quart pump type of extinguisher appeared in the United States in 1907. There was little resemblance between it and the extinguisher of today. A cylindrical tube with a perforated end contained the liquid. The user was expected to sprinkle the liquid over the fire just as salt is sprinkled from a saltcellar over meat.

One company applied the idea of pumping the liquid on the fire in 1909. They introduced a single-acting pump. The user inserted the nozzle in the liquid, drew it into the pump, and then ejected it on the flames. This company substituted a double-acting pump early in 1910. The container for the fluid and the pump were thus combined and the extinguisher had the general appearance of those now on the market.

*Illustrations by courtesy of the Pyrene Manufacturing Co.

Brass construction was substituted for tin in the latter part of 1910, and in 1911 all brass construction was adopted. The extinguisher has remained practically unchanged since 1911.

This was the only one-quart type extinguisher on the market until 1911. Since then several others have been marketed. All use an extinguishing liquid with carbon tetrachloride as a base. They differ principally in the manner of its ejection. The original type pumps the liquid out by hand. Others eject it by air pressure or by a combination of the two methods. The objection made by some people to the use of air pressure is that it demands attention and the use of a complicated mechanism which more readily gets out of order.

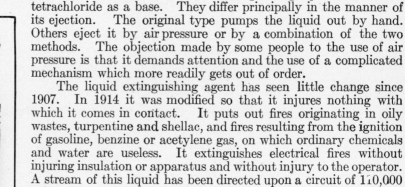

The liquid extinguishing agent has seen little change since 1907. In 1914 it was modified so that it injures nothing with which it comes in contact. It puts out fires originating in oily wastes, turpentine and shellac, and fires resulting from the ignition of gasoline, benzine or acetylene gas, on which ordinary chemicals and water are useless. It extinguishes electrical fires without injuring insulation or apparatus and without injury to the operator. A stream of this liquid has been directed upon a circuit of 110,000 volts without the least harm to the operator.

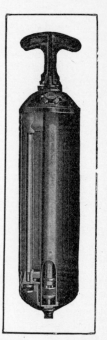

A German originated the soda and acid type of extinguisher from tests made in Denmark between 1830 and 1835. The enterprising Teuton divided a hogshead into two parts. He filled one part with a solution of alcohol and water; the other division was partly filled with sulphuric acid. His problem was to unite the two when he wanted to put out a fire. This was accomplished by fastening a charge of gunpowder in such a way that when exploded it would break the partition and mix the solutions. French ingenuity added slight improvements a short time later.

Alexander Graham, of Lexington, Virginia, applied for patents on this type of extinguisher a number of times between 1844 and 1849. He was unable to patent his invention. A fire extinguisher company in Chicago and one in Baltimore obtained patents on what was known as the "bicarbonate of soda and sulphuric acid" extinguisher by a special act of Congress in 1865. These patents were known as the Graham patents, and both extinguishers were called the "break-bottle type" because the soda and acid were mixed when a glass bottle containing the latter was broken.

The "up-set" type of soda and acid extinguisher was adapted by Meyerose in St. Louis in 1891. The improvement lay in the vessel containing the acid being upset instead of broken. This extinguisher was of copper construction and had a capacity of three gallons. One fire extinguisher company improved upon the original type of "up-set" extinguisher in 1893 by lining the extinguisher with lead which the acid did not affect. Since 1893 there have been no improvements of consequence on the soda and acid extinguisher. It consists of a cylindrical container with a solution of sodium bicarbonate. Over the bicarbonate is suspended a vessel containing sulphuric acid. When in use the acid is tilted over and comes in contact with the bicarbonate. This liberates carbon dioxide. The pressure generated is sufficient to throw a stream of the bicarbonate solution forty feet. The chief dis-advantages of the soda and acid type of extinguisher are that its weight makes it cumbersome to operate and it cannot be safely used on electrical fires until the current has been turned off.

How is Gold Leaf Made?

The gold is cast into ingots weighing about two ounces each, and measuring about three-quarters of an inch broad. These ingots are passed between steel rollers till they form long ribbons of such thinness that a square inch will weigh six and one-half grains. Each one of these is now cut into 150 pieces, each of which is beaten on an anvil till it is about an inch square. These 150 plates are interlaid with pieces of fine vellum about four inches square, and beaten till the gold is extended nearly to the size of the vellum leaves. Each leaf is then divided into four, interlaid with goldbeater's skin, and beaten out to the dimensions of the skin. Another similar division and beating finishes the operation, after which the leaves are placed in paper books ready for use. The leaves are about three and a quarter inches square and are produced in ten different shades of color, according as the gold was alloyed with much or little copper or silver.

What is the Natural Color of Goldfish?

It is greenish in color in the natural state, the golden-yellow color being found only in domesticated specimens, and retained by artificial selection.

These fishes are reared by the Chinese in small ponds, in basins or porcelain vessels, and kept for ornament. By careful selection, many strange varieties have been propagated.

They are now distributed over nearly all the civilized parts of the world, but in large ponds they readily revert to the color of the original stock.

When was "Liquid Fire" First Used in Warfare?

Long before the European war, an inflammable and destructive compound was used in warfare, especially by the Byzantine Greeks.

It was poured from caldrons and ladles, vomited through long copper tubes, or flung in pots, phials and barrels.

The art of compounding it was concealed at Constantinople with the greatest care, but it appears that naphtha, sulphur and nitre entered into its composition.

How did the Greyhound Get His Name?

The name appears to have no reference to the color, but is derived from the Icelandic "grey," meaning a dog. They are used chiefly in the sport of coursing, a work for which their peculiar shape, strength, keenness of sight and speed make them exceedingly well fitted. This sport is preferred by many people to horse racing. There are several varieties, as the Irish greyhound, the Scottish, the Russian, the Italian and the Turkish.

The common greyhound is of an elegant make of body, and is universally known as the fleetest of dogs.

A good hound has a fine, soft, flexible skin, with thin, silky hair, a great length of nose, contracting gradually from the eye to the nostril, a full, clear and penetrating eye, small ears, erect head, long neck, chest capacious, deep, but not wide, shoulders deep and placed obliquely, ribs well arched, contracted belly and flank, a great depth from the hips to the hocks of the hind-legs, fore-legs straight and shorter than the hind legs.

THE GATEWAY TO AMERICA

The famous statue of Liberty in New York Harbor. The grassy space in the foreground is Battery Park, and the round building is the Aquarium. Here in the early days stood a rude "castle" or fort, later supplanted by an opera house. Washington often walked in the old garden around the building, as did other great Americans.

Copyright by Underwood & Underwood, N. Y.

Why is It Called "Battery Park"?

The extreme southern end of Manhattan Island is both popularly and officially known as "Battery Park" because it was fortified in the seventeenth century for the protection of the town. In the picture the round building is the Aquarium, which is abundantly supplied with sea and river fishes. The picture was taken from a platform of the Elevated Railway, the trains of which run from this point to practically the northern extremity of the island, making stops en route at stations situated at approximately every eighth street.

Manhattan Island was first visited in 1609 by Henry Hudson. The first settlement was located three years afterward on the present site of Battery Park. The Dutch settlement here formed gradually grew into a town called New Amsterdam, which in 1648 had 1,000 inhabitants. In 1664 it surrendered to the British and took its new name from the Duke of York, into whose hands it came. It was the capital of the State of New York from 1784 to 1797, and from 1785 to 1790 it was the seat of the Federal Government. Washington was inaugurated to the presidency at New York in 1789. The opening of the Erie Canal in 1825 gave the city command of internal commerce and since that date its progress has been rapid, almost beyond example.

How do we Know that the Earth is Round?

We have all been taught that the earth is a nearly spherical body which every twenty-four hours rotates from west to east around an imaginary line called its axis —this axis having as its extremities the north and south poles respectively—while in the course of a year it completes a revolution around the sun.

To an observer whose view is not obstructed, any part of the earth presents itself as a circular and horizontal expanse, on the circumference of which the heavens appear to rest. Accordingly, in remote antiquity, the earth was regarded as a flat, circular body, floating on the water. But even in antiquity the spherical form of the earth began to be suspected.

It is only on this supposition that we can explain how the horizon of vision grows wider and wider the higher the position we choose, how the tops of towers and mountains at a distance become visible before the bases, how the hull of a ship disappears first as she sails away, and how, as we go from the poles towards the equator, new stars become visible. Besides these proofs, there are many others, such as the circular shadow of the earth seen on the moon during an eclipse, the gradual appearance and disappearance of the sun, and especially the fact that since 1519 the earth has been regularly circumnavigated.

The earth is not, however, an exact sphere, but is very slightly flattened at the poles, so as to have the form known as an oblate spheroid. In this way the polar diameter, or diameter from pole to pole, is shorter than the diameter at right angles to this—the equatorial diameter. The most accurate measurements make the polar diameter about twenty-seven miles less than the equatorial, the equatorial diameter being found to be 7,925.6 miles, and the polar 7,899.14.

What were "Ducking Stools"?

A ducking stool was a sort of a chair in which "common scolds" were formerly tied and plunged into water. They were of different forms, but that most commonly in use consisted of an upright post and a transverse movable beam on which the seat was fitted or from which it was suspended by a chain.

The ducking stool is mentioned in the Doomsday survey; it was extensively in use throughout the country from the fifteenth till the beginning of the eighteenth century, and in one rare case at least—at Leominster—was used as lately as 1809.

The Story in Photo-Engraving*

Modern advertising would not have been possible without photo-engraving. Attention has been attracted, desire has been created and goods have been sold, largely through the pictorial or other artistic embellishments which have lifted particular "ads" out of the mass and attracted the favorable attention of the cursory reader. Pictures are the universal language, not only to those of divers tongues, but to those of every stage of mental development.

Photo-engravings are a comparatively modern product. They superseded wood engravings, which for years has been the recognized medium for illustrations to print on a type printing press. Photo-engravings, broadly speaking, are divided into two classes—line engravings and halftones. The distinction between them lying in the fact that one, as its name implies, is a reproduction of a drawing made in lines or stipples, while the other, the halftone, gets its name from the method of its manufacture.

Briefly stated, the process of making halftones is as follows: The subject to be engraved is photographed through a halftone screen, so-called. This halftone screen is a glass plate ruled with lines at right angles ranging, for different purposes, from 60 to 200 lines to the inch. This screen is placed between the lens and the sensitized plate which is to be the negative. The necessity for this screen is due to the fact that a photograph is made up of "tones." That is to say, that the color changes imperceptibly in subtle gradations of light and shade. If this copy were photographed on a piece of copper it would present no chance for the etching fluid to act.

HALFTONE ENGRAVING

The idea is to break up the surface into various sized dots, as the various gradations of color on the original cannot be transferred by any other method to a sheet of copper and etched.

The various tones must be changed either to lines or dots, so as to make a printing surface for the ink roller of the press to operate. This is necessary to get the desired printing surface.

The dots are of various sizes, ranging from a minute stipple to a solid black, and they present to the eye the same effect as the unbroken tones of a photograph. The negative when finished shows the drawing exactly like the original. The whites are opaque, the solid blacks are clear glass, the intermediate tones showing the same values in stipples of various sizes. The film of the negative is next removed from the

*Illustrations by courtesy of Gatchel & Manning.

glass, turned and placed on a heavier plate glass with a number of others and printed on a sheet of metal which has been coated with a sensitized solution.

This plate of heavy glass containing the several negatives is placed with the sensitized metal in a printing frame. The light passes through the clear part of the negative, the solid parts prevent the passage of light; thus we have the light acting chemically on the sensitized surface.

After the print is removed from the printing frame, it is developed, the parts acted on by the light adhering to the metal. The opaque parts, through which no light has penetrated, leave the solution soft on the surface of the metal. This is removed by placing in water and wiping gently with absorbent cotton. The print is then dried and heated over a stove which bakes the sensitized solution to the metal. It can readily be seen that this sheet of metal is now in such shape that the etching fluid will etch away the uncovered portions of the metal and allow the protected parts, which represent the color of the original, to remain in relief.

This plate is etched—a flat proof, so called, is pulled on a hand press—and it is then taken up by the re-etcher. The re-etcher is the artist of the etching room. He takes the plate and by covering up certain parts and etching again gives

LINE ENGRAVING

additional play of color. Smaller developments of lights are worked out by careful manipulation of the etching fluid with small sable brushes. The differences in cost in the production of halftones is due largely to the length of time devoted to this

COMBINATION ENGRAVING

work. The engraver or finisher then takes charge of it, preparing the engraving for the routing department, where the superfluous metal is removed. The plate is then returned to the engraving department, which completes the work, burnishing darks, engraving highlights, removing slight imperfections and otherwise perfecting the plate.

It is then proofed and blocked. Nine separate men handle each engraving in the halftone department.

The making of line engravings follows the same general course, with the exception that no halftone screen is needed, the copy to be reproduced being already made up of lines or dots or a combination of them. In the handling of line work, eight skilled men successively handle each plate.

In addition to plates made by either line or halftone process, combinations of the two are frequently used, as, for instance, where decorative pen work is used to embellish a halftone picture, or where lettering is to be used in connection with a halftone and form part of the same plate. These plates made up of both line work and halftones are known as combination plates or double-prints, depending upon the way they are produced. In both cases, negatives are made of both the halftone and line copies.

Combination plates are made by combining the halftone and line negatives together and making one complete print on the metal.

Double-print is used where the surface is covered with halftone screen, either the line or halftone negative is printed on the metal, the other is superimposed on it.

The Ben Day process, so called, is the use of mechanical appliances for adding lines or stipples to either drawings or plates. Its use is very extensive in the making of tint blocks or color work, used either in connection with line or halftone key plates.

The highlight process, possible only with certain kinds of copy, is a modification of the halftone in which, by manipulation of the time of exposure and the screen when making the negative, the halftone stipples are lost and in this way halftones are produced in which there are pure whites, without the necessity of the finisher cutting them by hand.

BEN DAY ENGRAVING

Color Engravings.

Let us assume that we have a painting or a drawing in colors from which it is desired to produce a set of printing plates to produce that drawing in facsimile. Under the old method of procedure, lithography, it would have been necessary to make a stone for each of the colors, which would mean, roughly speaking, from twelve to eighteen stones to reproduce it—it will be understood that this means the finished print must go through the press once for each color. This would mean twelve to eighteen impressions to get the desired result. The expense of doing this limited the use of lithography.

HIGHLIGHT ENGRAVING

The modern or photo-engraving method of reproducing a colored copy is based on the theory of the three primary colors, yellow, red and blue. It is assumed that every color is formed by some combination of these three colors—the problem confronting us, therefore, is to separate these three colors and if possible make a printing plate of each color with the color values varying from light to dark in such proportions that when the three are printed in proper register over each other, with transparent printing inks, the varying color values will blend so as to reproduce the original.

We go about this by making three negatives, one of each color, the red negative is made by placing at the lens a so-called color filter, which separates the red rays, whether they appear as pure red or any part of an orange or a purple, or any of the many tones of which red may form a part. In like manner the yellow and blue plates are made by the use of appropriate color filters, each of which acts for its required color as that used for the red.

So far this would appear to be a purely mechanical operation, requiring simply the usual care in negative making, but unfortunately this theory does not work out so absolutely in practice, and for this reason, while any color may be produced in light rays by the union of the three primary colors of the proper quality, when the operation is attempted with material pigments or ink, produce results varying widely from the ideal. No pigment is absolutely pure, the adulterants or foreign substances will cause sufficient deviation from the abstract standard to cause a very noticeable difference in the finished result when united with another color which is of itself impure. The result is that the three negatives, instead of each being a true unit, ready for combination with the others, is really only a basis for further work. It might justly be compared with a sketch which is all right as far as it goes, but which requries toning down and elaboration before becoming a finished work of art.

The three negatives are each printed on sensitized copper, as was noted with the black and white halftone; they are then turned over to the re-etcher, who may be rightly termed an "artist-etcher." He has before him three prints on copper; on each of them are tones which to his trained eye are too light or too dark to produce the desired result when printed with the other two, which also vary more or less. It is his duty to strengthen and reduce and otherwise manipulate the plates so that they will, when finally printed, have the desired result.

For every particular use to which an engraving can be put, there is some particular style or grade of engraving better adapted than any other. The successful use of halftones, whether in black and white or in colors, depends on the care with which the particular screen is selected to suit the paper stock and printing conditions. To illustrate this, the 150-line screen has 22,500 stipples to the square inch. It is apparent, therefore, that only certain kinds of paper can be used for such halftones, whereas a 60-line screen contains only 3,600 stipples to the square inch, which permits its use on a newspaper stock.

The production of engravings is just as highly technical and scientific and involves as much experience and judgment in their application as any of the learned professions.

Where are Milk-Pails Filled from Trees?

In South America there are some trees known as "cow-trees" which, when wounded, yield a rich, milky, nutritious juice in such abundance as to render it an important article of food. This fluid resembles in appearance and quality the milk of the cow.

The cow-tree is a member of the bread-fruit family, and is most common in Venezuela, growing to the height of a hundred feet. The leaves are leathery, about a foot long and three or four inches broad.

In British Guiana the name is given to another large, much-branched tree, and there are also other varieties in Para and along the Rio Negro, which is a tributary of the Amazon River.

How did the Wearing of a Crown Originate?

When we speak of a crown now we mean the head-dress worn by royal personages as a badge of sovereignty, but it was formerly used to include the wreaths or garlands worn by the ancients upon special occasions.

Among the Greeks and Romans, crowns made of grass, flowers, twigs of laurel, oak, olive and so forth, and later of gold, were made use of as honors in athletic contests, as rewards for military valor, and at feasts, funerals and so forth.

It is, however, with the eastern diadem rather than with the classic corona that the crown, as a symbol of royalty, is connected; indeed, it was only introduced as such a symbol by Alexander the Great, who followed the Persian usage. Antony wore a crown in Egypt, and the Roman emperors also wore crowns of various forms, from the plain golden fillet to the radiated or rayed crown.

In modern states they were also of various forms until heralds devised a regular series to mark the grades of rank from the imperial crown to the baron's coronet.

CROWNS

1. Crown of England. 2. Russian Crown. 3. French Crown. 4. Austrian Crown. 5. Imperial Crown (Charlemagne's).

The English crown has been gradually built up from the plain circlet with four trefoil heads worn by William the Conqueror. This form was elaborated and jeweled, and finally arched in with jeweled bands surmounted by the cross and scepter. As at present existing, the crown of England is a gold circle, adorned with pearls and precious stones, having alternately four Maltese crosses and four fleur-de-lis. From the top of the crosses rise imperial arches, closing under a mound and cross. The whole covers a crimson velvet cap with an ermine border.

The crown of Charlemagne, which is preserved in the imperial treasury of Vienna, is composed of eight plates of gold, four large and four small, connected by hinges. The large plates are studded with precious stones, the front one being surmounted with a cross; the smaller ones, placed alternately with these, are ornamented with enamels representing Solomon, David, Hezekiah and Isaiah, and Christ seated between two flaming seraphim.

The Austrian crown is a sort of cleft tiara, having in the middle a semicircle of gold supporting a mound and cross; the tiara rests on a circle with pendants like those of a miter.

The royal crown of France is a circle ornamented with eight fleur-de-lis, from which rise as many quarter-circles closing under a double fleur-de-lis. The triple crown of the popes is more commonly called the tiara.

Why do Lobsters Change Colors?

Before a lobster is cooked he is green, that being the color of the rocks around which he lives on the bottom of the ocean. However, as soon as a lobster is placed in boiling water his shell changes from green to red. This is due to a certain chemical substance contained in the shell which acts in that way when boiled.

How do Fishes Swim?

The fish is entirely surrounded by water which exerts an equal pressure on all sides. When the fish moves its tail, or makes any movement at all, he moves in the water. Of course, by moving his tail from side to side he propels himself forward and by bending his tail he goes in the direction in which it is bent.

Where do Pearls Come From? *

Below the surface of the ocean, there's a strange, enchanted world. Living in the midst of its grandeur are most marvelous and delicate creatures that ceaselessly toil to strew the ocean's bed with lustrous gems—pearls.

Nature provides for the denizens of the deep that make these beautiful gems. The ocean pearl oyster or bivalve (*avicula margaritifera*) and fresh water mussel (*unio margaritifera*) have wonderful homes—their shells. Coarse, rough, rugged, often distorted on the outside, within they are lined with smooth, softly-glowing, iridescent "mother of pearl." The membrane, attaching the bivalve to its shell, extracts lime from the water, building the shell from the inside outward in successive layers, preserving the finest nacreous secretions for the smooth inside lining, thus protecting its delicate body.

In this comfortable home the mollusk is contented, but an enemy sometimes attacks it by boring through its hard shell. Leucodore, clione and other borers, parasitic or domiciliary worms work into the shell, and instinctively the protecting nacreous fluid envelops the intruder. This is the birth of the pearl. The intruder, now covered entirely with the pearl-nacre, is constantly rolled and lapped about, and successive layers of nacre are applied until in a few years a pearl of great size and value is formed and awaits the hardy, daring pearl fisher.

Pearls were the first gems discovered and used as ornaments in prehistoric ages. Found in their natural state in utmost perfection, needing no cutting nor polishing, these glowing beads of the sea were the first baubles of savages, tribes and nations. Today the pearl is the favored gem of those who are surfeited with valuable jewels. It is essentially a gem for the wealthy. The connoisseur, accustomed to the possession of jewels, finds in its soft luster a grandeur above that of all the sparkling stones.

Fancy pearls include all those of decided color, having a rare and beautiful tint. "White pearls" include pure white and white slightly tinted witn pink, blue, green or yellow. Of these colored white pearls, the delicate, lightly-tinted, pink pearl of fine color and luster known as "rose" is most beautiful. Every white pearl is classified according to its respective tint and thus its price is determined, the values ranging in the order named above, from highest for pure white, to lowest for yellowish-white.

What is Cork?

Cork is the outer bark of a species of oak which grows in Spain, Portugal and other southern parts of Europe and in the north of Africa. The tree is distinguished by the great thickness and sponginess of its bark, and by the leaves being evergreen, oblong, somewhat oval, downy underneath, and waved.

The outer bark falls off of itself if let alone, but for commercial purposes it is stripped off when judged sufficiently matured, this being when the tree has reached the age of from fifteen to thirty years. In the course of eight or nine years, or even less, the same tree will yield another supply of cork of better quality, and the removal of this outer bark is said to be beneficial, the trees thus stripped reaching the age of 150 years or more.

The bark is removed by a kind of ax, parallel cuts being carried around the tree transversely and united by others in a longitudinal direction, so as to produce oblong sheets of bark. Care must be taken not to cut into the inner bark, or the tree would be killed. The pieces of cork are flattened out by heat or by weights, and are slightly charred on the surface to close the pores.

Cork is light, impervious to water, and by pressure can be greatly reduced in bulk, returning again to its original size. These qualities render it peculiarly serviceable for the stopping of vessels of different kinds, for floats, buoys, swimming-belts or jackets, artificial limbs, etc. Corks for bottles are cut either by hand or by means of a machine. The best corks are cut across the grain.

25 * Courtesy of Mr. Charles L. Trout.

The Story in a Giant Cannon

Origin of the Cannon.

The shotgun and rifle, the familiar weapons of the sportsman and the foot-soldier, are not the ancestors of the cannon, as might be surmised. On the contrary, the cannon was the predecessor of the musket, and its successors. The rifle, however, antedated the rifled cannon, the type of modern artillery. We do not know when cannon first appeared, but it may have been soon after the discovery of gunpowder

THREE-INCH FIELD GUN UNDER TEST AT FORT RILEY, KANSAS

In the trials conducted by the Board of Ordnance and Fortification of the United States Army. This gun and carriage, complete, weighs 2,020 pounds   Charge 18.5 ounces of smokeless powder. Weight of projectile, 15 pounds. Muzzle velocity, 1,800-foot seconds.

Courtesy of the Bethlehem Steel Co.

in Europe. This explosive seems to have been known in China long before knowledge of it reached the West, but we do not know to what extent it was developed and used in that country.

The earliest cannon of which we have any knowledge were clumsy contrivances, at first wider at the mouth than at the chamber, and made of wood, and later of iron bars, hooped together with iron rings, a system of the same type as that now in use in the wire-wound cannon. They at first seem to have fired balls of stone, iron balls coming later. A doubtful statement exists to the effect that cannon were used at the siege of Belgrade in 1073, and it is said that Edward III used them against the Scotch in 1327. Other dates of their use are 1338 and 1346, in which latter year Edward III employed them against the French at Crecy. For this we have the authority of Froissart. They were known under the varied names of bombards, serpentines, etc. Twelve cannon cast by Louis VII were named after the twelve peers of France, and Charles V gave twelve others the names of the twelve apostles. Other titles came later into general use, the royal or carthorne, carrying 48 pounds; the culverin, 18 pounds; the demi-culverin, 9 pounds; the basilisk, 48; the siren,

THREE-INCH NAVAL LANDING GUN, CARRIAGE AND LIMBER

Weight of gun and mechanism, 675 pounds. Length of gun, 74.35 inches (25 calibers). Weight of projectile, 13 pounds. Travel of projectile in bore, 62.9 inches (20.97 calibers). Weight of charge, 18 ounces of smokeless powder. Muzzle velocity, 1,650-foot seconds. Muzzle energy, 246-foot tons. Weight of gun, carriage, limber, drag ropes, tools, etc., and 60 rounds of ammunition, complete, 3,420 pounds. The carriage and limber have each two removable interchangeable ammunition boxes for 12 rounds each, with a box for 12 rounds below the axle of the limber.
Courtesy of the Bethlehem Steel Co.

60, etc. In still later times cannon became known by the weight of the balls they carried, 6-pounders, 12-pounders, etc. But they are now usually called after the size of their bores, as 6-inch, 8-inch, or 12-inch cannon. The oldest example still in existence is "Mons Meg," preserved at Edinburgh Castle. This is one of the iron-bar type, hooped by iron rings. It is supposed to have been used by James II of Scotland, at the siege of Threave Castle in 1455.

Louis VI used bombards of great length and power against the Flemish in 1477, while as early as 1401 bronze cannon had been cast in several cities of West Prussia. Iron cannon were not cast until near the end of that century. Coming down to the seventeenth century, we are told of the great Bijapur cast-iron gun, the "Lord of the Plain," cast by the Mogul emperor Aurungzebe or by his foes the Mahrattas. This huge gun was 14 feet long, 28 inches bore, and fired a ball of 1,600 pounds weight. Smooth-bore cannon and mortars of cast-iron and bronze are still retained in some fortresses, though rifled cannon are the only type now made. As late as 1864 smooth-bore 100- and 150-pounder wrought-iron guns were made for the British navy and

A SIXTEEN-INCH FRENCH GUN ON A RAILWAY MOUNT

Ordnance of this character requires a special train consisting of ammunition cars and living quarters for the gun crew. The car carrying the gun is built of heavy steel trusses and equipped with hydraulic jacks which are used between the car and the ground to take the shock of the recoil. The range of the gun is about twenty miles and the shell weighs 2400 pounds.

© Committee on Public Information, From "International."

Conquering the Alps.

Immense labor and great ingenuity were required to haul the monster Italian guns up the steep mountain sides to their positions.

The Most Formidable of the French Army's Trench Artillery

80-m.m. mountain gun loaded with air-mine weighing 130 pounds. These mines can be thrown for a considerable distance and create havoc in the enemy's trenches if the aim is true.

THE BENNETT-MERCIER MACHINE GUN

This new automatic machine gun has been adopted by the United States Army, Navy and Marine Corps. It is handled by two men, one to aim and fire it, the other to feed the cartridges which are held in brass clips of 30 each. The complete gun weighs only about 35 pounds, fires 400 shots per minute, using regular 30-caliber Springfield rifle cartridges, with a maximum range of 3 miles and an effective range of about 2,000 yards. The weapon is air cooled and can be fired steadily for about 10 minutes without undue heating.

a few bronze rifled guns were made in 1870 for service in India, but all such guns are now obsolete.

The development of the rifle from the old smooth-bore musket, by cutting grooves or channels in the form of a screw in the interior surface, was found so advantageous in increase of precision of aim and length of range, that the rifling of cannon in time followed and is now universally used. Breech loading has also replaced muzzle loading, another vast advantage in the use of artillery. A form of breech-loading cannon was introduced in the sixteenth century, but the advantageous use

THREE-INCH FIELD GUN, LONG RECOIL CARRIAGE AND LIMBER

Weight of gun, carriage and limber complete, including 36 rounds of ammunition, 4,200 pounds; ground clearance, 22.5 inches. Seats are provided on axle of carriage for two gunners in transportation, one of whom operates the road brake.
Courtesy of the Bethlehem Steel Co.

of this device is of late invention. An important result of these changes is the use of elongated instead of round balls, this permitting of the employment of much heavier projectiles for the same width of bore.

Modern Cannon.

Until 1888 the largest cannon in use was the 119-ton Krupp, made in 1884 for Italy; but in 1888–90 the same house produced a 135-ton gun for Cronstadt. The heaviest British gun at that time was of 111-ton weight. This threw a projectile of 1,800 pounds with a muzzle velocity of 2,216 feet per second. But there later came a reaction in favor of lighter guns and quicker firers. The heavy cannon of recent times are not cast, as of old, but are made of forged-steel by what is known as the building-up process. The different parts of these are called the tube, jacket, hoops, locking rings, trunnion rings, wire winding, etc.

Cannons are subject to great stress in firing, this being of two kinds. One is the longitudinal stress, acting in the direction of the length and tending to pull the muzzle away from the breech. The other is the circumferential or tangential stress, which tends to split the gun open in lines parallel to the axis of the bore. These stresses are results of the longitudinal and radial pressures of the gas developed by the ignition and explosion of the powder. Such destructive forces have to be

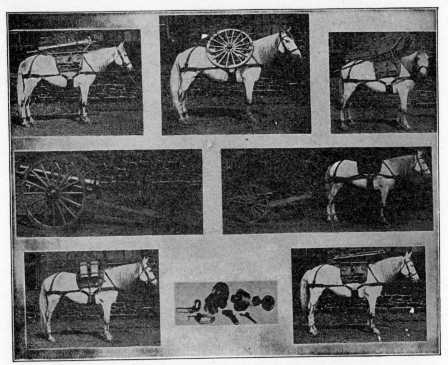

THREE-INCH MOUNTAIN GUN AND CARRIAGE

Weight of gun, 206½ pounds. Length of gun, 27.25 inches (12.4 calibers). Weight of projectile, 12 pounds. Travel of projectile in bore, 27.55 inches (9.2 calibers). Weight of charge, 12.5 ounces of smokeless powder. Muzzle velocity, 1,224-foot seconds. Muzzle energy, 123-foot tons. Weight of gun and carriage complete, 726 pounds. This gun and carriage break up into four loads of approximately 200 pounds each. The equipment carried 16 complete rounds of ammunition with it, which are divided equally among four boxes. The saddles are so made that the load will go on any saddle.
Courtesy of the Bethlehem Steel Co.

guarded against in the building of a cannon and have led to a great development over the old-time casting processes. As long as projectile velocities under 1,500 feet per second were employed cannons cast in one piece sufficed, but when greater velocities were sought, the pressure grew so extreme that no cast or forged metal tube would stand the strain.

How Cannon are Now Made

It was found that the inner surface of the tube stretched more than the outer surface, and that after the inner surface has been stretched to its limit of elasticity the outer part failed to add to its strength, so that further thickness was of no benefit.

To do away with this condition cannon were constructed on the principle of varying elasticity, the metal with the greatest elongation within its elastic limit being placed next to the bore, yet in high-powered guns this system failed to yield the result desired and it was replaced by what is known as the initial tension system.   This

RAPID-FIRE GUN

Six-inch rapid-fire gun equipped with patented two-handed elevating gear, consisting of two hand wheels on opposite ends of the same shaft, the handles being 180 degrees apart.   The pointer uses both hands in elevating and depressing the gun.   The electric firing trigger A is worked by the index finger of the right hand without releasing the handle.   There is a second firing handle B attached to the slide, for firing either electrically or percussively.
Courtesy of the Bethlehem Steel Co.

comprised two methods: the plain built-up gun and the wire-wound gun.   In the latter certain parts of the gun were wrapped with wire in the form of a ribbon.

Built-Up and Wire-Wound Guns.

A built-up gun is made of several layers of forged steel.   The parts of such a gun are known as the liner, the tube, the jacket and the hoops.   The liner is a single piece which extends the length of the bore and is intended to contain the rifling and the powder chamber.   This is inclosed by the tube, which is also in one piece, surrounding the liner throughout its length.   Outside this is the jacket, made in two pieces and shrunk on the tube.   Over the jacket lie the hoops, six or seven of these being used in a big gun.   Like the jacket, these also are shrunk on.   All these parts are made of the finest quality of open-hearth steel.

These pieces are prepared with the utmost care to prevent any defective material entering into the make-up of the gun.   After the parts are put together a thorough

FIVE-INCH NAVAL GUN AND MOUNT

The latest type of gun used in the U. S. Naval Service in the secondary batteries on a battleship.

COAST DEFENSE GUN

A modern 14-inch coast defense gun at Sandy Hook. The gun is mounted on a disappearing carriage, which lowers it out of sight behind the breastworks after firing. This is one of the most powerful guns in the world, firing a projectile which would pierce the armor of a battleship more than five miles away.

Copyright by Underwood & Underwood, N. Y. A BATTERY OF 12-INCH COAST DEFENSE MORTARS

These powerful weapons fire a projectile which weighs from 700 to 1,046 pounds, depending on the range desired, and which is capable of piercing the deck armor of any battleship. They have a range of 20,000 yards with the 700-pound projectile. The gun is 16⅔ feet long and is fired only at elevations between 45° and 65°.

GIANT GUNS—THEIR MUZZLE-ENERGY, PROJECTILES, AND PENETRATING POWERS

The British 13.5, which was known as the 12-inch-A until the "Lion" was launched, has a length of 45 calibers, and a muzzle-energy ten per cent greater than that of the 50-caliber 12-inch of 1909 and 1910. It may be noted that the caliber is the diameter of the bore of a gun. The statement that a gun has a length of 45 calibers, for example, implies that the gun is forty-five times the bore's diameter. Thus a 12-inch gun of 45 calibers is 45 feet long.

forging follows, either by use of hammer or press, the latter being now used in preference. The usual practice in forging is to continue it until the ingot is decreased to one-half its original thickness and is within two inches of the desired diameter of the finished work. It is then annealed with great care to relieve the strains set up in the metal by the forging and next goes to the machine shop to be rough bored and turned. The final boring takes place after a second annealing. The above is

ORDNANCE PROVING GROUND
View showing smoke cone occurring during the proof firing of a twelve-inch gun with brown powder.

Courtesy of the Bethlehem Steel Co.

only a rapid sketch of the total process, in which elaborate care is taken to prevent imperfection of any kind.

In a wire-wound gun an inner tube of steel is thoroughly wrapped by successive layers of ribbon wire, each layer being wound with wire at a different tension. This type of gun is preferred by foreign manufacturers, but within the United States the built-up system is in higher favor and is almost exclusively employed. The makers of the wire-wound cannon claim for it a positive soundness of material impossible to secure in a built-up gun, and that it has greater firmness of material and superior tangential strength. But with this come certain disadvantages, a notable one being a lack of rigidity in the longitudinal direction, this tending to increase the "droop" of the muzzle and give a certain "whip" to the piece when fired that reduces accuracy. This and other disadvantages have given the built-up guns general preference in this country, they being found strong enough to bear any pressure desirable in service. In addition they are much cheaper to build than the wire-wound guns.

Modern heavy guns are made of medium open-hearth carbon steel, forged as stated. The liner and tube are then placed upright in an assembling pit, the jacket and hoops shrunk on, and the finishing work done, as above said, the breech mechanism being finally fitted. Within recent years there has been a steady increase in the size and range of cannon, until an immense size and weight have been attained. For naval purposes the 14-inch gun is the largest now used in American battleships, but in the United States coast defense forts, 16-inch guns are installed. England has equipped several of her latest battleships with 15-inch guns and other nations

FOUR-INCH FIFTY CALIBER RAPID-FIRE GUN ON PEDESTAL MOUNT

Extraction of cartridge case by opening of breech mechanism. Weight of gun, 6,170 pounds. Length of gun, 205 inches (51.2 calibers). Weight of projectile, 33 pounds. Travel of projectile in bore, 165.6 inches (41.4 calibers). Weight of charge, 15 pounds of smokeless powder. Muzzle velocity, 2,900-foot seconds. Muzzle energy, 1,928-foot tons. Weight of mount with shield, 9,470 pounds. Thickness of shield, 2 inches of nickel steel. Gun equipped with telescopic and night sights and with electric and percussion pull-off firing gear.
Courtesy of the Bethlehem Steel Co.

are following in the same direction. In recent great battleships four turrets are used, each carrying three of these great guns, giving a broadside of twelve of these monster weapons of war. Of the three guns, the middle one is raised above the line of the others. A battleship thus armed is able to fire six guns ahead and six astern by raising the second and third turrets so as to fire over the others.

Military cannon are divided into three classes, based upon the length of caliber, and technically known as guns, mortars and howitzers. In guns the length is relatively great, in mortars relatively small, compared to their calibers. Howitzers form a class between guns and mortars in length. The field guns of the American army are the 3.6-inch breech-loading mortars, and the 3.6-inch heavy and 3.2-inch light guns. The siege guns in the service are the 5-inch siege guns, the 7-inch howitzer, and the 7-inch mortar. The coast defense artillery consists of the 8-, 10-, 12- and 16-inch guns and the 12-inch mortars. In the recent World War very heavy cannon were used for field service, pieces of the size usually placed in forts being

FLUID COMPRESSION PLANT

While still in a molten condition in the mold, the steel used in manufacturing guns and shafting is subjected to hydraulic pressure until the ingot has cooled, thus insuring the solidity of the metal. The upper head of the compressor weighs 125 tons, and the lower one, including the cylinder through which the hydraulic pressure is applied 135 tons.

Courtesy of the Bethlehem Steel Co.

drawn to the field by powerful tractors, set on concrete platforms and used in attacks on fortified cities. It was through the use of such ordnance that the German army so easily reduced the strongly fortified Belgian cities.

The range of these giant cannon is enormous and their destructive power great, this being added to by the fact that the explosive shell has replaced the solid round shot of old-time gunnery. A 14-inch gun of 45 caliber can discharge a 1,400-pound

AMMUNITION.*   (See page 410.)

TWO-HANDED ELEVATING GEAR.*   (See page 410.)

* Illustrations by courtesy of the Bethlehem Steel Co.

RANGE FINDER AND PREDICTOR; HOME AND DISTANT STATION INSTRUMENTS.*
(See page 410.)

ARMOR PIERCING PROJECTILES, CAPPED AND UNCAPPED.*   (See page 410.)

* Illustrations by courtesy of the Bethlehem Steel Co.

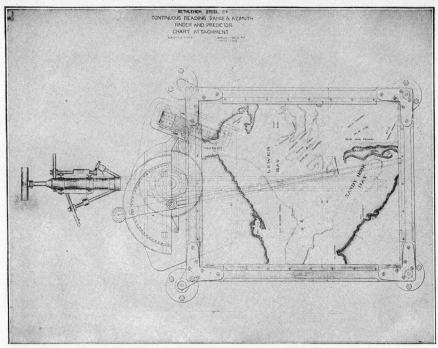

RANGE FINDER AND CHART ATTACHMENT*   (See page 410.)

EIGHTEEN-INCH, THIRTY-CALIBER TORPEDO GUN.*   (See page 410.)

* Illustrations by courtesy of the Bethlehem Steel Co.

FIRING GEAR FOR GUNS.*   (See page 410.)

FUSES.*   (See page 410.)

* Illustrations by courtesy of the Bethlehem Steel Co.

projectile at a muzzle velocity of 2,600 feet per second. If we compare this with a
locomotive going at the speed of sixty miles an hour, we have in the latter a speed of
eighty-eight feet per second to compare with the 2,600 feet per second of the
cannon ball. From this we can well conjecture the vast speed with which the
latter moves, its enormous range and vast powers of destruction.

As facts are better than theories, it will be of interest to adduce a recent example
of gunnery of a most illuminating type, both as regards distance and remarkable
accuracy of aim. In September, 1916, the American battleship "Pennsylvania,"

THREE-INCH HORSE ARTILLERY GUN, LONG RECOIL CARRIAGE AND LIMBER
Length of gun, 85 inches (28 calibers). Weight of projectile, 12 pounds. Travel
of projectile in bore, 74.65 inches (24.88 calibers). Weight of charge, 17.1 ounces of
smokeless powder. Muzzle velocity, 1,750-foot seconds. Muzzle energy, 255-foot tons.
Weight of gun, carriage and limber, containing 36 rounds of ammunition, 3,355 pounds.
Ground clearance, 18 inches.
Courtesy of the Bethlehem Steel Co.

armed with a main battery of twelve 14-inch guns, fired these simultaneously at a
target in the Chesapeake 22,000 yards, or more than twelve miles, away. The target
was the sunken hulk of the "San Marcos," formerly the battleship "Texas," which
for several years had been used for similar purposes. As the target was invisible
to the gunners it was hardly to be expected that any of the shots should fall near
the target. But the extraordinary result appeared that five of these twelve shots
struck the hulk. As each of these projectiles weighed 1,400 pounds any battleship
receiving such a broadside would probably have gone promptly to the bottom. The
result, which has never before been equaled in accuracy, sufficiently attests the
remarkable proficiency in range-finding that modern engineers have developed.

As for the penetrating powers of such huge shot we may take the 15-inch gun, the type of the largest guns in our fortifications and which is claimed to be able to pierce sixteen inches of armor at a range of 18,000 yards and ten inches at a range of 20,000 yards. A notable example of this took place on September 15, 1916, at the proving grounds at Indian Head, on the Potomac River, when a 16-inch, 2,100-pound, solid steel shell, said to be the first ever fired from a naval gun of that caliber, with a small charge of explosive, went through a plate of armor, penetrated a thick sand backing, and continued its course, striking the house of an employee of the

PATENTED CHAIN RAMMER

As applied to loading twelve-inch turret guns. The space occupied by this rammer in the rear of the gun is less than one foot, with a possible ramming stroke of fifteen feet. The rammer being attached to the gun's cradle or slide, moves with the gun in elevation and depression. The ammunition car also moves with the gun. Loading can be performed while the gun is kept in motion following a moving target. This rammer is stiff in all directions when extended.

Courtesy of the Bethlehem Steel Co.

proving grounds and plunging through the kitchen rending all before it. This was a naval gun, the largest yet made for naval purposes.

In the make-up of modern guns the breech-loading mechanism is of essential importance, it being necessary that the breech should be capable of rapid opening for the insertion of the charge into the loading chamber, as rapidly closed and firmly secured to prevent its being forced open by the reaction of the discharge. It also must fit with such tightness as to prevent any escape of the gas in that direction, and force it to exert all its impelling power upon the ball. Various methods are used for this purpose, with the result that loading and firing can be very quickly and effectively performed. In the case of guns in fortifications, the disappearing carriage is a highly important invention of recent date. By its aid the gun is quickly lifted to fire over the walls of the fort and is driven backward by the force of its discharge, sinking to a place of safety behind the walls. This saves the gun and its crew from injury by return fire.

We may say in conclusion that the great World War was notable for the use of artillery to an extent far surpassing its employment in any previous war. This great conflict, indeed, was very largely a contest of gun fire, in which opposing fields of the battling armies were so swept with shells and other explosives as to render life impossible on the open land, trench digging being one of the main employments of the embattled hosts. Never before had the supreme value of gunnery in warfare been so fully demonstrated.

GEAR WHEEL AND DRUM FOR COAL HOISTING PLANE

Diameter of wheel, 20 feet 9½ inches; face, 43½ inches; diameter of hub, 26 inches; number of teeth, 128; pitch, 6⅛ inches; pitch diameter, 249.554 inches; shipping weight, 108,873 pounds.

Courtesy of the Bethlehem Steel Co.

Six-Inch Ribbed Cavity Armor-Piercing Shell

Projectile was loaded with two pounds of black charcoal powder and fused with magazine fuse. Fired at six-inch Krupp hard-faced armor plate. Shell burst about eight feet to rear of plate after penetrating the same. Weight of largest fragment recovered $10\frac{1}{4}$ pounds. Average weight of fragments, $2\frac{5}{16}$ ounces. Total number of pieces recovered, 650.

Courtesy of the Bethlehem Steel Co

AMMUNITION. (See page 402.)

Made-up ammunition, with brass cartridge cases, and cast-iron and forged steel shells and armor-piercing projectiles. The rounds shown are as follows: Rounds with forged steel shell for one-pounder gun, for three-pounder gun and for six-pounder gun respectively; round with cast-iron shell for three-inch field gun; round with capped armor-piercing shell for three-inch fifty-caliber rapid-fire gun; round with forged steel shell for four-inch forty-caliber rapid-fire gun; round with capped armor-piercing projectiles for the four-inch and twelve-centimeter fifty-caliber rapid-fire guns respectively, and round with forged shell for six-inch gun.

TWO-HANDED ELEVATING GEAR. (See page 402.)

Method of obtaining a variable movement of a miniature target, corresponding to rolls of a vessel of from 1 to 10 degrees. A series of 25,000 shots were fired thus, by eight gun pointers, at targets corresponding to the size of a battleship as seen at ranges of 1,500, 3,000, 6,000 and 9,000 yards. Using a sub-caliber rifle rigidly attached to the muzzle of the gun and fired electrically by the firing gear of the big gun. The record shows that under circumstances of average difficulty at sea (say 5 degrees roll and range of 3,500 yards), the gain in accuracy (increase in hits with a given expenditure of ammunition) is about 25 per cent, and the gain in speed of hitting (number of hits in a given time) is 50 per cent, with the two-hand gear as compared with the usual one-hand gear.

RANGE FINDER AND PREDICTOR; HOME AND DISTANT STATION INSTRUMENTS. (See page 403.)

Continuous readings, by means of automatic indicators, of either the actual or the predicted ranges and azimuths of moving target at every instant and for any distance from 1,000 to 15,000 yards and through an azimuth of 160 degrees, are clearly presented at all times. The ranges are read in scales of 10-yard steps, and the azimuths for each .01 degree are traversed. The corrected ranges for the various guns served by the instruments, either actual or automatically predicted for any interval of time, are constantly communicated to the various guns whose fire is being directed by the observation instrument.

ARMOR-PIERCING PROJECTILES, CAPPED AND UNCAPPED. (See page 403.)

The projectiles shown are a three-inch capped, a four-inch capped, a five-inch and a six-inch uncapped, eight-inch uncapped and capped, ten-inch uncapped and capped and twelve-inch capped.

RANGE FINDER WITH CHART ATTACHMENT. (See page 404.)

The chart is drawn on the lower and ground side of a ground glass plate. A pencil point is secured to moving cross-head and marks position of target on ground glass, tracing movement of same thereon. The pillar mounting allows of ready removal of chart attachment when it is not desired to use the same.

EIGHTEEN-INCH, THIRTY-CALIBER TORPEDO GUN. (See page 404.)

Weight, 134,000 pounds. Length of gun, 528 inches. Weight of projectile, 2,000 pounds. Travel of projectile in bore, 432.4 inches (24.02 calibers). Weight of charge, 310 pounds of smokeless powder. Muzzle velocity, 2,000-foot seconds. Muzzle energy, 55,500-foot tons. Greatest diameter of gun, 45 inches. Its breech mechanism was opened and closed by one man in nine seconds. It was also opened without great effort by a boy twelve years of age.

FIRING GEAR FOR GUNS. (See page 405.)

External firing gear for guns using loose ammunition. The primer is inserted in the firing gear when the breech mechanism is open, but is held at an angle to the lighting vent until the final locking motion of the breech block, making it impossible to light the gun's charge before the breech mechanism is safely closed, even if the primer should be prematurely exploded. The primer case is automatically ejected by the opening of the breech mechanism.

FUSES. (See page 405.)

The fuses shown from left to right are: minor caliber percussion fuse, minor caliber magazine percussion fuse, major caliber percussion fuse, major caliber magazine percussion fuse, triple, double and single train time fuses. The time fuses all contain a percussion element to insure their exploding on impact if not previously exploded. No special tool is required for setting these fuses. They are made up to 27 seconds burning time for guns of 2,600-foot seconds muzzle velocity, and up to 36 seconds for mortars and guns of 1,400-foot seconds muzzle velocity.

What is a Deep-Sea Diver's Dress Like?

There are now two general types of deep-sea diving equipment: an India rubber dress, covering the entire body, except the head, which is covered by a helmet, and another apparatus which is constructed entirely of metal.

The India rubber dress has a neck-piece or breast-plate, fitted with a segmental screw bayonet joint, to which the head-piece or helmet, the neck of which has a corresponding screw, can be attached or removed. The helmet has usually three eyeholes, covered with strong glass, and protected by guards. Air is supplied by means of a flexible tube which enters the helmet and communicates with an air pump above. To allow of the escape of the used air there is sometimes another flexible tube, which is led from the back part of the helmet to the surface of the water. But in the more improved forms of the dress, the breathed air escapes by a valve so constructed as to prevent water from getting in, though it lets the air out. Leaden weights are attached to the diver, and his shoes are weighted, that he may be able to descend a ladder, walk about below, etc.

Communication can be carried on with those above by means of a cord running between the diver and the attendants; or he may converse with them through a speaking tube or a telephonic apparatus. One form of diving-dress makes the diver independent of any connection with persons above the water. It is elastic and hermetically closed. A reservoir containing highly compressed air is fixed on the diver's back, which supplies him with air by a self-regulating apparatus at a pressure corresponding to his depth. When he wishes to ascend he simply inflates his dress from the reservoir.

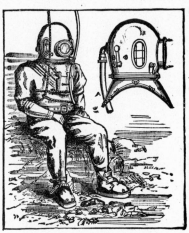

DIVING-DRESS AND DIVING-HELMET,
BY SIEBE, GORMAN & CO.

A. Pipe by which air is supplied.
B. Valve by which it escapes.

Another form, known as the Fleuss dress, makes the diver also independent of exterior aid. The helmet contains a supply of compressed oxygen, and the exhaled breath is passed through a filter in the breast-piece which deprives it of its carbonic acid, while the nitrogen goes back into the helmet to be mixed with the oxygen, the supply of which is under the diver's own control, and to be successively breathed. A diver has remained an hour and a half under thirty-five feet of water in this suit.

A considerable enlargement of the field of deep-sea diving is the result of the invention recently of a form of diving apparatus which is unaffected by the limitations hitherto imposed on work of this kind. A possible depth of 204 feet is recognized by the British Admiralty regulations under the conditions that obtain with the common form of diving suit. Yet this depth has probably never been reached. One hundred feet is the rare descent of the average diver and 150 feet his maximum. With the new apparatus a submergence of 212 feet has been obtained, and this might have been indefinitely extended had there been a greater depth of water at the place where the experiment took place—Long Island Sound during the latter part of 1914.

The new diving apparatus is constructed entirely of metal, is rigid and is made of such materials that it is strong enough to resist the great pressures found in the depths to which it can penetrate. The material used is an alloy of aluminum, and the diving case weighs complete about 500 pounds. When in the air, the man inclosed in it is incapable of imparting movement to it, but in the water, which counterbalances the dead weight of the apparatus, he can easily move the articulated sections as well as give himself motion through the water. The articulated portion consists of about fifty turning joints, fitted with leather packing, which swells and has an increased effectiveness under increased water pressure. To prevent the pressure-force of the deep sea from jamming the joints, roller bearings are so arranged about them that freedom of action is constantly maintained.

The diving case is not absolutely water-tight, nor is it desired that it should be so, as the slight leakage acts as a lubricant to the joints, and aids in their movements. The danger arising from the intake of water thus into the diving case is averted by the action of an ingenious pump appliance, which serves two purposes: that of pumping the water out and pumping the air in. The diver in this invention carries his pump with him and has air supplied to him at atmospheric pressure.

At the back of the diving case is a recess and in it is installed a compact but powerful pump, which sucks from the feet of the suit all leakage and forces it at once outward. This pump is worked by compressed air, and the air, after performing its mechanical part of driving the pump, is exhausted into the suit for the diver to breathe and then passes to the surface through the free space in an armored rubber tube, within which are led down to the diver the compressed air pipe for driving the pump, and the electrical connections for telephone and lamp. Thus the diving case receives a thorough ventilation, and it has been found that should the pump fail to work for a number of minutes there would still be enough air remaining in the diving case and the tube space to supply the diver's needs for at least the length of time he is being hauled to the surface.

During the experiment in Long Island Sound the pump was stopped for ten minutes, while the diver was at a depth of 100 feet. He suffered no inconvenience, and when the compressor again was started he was lowered to a depth of 212 feet. If such a condition as failure of the pump to work for ten minutes had arisen during a descent in the old elastic diving dress the result must necessarily have been fatal. Nor is a delay necessary in hoisting the diver clad in the new diving apparatus to the surface. According to the British Admiralty regulations, should a diver go down to a depth of 204 feet, the time of his ascent must be not less than one hour and a half. In the Long Island Sound experiments the diver was hoisted to the surface in eighty-seven seconds. He was totally unaffected by the abrupt change in pressure, although the deepest he had ever been was ninety feet, and on that occasion he had suffered from bleeding at the nose and ears.

Why do We Smile when We are Pleased?

We smile to express our pleasure. When you meet a friend on the street you smile as you greet him. This is an indication of your pleasure at seeing him. This is often caused by an unconscious nervous action produced by the impression the occurrence creates on the brain. You do not have to think about smiling, but the muscles of your face contract and give you that pleased look without any effort on your part.

Why do Some of Us have Freckles?

Some people have freckles, when others do not, because all skins are not alike, just the same as eyes are not all of one color. People with certain kinds of skin freckle more quickly when the skin is exposed to the sun. The action of the sun on their skin causes small parts of the second layer of skin to give out a yellow or yellowish brown substance. Freckles are most common in persons of fair complexion and hair. In some cases freckles are permanent, but in most cases they disappear with the coming of cold weather.

MINING ORE, ISLAND OF CUBA.* (See page 415.)

LOADING ORE, ISLAND OF CUBA.* (See page 415.)

* Illustrations by courtesy of the Bethlehem Steel Co.

PIG IRON CASTING MACHINE.* (See Page 415.)

OPEN-HEARTH FURNACE STOCK YARD.* (See Page 415.)

*Illustrations by courtesy of the Bethlehem Steel Co.

Mining Ore, Island of Cuba. (See page 413.)

The immense veins of magnetic ore lie close to the surface and are mined or quarried by working along a series of benches or ledges.

Loading Ore, Island of Cuba. (See page 413.)

The ore is loaded into small buggies at the mines and run down an inclined plane, where it is dumped into railroad cars for transportation to the shipping wharves, seventeen miles distant.

Pig Iron Casting Machine. (See page 414.)

No. 1 casting machine has a capacity of 1,000 tons per day. There are 180 molds, each pig weighing about 125 pounds.
No. 2 machine has a capacity of 1,800 tons per day. It has 278 molds, each for 125-pound pig. Product, low phosphorus, Bessemer and basic, or high phosphorus machine-cast pig iron.

Open-Hearth Furnace Stock Yard. (See page 414.)

The raw materials for the open-hearth furnaces are received on elevated railroad tracks graded and piled preparatory to sending to the furnaces. Yard No. 1 is 950 feet long and 87 feet wide, and is served by three electric traveling cranes of twenty tons and sixty tons capacity. Yard No. 2 is 790 feet long and 84 feet wide, and is served by two ten-ton electric traveling cranes.

Open-Hearth Furnaces. (See page 416.)

No. 1 open-hearth plant consists of twelve furnaces, two ten-ton, two twenty-ton, five forty-ton and two fifty-ton basic furnaces and one forty-ton acid furnace with gas producers. Length of floor, 623 feet.
No. 2 plant consists of ten fifty-ton furnaces with gas producers. Length of floor, 890 feet.

Charging Floor of Open-Hearth Furnaces. (See page 416.)

The stock is delivered to the charging floor in iron boxes loaded on narrow-gauge buggies, and is charged into the furnaces by electric charging machines. Length of floor of No. 1 open-hearth plant, 477 feet; width, 28 feet. Length of floor of No. 2 open-hearth plant, 890 feet; width, 50 feet.

Blast Furnace Storage Plant. (See page 417.)

The coal, coke, ore, etc., is delivered direct by the railroad cars under a traveling cantilever crane running on tracks laid the length of a wharf and is dumped from the cars through chutes into buckets and piled until needed at the furnaces. The plant is capable of storing over 1,000,000 tons of material.

Blast Furnaces. (See page 417.)

Showing stock house, blowing-engine house, etc. Plant consists of four furnaces 70 feet high, 18-foot boshet and 12-foot hearth. One furnace 90 feet high, 22-foot boshet and 11 feet 6 inches hearth. Blowing engines are of horizontal compound and horizontal vertical compound types, capable of blowing a pressure of 25 pounds of air. Four furnaces provided with fire-brick regenerator stoves 100 feet high and 18 feet in diameter. Large furnace has six stoves 100 feet high by 22 feet in diameter. Boilers fired with waste got from furnace.

OPEN-HEARTH FURNACES.*   (See page 415.)

CHARGING FLOOR OF OPEN-HEARTH FURNACES.*   (See page 415.)

* Illustrations by courtesy of the Bethlehem Steel Co.

BLAST FURNACE STORAGE PLANT* (See Page 415.)

BLAST FURNACES.* (See Page 415.)

*Illustrations by courtesy of the Bethlehem Steel Co.

27

15,000-Ton Hydraulic Forging Press

In all respects this press is the largest and most powerful forging press in the world. Water is supplied to the two plungers under a pressure of 7,000 pounds per square inch, giving it a maximum capacity of 15,000 tons. The columns supporting the cross-head are 14 feet 6 inches apart, and the working height under cross-head is 17 feet 1¼ inches.

Courtesy of the Bethlehem Steel Co.

Drop Forge Die Shop.* (See Page 421.)

View of a Section of Projectile Forge Shop.* (See Page 421.)

*Illustrations by courtesy of the Bethlehem Steel Co.

Forging Hollow Heavy Shaft.*   (See page 421.)

Oil-Tempering Heavy Shaft*.   (See page 421.)

* Illustrations by courtesy of the Bethlehem Steel Co.

DROP FORGE DIE SHOP. (See page 419.)

This shop has a floor space of 20,400 square feet. With full equipment of most modern die sinking tools.

VIEW OF A SECTION OF PROJECTILE FORGE SHOP. (See page 419.)

This shop has a floor space of 22,000 square feet and is thoroughly equipped with the necessary hammers, presses, furnaces, etc., for the forging, punching, closing in, treating and tempering of all sizes of armor-piercing and explosive projectiles and shells.

FORGING HOLLOW HEAVY SHAFT. (See page 420.)

No. 22. The block has a hole bored through its center, and in this the mandrel is inserted, the tube being forged around it. The hydraulic pressure for this 5,000-ton press is furnished by Whitworth pumping engines. This department contains also a 2,500-ton press of similar design.

OIL-TEMPERING HEAVY SHAFT. (See page 420.)

Showing a shaft weighing about 33,000 pounds being taken from the vertical heating furnace and suspended over the oil-tank preparatory to being lowered for tempering. The heating furnace and oil tank are served by a sixty-ton traveling crane and forty-ton jib crane. The shrinking pit for assembling is situated between the heating furnace and oil tank.

ARMOR PLATE MACHINE SHOP. (See page 423.)

The varied and complex machining required on armor plate demands tools of enormous size and strength as well as varied capacity. The equipment of this shop consists of large saws, planers, etc., together with numerous portable drill presses, grinders, etc. In this shop the different groups of armor are assembled in the positions they will occupy on the vessel and are finally inspected before shipment.

FORGING ARMOR. (See page 423.)

After heating, the ingot is placed under a 14,000-ton hydraulic forging press and forged to the required dimensions. The press is served by two 200-ton cranes with hydraulic lift and pneumatic travel. Weight of the porter-bar and chuck which hold the plate for forging is 125,000 pounds, exclusive of counter-weights used.

SPECIAL CAR BUILT FOR THE SHIPPING OF LARGE AND HEAVY MATERIAL. (See page 424.)

Length of car over couplers, 103 feet 10½ inches; capacity, 300,000 pounds. Weight of car, 196,420 pounds. Shown here loaded with casting of large 5,000-ton flanging press. Weight of casting, 252,000 pounds.

THE LARGEST STEEL CASTING IN THE WORLD. (See page 424.)

Combining the product of five 40-ton open-hearth furnaces. Steel casting forming part of a 12,000-ton armor-plate hydraulic forging press. Weight of casting, 325,000 pounds (145 gross tons).

BENDING ARMOR PLATE

After being rough-forged to size and re-heated, the plate is sent to the bending press to be straightened or bent to shape. The one shown is a nickel steel side armor plate, 14 inches thick. The press exerts a hydraulic thrust of 7,000 tons, with two independently operated plungers, and is served by direct-fired furnaces with movable car bottoms and two seventy-five ton hydraulic cranes.

Courtesy of the Bethlehem Steel Co.

ARMOR PLATE MACHINE SHOP.*   (See page 421.)

FORGING ARMOR.*   (See page 421.)

*Illustrations by courtesy of the Bethlehem Steel Co.

SPECIAL CAR BUILT FOR THE SHIPPING OF LARGE AND HEAVY MATERIAL.
(See page 421.)

THE LARGEST STEEL CASTING IN THE WORLD.* (See page 421.)

*Illustrations by courtesy of the Bethlehem Steel Co.

BATTLESHIP TURRET.* (See page 427.)

NICKEL STEEL FIELD RING FORGED WITHOUT WELD FOR A 5,000-HORSE-POWER
DYNAMO.* (See page 427.)

* Illustrations by courtesy of the Bethlehem Steel Co.

TURRET FOR TWO TWELVE-INCH GUNS FOR UNITED STATES BATTLESHIP "ALABAMA".*
(See Page 427.)

CONNING TOWER AND ENTRANCE SHIELD FOR UNITED STATES BATTLESHIP
"MASSACHUSETTS."*   (See Page 427.)

*Illustrations by courtesy of the Bethlehem Steel Co.

BATTLESHIP TURRET. (See page 425.)

Twelve-inch turret carrying two forty-five caliber twelve-inch guns for the U. S. Navy. These guns can be loaded at any angle of elevation or azimuth or while in motion. The turret is equipped with a broken or double hoist. The lower hoist supplying ammunition from the magazine to an upper handling room immediately below, and revolving with, the turret pan. This makes the upper or gun hoist shorter and increases the speed of ammunition service, besides interposing two fireproof bulkheads between the guns and the magazine handling room.

NICKEL STEEL FIELD RING FORGED WITHOUT WELD FOR A 5,000-HORSE-POWER DYNAMO. (See page 425.)

Forged dimensions: outside diameter, 141 inches; inside diameter, 131 inches; width, 51 inches. Rough machined dimensions: outside diameter, 139⅜ inches; inside diameter, 130 inches; width, 50¾ inches; weight, 28,840 pounds. Average physical properties shown in United States Standard test bar taken from full-sized prolongation of end of forging: Elastic limit, 53,560 pounds per square inch. Elongation, 27.05 per cent.

TURRET FOR TWO TWELVE-INCH GUNS FOR UNITED STATES BATTLESHIP "ALABAMA." (See page 426.)

Balanced type. Thickness of inclined plate, 14 inches; of side plates, 10 inches. Height of side plates, 7 feet. Largest diameter of turret, 393 inches. Weight of turret, 192.41 tons.

CONNING TOWER AND ENTRANCE SHIELD FOR UNITED STATES BATTLESHIP "MASSACHUSETTS." (See page 426.)

Conning tower, one piece hollow forging, nickel steel, oil tempered. Thickness of walls, 10 inches. Inside diameter, 83 inches. Height, 82½ inches. Top plate, nickel steel, oil-tempered, 1½ inches thick. Shield, face-hardened nickel steel, 10 inches thick, 66 inches high.

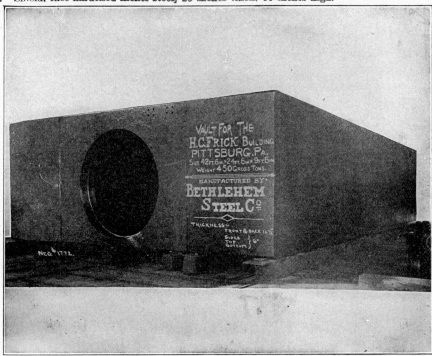

SAFE DEPOSIT ARMOR PLATE VAULT

Size, 42 feet 6 inches by 24 feet 6 inches by 9 feet 6 inches high; weight 450 gross tons.
Courtesy of the Bethlehem Steel Co.

FRONT DOOR, WITH TIME LOCK, FOR ARMOR PLATE
SAFE DEPOSIT VAULT

Thickness of front door plate, 12½ inches; weight of door plate,
12,000 pounds.

Courtesy of the Bethlehem Steel Co.

Reproduced by permission of the Philadelphia Museums.   CASTING PIG IRON

Molten iron from the blast furnace in the rear is allowed to flow out on this molding floor in which the shape of the "pig" is molded in the sand. After cooling, the pigs are broken apart and stored.

Courtesy of Indiana Steel Co.

OPEN-HEARTH FURNACES

Iron is converted into steel by the basic or open-hearth method in the furnaces shown here. The 100-ton ladles are in position at the tapping side of the furnaces to receive the molten steel.

Reproduced by permission of the Philadelphia Museums. POURING STEEL INTO MOLDS

The great ladle in the upper portion of this picture is filled with steel at the furnace. A traveling crane then takes it to the train of flat cars on which the molds stand and the steel is poured. After cooling, the molds are removed and the steel in the form of a "billet" is taken to the next process in manufacture.

— GIRDLING THE EARTH WITH STEEL

A steel beam, red-hot, drawn out 90 feet long in a huge steel mill in Pittsburgh. Steel rolled here may find its place as part of a skyscraper in the Babel of New York, be builded into the framework of a vessel in the shipyards of San Francisco, or help to construct a railroad into the heart of China.

Copyright by Underwood & Underwood, N. Y.

ARMOR PLATE FORGING PRESS

The Bethlehem Steel Company installed this great hydraulic press to replace a 135-ton steam hammer, which was abandoned because the shock of its blow disturbed the alignment of the big machines in nearby shops. This press is the largest of its kind in the world, having a capacity of 15,000 tons, induced by pressure as much as 7,000 pounds per square inch in its two hydraulic cylinders of over 50½ inches diameter.

28

MAKING ARMOR PLATE

View of the armor plate machine shop at the Bethlehem Steel Company. The varied and complex machining required on armor plate demands tools of enormous size and strength as well as varied purpose. In this shop the different groups of armor are assembled in the position they will occupy on the vessel for which they are intended, and inspected before shipment.

Courtesy of Bethlehem Steel Co.   FORGING

One-piece, 90-degree, double-throw crank shaft for 5,400 H. P. gas engine.   Diameter of shaft, 37 inches, with 10-inch hole.   Length over all, 25 feet 5 inches.   Crank webs, 16⅜ inches thick, 6 feet 1½ inches long, 4 feet 1 inch wide.   Forged weight of shaft, 133,400 pounds.   Finished weight, 83,855 pounds.

We have always said "a white elephant" when we have meant something we didn't know what to do with, since a King of Siam first sent a white elephant to a courtier whose fortune he wished to destroy.

What do We Mean by "Deviation of the Compass"?

When people speak of "deviation of the compass" they mean the difference of a ship's compass from the magnetic meridian, caused by the near presence of iron. In iron ships the amount of deviation depends upon the direction, with regard to the magnetic meridian, in which the ship lay when being built.   It is least when the ship has been built with her head south.   Armor-plated ships should be plated with their head in a different direction from that in which they lay when built.

The mode now generally employed to correct deviation is by introducing on board ship masses of iron and magnets to neutralize the action of the ship's magnetism so far as possible.

Compasses are sometimes carried on masts in iron vessels as a means of removing them from the disturbing influence of the iron of the hull.   In this position they serve as standards of comparison for the binnacle compass.

Wooden ships are also affected, though in a far less degree, by the direction in which they lie when building.

The Story in the Making of a Pair of Shoes*

The covering and protection of the feet has been a necessity in all but the warm climates for very many centuries, various articles being used for this purpose. Leather is now very generally employed, though wood is often used in Holland and France and paper in China and Japan. The moccasin of the American Indian was made of untanned deer skin. The first historical mention of a shoe is in the Old Testament, where Abraham refused to take as much as a "shoe-latchet" from the King of Sodom. This probably meant a sandal, leather strapped to the foot, though the Jews wore shoes as well, and both shoes and sandals were worn in Greece and Rome. Both in ancient and modern times the styles of shoes worn have varied greatly, fashion taking hold of them. In the reigns of the English kings Henry I and Stephen, the people of the court wore shoes with long points stuffed with tow and made to coil like a ram's horn, and by the time of Richard II the points had grown so long as to reach the knee, to which they were fastened by silver or gold chains. In the eighteenth century ladies wore shoes with absurdly high heels, a ridiculous fashion which has come back within our own times. An improvement which was adopted in the early nineteenth century was that of making shoes right and left. Boots, which have at times been much worn, are a variety of shoe lengthened to protect part of the legs.

Until within a recent period the trade of shoemaker was an active one, all boots and shoes being made by hand. At the present time, however, the old-time shoemaker, with his bench, lapstone, last and awls has almost gone out of business, except as a cobbler, mending instead of making having become his usual occupation. In his place has come the factory hand, nearly all footwear being now a product of machinery, and this of greatly varied and effective character. In this form shoemaking has become a thriving industry in New England and in some other parts of the United States. This method has greatly decreased the cost of shoes, invention having so hastened and cheapened all its processes that the number of shoes that it would take an old-time shoemaker a year to make can be turned out in a few hours by modern machinery.

Shoemaking by Machine.

The variety of inventions used in shoe factories is rather bewildering, every one of the many processes having a machine of its own, and each of these doing its work with admirable precision. We can name here only the more important of these implements.

First comes the clicking machine. This has a cutting board resembling that used by the hand workmen. Over this is a beam containing a cutting die under which the leather is passed. At every descent of the die a piece of leather is cut out of the skin of the size and shape needed for the upper leather of a shoe. Thus in an instant is done what was slowly done by a sharp knife moved around a pattern in the old method.

The piece of leather thus cut out is next passed under the skiving machine, which shaves down its edges to a bevel, the thinned edge being then folded, after which

*Illustrations by courtesy of United Shoe Machinery Co.

IN THE DAYS OF THE AWL, LAPSTONE
AND HAMMER

AMAZEEN SKIVING
MACHINE

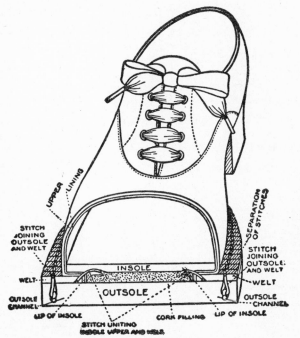

CROSS-SECTION OF GOODYEAR WELT SHOE, SHOWING THE
DIFFERENT PARTS AND THEIR RELATION TO EACH OTHER

INSOLE TACKING MACHINE

IDEAL CLICKING MACHINE

DUPLEX EYELETING MACHINE

ENSIGN LACING MACHINE

REX UPPER TRIMMING
MACHINE

REX PULLING-OVER MACHINE

CROWN TIP PUNCHING MACHINE

BED LASTING MACHINE

GOODYEAR UNIVERSAL INSEAM TRIMMING MACHINE

TACK-PULLING AND RE-SETTING MACHINE

CONSOLIDATED HAND METHOD WELT LASTING MACHINE

IMPROVED SOLE LAYING MACHINE

STAR CHANNEL CEMENTING
MACHINE

GOODYEAR AUTOMATIC SOLE LEVELING MACHINE

AMERICAN LIGHTNING NAILING
MACHINE

the toe caps are passed through a punching machine which cuts a series of ornamental perforations along the edge of the cap. The linings of the shoe are then prepared and put in place and the whole goes to the stitchers, by which all the parts of the upper are united. This is done by a range of machines, which perform the varied operations with wonderful rapidity and accuracy. The eyelets are next added by a machine which places them in both sides of the shoe at the same time and directly opposite each other, this operation finishing the upper part of the shoe.

The sole leather portions of the shoe pass through another series of machines, being cut from sides of sole leather by the dieing-out machine, cut to exact shape by the rounding machine and to exact thickness by the splitting machine, and then toughened by passing under a heavy rolling machine. These and other machines complete the soles and heels, which are finally sent to the making or bottoming room, where the completed shoe uppers awaits them.

The first process here is that of the ensign lacing machine, which puts a strong twine through the eyelets and ties it in an accurate manner. This is done very swiftly and exactly, its purpose being to hold the parts of the shoe in their normal position while the shoe is being completed. The last, made of wood, is now put in place and tacked fast by the insole tacking machine, when the upper is placed over it and fastened by two tacks to hold it in place. Then comes the pulling-over machine, the pincers of which draw the leather securely against the wood of the last, to which it is fastened by other tacks. These tacks in the upper are driven only part way in, so that they may be easily drawn out when no longer needed.

The welt lasting machine next takes the job in hand, it being almost human-like in the evenness and tightness with which it draws the leather around the last, other tacks being driven partly in to hold it in place. A second lasting machine of different kind, draws it around the toe and heel. Then comes the upper trimming machines, which cuts away the surplus parts of the leather, the Rex pounding machine, which hammers it around the heel, the tack pulling machine which removes the lasting tacks and puts in others to hold the new placed leather, and the upper stapling machine, which forms a little staple fastening from wire which securely holds the shoe upper to the channel lip of the insole.

The shoe is now ready to receive the welt, a narrow strip of prepared leather which is sewed along the edge of the shoe and holds all its parts firmly together. This used to be one of the most difficult tasks in hand-work, but is done rapidly and exactly by this machine. After this all protruding parts of the welt and upper are trimmed off by another machine, the insole tack pulling machine removes all the remaining temporary tacks, and the welt-beating and slashing machines beats the welt with little hammers till it stands out evenly from the side of the shoe.

It may seem as if the number of machines engaged in this work are almost beyond number, but there are nearly as many more to come. In fact, a factory shoe in many cases is not completed until 170 machines and 210 pairs of hands have taken part in putting it together and getting it into shape for the wearer, and each of these machines works with an accuracy which no hand-work can equal. We have so far witnessed the assembling of the several parts of the shoe into one connected whole. The remaining processes must be run over more rapidly.

There is a sole-laying machine, a rounding and channeling machine, a loose nailing machine (the latter driving nails into the heel at the rate of 350 per minute), a heel seat rounding machine, and various others, one sewing the welt to the shoe, a leveling machine, a second nailing machine, which does the final work of attaching the heel to the shoe, and so on somewhat indefinitely.

The remaining machines have to do with the final finishing. They include trimmers, stitch separators, edge setters, buffers, finishers, cleaners, stampers, shoe treers, creasers, etc., each playing a part of some importance in giving a final finish

EDGE TRIMMING MACHINE

CLIMAX FINISHING SHAFT

GOODYEAR HEEL SEAT
ROUNDING MACHINE

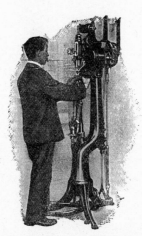

LOOSE NAILING MACHINE

THE HADAWAY STITCH
SEPARATING MACHINE

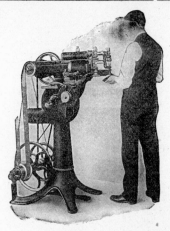

NAUMKEAG BUFFING MACHINE

REGENT STAMPING MACHINE

GOODYEAR UNIVERSAL ROUNDING AND CHANNELING MACHINE

GOODYEAR WELT AND TURN SHOE MACHINE

STITCH AND UPPER CLEANING
MACHINE

TWIN EDGE SETTING MACHINE

Goodyear Outsole Rapid Lockstitch Machine

Improved Vamp Creasing Machine

Miller Shoe Treeing Machine

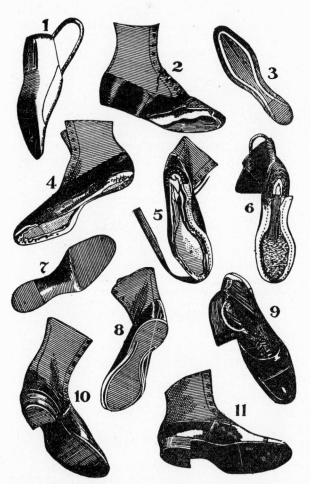

THE EVOLUTION OF A GOODYEAR WELT SHOE

1. A last. 2. An upper. 3. An Insole. 4. Shoe lasted and ready to have welt sewed on. 5. Welt partly sewed on. 6. Welt entirely sewed on the shoe. 7. An outsole. 8. Shoe with outsole laid and rounded; channel lip turned up ready to be stitched. 9. Shoe with sole stitched on. 10. Shoe with heel in place. 11. Heel trimmed and shoe ready for finishing

to the shoe and making it presentable to the wearer. The whole operation, as will be seen, is a highly complicated one, and is remarkably effective in preparing an article that shall appeal to the salesman and purchaser and prove satisfactory when put into use.

Such is the complicated process of making a shoe by machinery. It would be hard to find any machine process that surpasses it in complexity and the number of separate machines involved. Poor old St. Crispin would certainly expire with envy if he could see his favorite thus taken out of the hands of his artisans and the shoe whirled rapidly through a host of odd but effective contrivances on the way to become made fit for wear.

What is " Standard Gold "?

Gold is one of the heaviest of the metals, and not being liable to be injured by exposure to the air, it is well fitted to be used as coin. Its ductility and malleability are very remarkable. It may be beaten into leaves so exceedingly thin that one grain in weight will cover fifty-six square inches, such leaves having the thickness of only 1/282000th part of an inch. It is also extremely ductile; a single grain may be drawn into a wire 500 feet long, and an ounce of gold covering a silver wire is capable of being extended upwards of 1,300 miles. It may also be melted and remelted with scarcely any diminution of its quantity. It is soluble in nitromuriatic acid and in a solution of chlorine. Its specific gravity is 19.3, so that it is about nineteen times heavier than water. The fineness of gold is estimated by carats, pure gold being twenty-four carats fine.

Jeweler's gold is usually a mixture of gold and copper in the proportions of three-fourths of pure gold with one-fourth of copper. Gold is seldom used for any purpose in a state of perfect purity on account of its softness, but is combined with some other metal to render it harder. Standard gold, or the alloy used for the gold coinage of Britain, consists of twenty-two parts of gold and two of copper (being thus twenty-two carats fine).

Articles of jewelry in gold are made of every degree of fineness up to eighteen carats, i. e., eighteen parts of gold to six of alloy. The alloy of gold and silver is found already formed in nature, and is that most generally known. It is distinguishable from that of copper by possessing a paler yellow than pure gold, while the copper alloy has a color bordering upon reddish yellow. Palladium, rhodium and tellurium are also met with as alloys of gold.

Gold has been found in smaller or larger quantities in nearly all parts of the world. It is commonly found in reefs or veins among quartz, and in alluvial deposits; it is separated, in the former case, by quarrying, crushing, washing and treatment with mercury. The rock is crushed by machinery and then treated with mercury, which dissolves the gold, forming a liquid amalgam; after which the mercury is volatilized, and the gold left behind; or the crushed ore is fused with metallic lead, which dissolves out the gold, the lead being afterwards separated by the process of cupellation.

By the "cyanide process," in which cyanide of potassium is used as a solvent for the gold, low-grade ores can be profitably worked. In alluvial deposits it is extracted by washing, in dust grains, laminæ or nuggets.

In modern times large supplies of gold were obtained after the discovery of America from Peru, Bolivia, and other parts of the New World. Till the discovery of gold in California, a chief source of the supply was the Ural Mountains in Russia. An immense increase in the total production of gold throughout the world was caused by the discovery of gold in California in 1848, and that of the equally rich

CASTING INGOTS

ROLLING ROOM

The upper view shows the melting room in the United States Mint, Philadelphia. The man at the right is about to pour hot metal into the iron molds. The lower view is in the coining department, where the ingots such as are seen on the truck in foreground, are rolled into long strips of the thickness of the several coins, and then cut into blanks or planchets.

29

gold fields of Australia in 1851.   The yield from both sources has considerably decreased.   Other sections of the United States have of late years proved prolific sources of gold, especially Colorado, which now surpasses California in yield, and Alaska, which equals it.   Canada has gold fields in several localities, the richest being those of the Klondike.

At present the richest gold field in the world is that of South Africa, which yielded in 1910 a value of $175,000,000, somewhat exceeding the combined yield of the United States and Australia.   Russia and Mexico followed these in yield. The total production throughout the world amounted to over $450,000,000, of which the United States produced $96,000,000.

What are Cyclones?

A cyclone is a circular or rotatory storm, or system of winds, varying from 50 to 500 miles in diameter, revolving around a center, which advances at a rate that may be as high as forty miles an hour, and towards which the winds tend.

Cyclones of greatest violence occur within the tropics, and they revolve in opposite directions in the two hemispheres—in the southern with, and in the northern against, the hands of a watch—in consequence of which, and the progression of the center, the strength of the storm in the northern hemisphere is greater on the south of the line of progression and smaller on the north than it would if the center were stationary, the case being reversed in the southern hemisphere.

An anti-cyclone is a storm of opposite character, the general tendency of the winds in it being away from the center, while it also shifts within comparatively small limits.   Cyclones are preceded by a singular calm and a great fall of the barometer.

What Metals can be Drawn into Wire Best?

The wire-drawing of metals depends on the property of solid bodies, which renders them capable of being extended without any separation of their parts, while their thickness is diminished.   This property is called "ductility."

The following is nearly the order of ductility of the metals which possess the property in the highest degree, that of the first mentioned being the greatest: gold, silver, platinum, iron, copper, zinc, tin, lead, nickel, palladium, cadmium.

Dr. Wollaston succeeded in obtaining a wire of platinum only 1/30000th of an inch in diameter.   The ductility of glass at high temperatures seems to be unlimited, while its flexibility increases in proportion to the fineness to which its threads are drawn.

How are Cocoanuts Used to Help Our Warships?

The fibrous husks of cocoanuts are prepared in such a way as to form "cellulose," which is used for the protection of warships, preventing the inflow of water through shot holes.

The United States adopted the preparation for this purpose in 1892.

It is very light and compressible and when tightly packed between the steel plating and the side of the vessel will expand when wet and fill up the space through which a shot may have passed.

Another and cheaper product experimented with is the pith of the cornstalk, which is much lighter than the cocoanut fiber and serves the same purpose.

How did the Dollar Sign Originate?

The sign, $, used in this country to signify a dollar, is supposed to date from the time of the pillar dollar in Spain.   This was known as the "Piece of Eight" (meaning eight reals), the curve being a partial representation of the figure 8.   The two vertical strokes are thought to represent the Pillars of Hercules, which were stamped upon the coin itself.

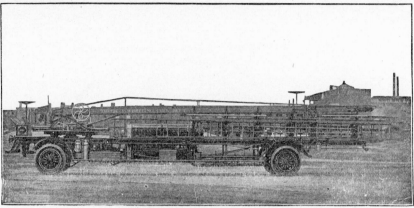

MOTOR DRIVEN AERIAL TRUCK*

The 66-foot ladder of this truck is raised by the motor which drives the machine. A full equipment of scaling ladders and fire-fighting apparatus is carried.

MOTOR FIRE ENGINE AND HOSE TRUCK*

One of the latest fire-fighting units. A powerful gasoline engine supplies the motive power and drives the pump which has a capacity of 700 gallons per minute. The machine also acts as a hose cart and carries a full complement of firemen.

*Courtesy of James Boyd & Bro., Inc.

A CRANE NECK HAND FIRE ENGINE*

This engine was manned by sixty trained men and under expert operation would throw a stream of 1.53 gallons per stroke more than 200 feet.

THE FIRST STEAM FIRE ENGINE BUILT IN 1841*

* Courtesy of American LaFrance Fire Engine Co.

THE SPLENDID HORSES BY WHICH THE HAND-DRAWN FIRE APPARATUS WERE SUPPLANTED ARE IN TURN GIVING WAY TO POWERFUL MOTOR ENGINES AND TRUCKS.*

AN OLD-TIME LaFRANCE PISTON STEAM FIRE ENGINE

Built in 1894, at which time it had a capacity of 900 gallons per minute. This steam engine was equipped with a LaFrance boiler This particular engine was in service in Superior, Wis., and was in continuous service pumping water on a coal fire night and day from November 18, 1913, to February 18, 1914 (just exactly three months), during which time it was only shut down twice to replace burned-out grates and three times to replace broken springs. During all of this time this steamer was incased in snow and ice.

* Courtesy of American LaFrance Fire Engine Co.

GASOLINE TWO-WHEEL FRONT-DRIVE, FIRST SIZE STEAM FIRE
ENGINE*

Seventy horse-power, four-cylinder motor; speed, 35 miles per
hour; locomotive bell and hand-operated siren horn; boiler, 36x66
inches; suction hose, 2 lengths, 4½-inch diameter; lanterns, three,
fire department standard; hydrant connections; carrying capacity,
four men.

COMBINATION CHEMICAL ENGINE AND HOSE CAR*

Seventy horse-power, four-cylinder motor; speed, 60 miles per hour; hose capacity,
1,200 feet 2½-inch hose; chemical cylinder, one 40-gallon capacity; chemical hose,
200 feet ¾-inch chemical hose; acid receptacles, two; one 10-inch electric searchlight;
locomotive bell and hand-operated siren horn; extinguishers, two 3-gallon Babcock, fire
department standard; ladders, one 20-foot extension ladder, one 12-foot roof ladder with
folding hooks; lanterns, four, fire department standard; axe, one, fire department standard; pike pole, one; crowbar, one of steel held by snaps; carrying capacity, seven men.

* Courtesy of American LaFrance Fire Engine Co.

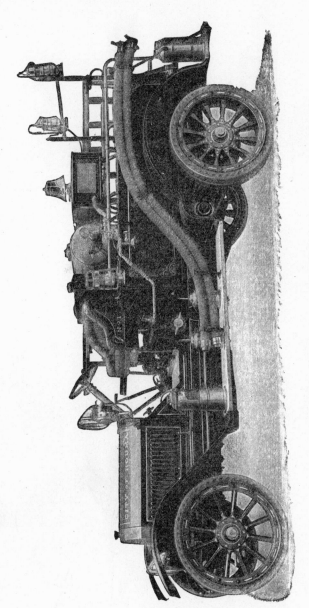

COMBINATION CHEMICAL AND HOSE CAR

Equipped with Junior Pump. This pump is intended to boost the pressure of the chemical tank and can also be used as an auxiliary pump. On this type of steamer the pump will deliver 250 gallons of water at 120 pounds pump pressure.

Courtesy of American LaFrance Fire Engine Co.

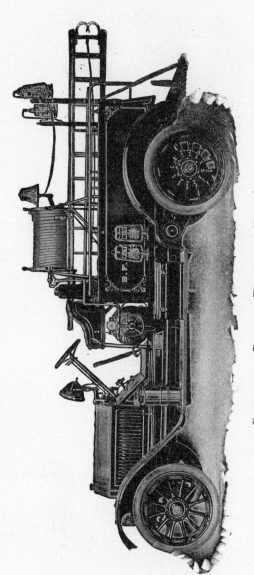

COMBINATION CHEMICAL ENGINE AND HOSE CAR
Equipped with hose reel instead of hose basket as in other types illustrated.
Courtesy of American LaFrance Fire Engine Co.

THE BODY OF THIS CAR HAS A CAPACITY OF 800 FEET OF 2½-INCH FIRE HOSE AND IS ALSO EQUIPPED WITH A 40-GALLON TANK, WITH CHEMICAL HOSE, FIRE EXTINGUISHER AND EXTENSION LADDER.*

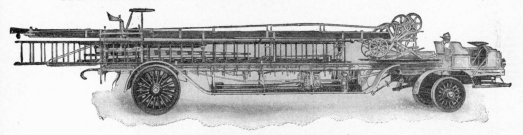

GASOLINE TWO-WHEEL FRONT-DRIVE AERIAL TRUCK*

One hundred horse-power; six-cylinder motor; speed, 25 miles per hour; locomotive bell and hand-operated siren horn; extinguishers, two 3-gallon Babcock, fire department standard; lanterns, four, fire department standard; axes, four, fire department standard; wall picks, two; crowbars, two; shovels, two; wire cutter, one; door opener, one; tin roof cutter, one; pitchforks, two; battering ram, one; Manila rope, tackle and snatch block; pull-down hook with pole, chain and rope; rubber buckets, four; crotch poles, two; pike poles, six, assorted lengths; wire basket, one under frame; one 10-inch electric searchlight.

GASOLINE TWO-WHEEL BEVEL-GEAR FRONT-DRIVE WATER TOWER*

One hundred horse-power; six-cylinder motor; speed, 25 miles per hour; one 10-inch electric searchlight; locomotive bell and hand-operated siren horn; deck turret, one, mounted; nozzle tips, three for deck turret, 1½-inch, 1¾-inch, 2-inch; three for tower nozzle, 1½-inch, 1¾-inch, 2-inch; hose, one 35-foot length, 4-inch cotton, rubber lined; lanterns, two, fire department standard; axes, two heavy pick back, fire department standard; crowbar, one of steel, held by snaps.   * Courtesy of American LaFrance Fire Engine Co.

The Story of the Taking of Food From the Air*

What is the greatest discovery of the last twenty-five years? Probably you will say the wireless telegraph, the flying machine, moving pictures or the phonograph, but it would be none of these, according to the *Scientific American*. This publication discussed at great length the subject of what invention of the last twenty-five years was of greatest value to mankind. First place was given not to the wonderful inventions that are so large in the public eye, but to the fixation of nitrogen from the air for fertilizer purposes. Why? Simply because this discovery stands between man and starvation. Other inventions are vastly important, but this one is vital. Looking at it from the broadest view there can be no other decision. The time is here when to feed the world is becoming a more and more difficult problem.

WRAPPER LEAF TOBACCO CROP FERTILIZED WITH CYANAMID MIXTURES. GROWN IN HATFIELD, MASS.

During the past ten years our population has increased at the rate of two per cent per annum, while our crop production has increased only one-half as fast. In six years the number of beef cattle produced in this country has fallen off about five per cent per annum. The cost of foodstuffs recently has been increasing at the rate of five per cent per annum. The hardships experienced by wage-earners, particularly in the United States, have been very great in view of the fact that the cost of food increased more rapidly than wages—at a rate approximately double. The same tendencies apply with some modifications to the clothing of mankind. These facts point to the necessity of increasing the yields both of the food crops and the crops that are used in the making of clothing.

The problem of decreasing the cost of living has been given far more attention abroad than it has in this country, owing to the much greater density of population in the principal nations of Europe. For a long time it has been known that plants require food the same as animals and human beings. Without food plants cannot live and grow, and just to the extent that plant food is present in the soil, to that extent will a crop be produced. The most important of plant foods is nitrogen. While the earth is literally bathed in nitrogen, this element is found to only a very slight degree in the soil. That is to say, the air which we breathe and in which we move is four-fifths nitrogen, yet in the richest soil there is seldom more than one-tenth or two-tenths of one per cent of nitrogen. Put on a wheat crop one pound

*Illustrations by courtesy of American Cyanamid Company.

of nitrogen and you can take off twenty pounds more wheat and forty pounds more straw than you could if you failed to make this application.   One pound of nitrogen properly applied to a cornfield will add thirty-five pounds to the crop; one pound of nitrogen will produce one hundred pounds of increase in the potato crop; one pound of nitrogen will produce five pounds of cotton, without any extra labor being devoted to the production of the crop.   Nitrogen is the heart and soul of the problem of growing more crops and cheaper crops.   Take any nation that produces large crop yields per acre and you will find that the nation that uses the most nitrogen per acre grows the largest crops.

For years the nations of Europe have been depending to a great extent upon supplies of nitrate of soda obtained from Chile, in South America.   Germany alone imported nearly a million tons of this salt annually before the war.   Then, too, the

by-products of many industries furnish a quantity of nitrogen, but all this, it was realized, furnished but a small part of what was required to combat the constantly rising cost of producing food.

For years it was the dream and life-ambition of the world's greatest scientists to discover how to make the supplies of nitrogen in the air available to plants as food.   The only way that this could be done in nature was through the agency of bacteria working on the roots of certain plants, such as clovers, but this process was

Sugar Cane Crop Fertilized with Cyanamid Mixtures. Grown in Calumet, La.

entirely too slow for practical purposes and could be applied on only a small acreage at one time.   The free nitrogen of the air cannot be utilized directly by plants.   It must first be converted into some combination with other chemicals, as a solid or liquid, which can be absorbed by the plant.   Among others who worked on the problem of fixing atmospheric nitrogen were two German chemists, Doctors Caro and Frank, who found that a compound of calcium and carbon heated to a high temperature would absorb nitrogen and retain it in a form that could be applied to the soil and serve as a food for plants.

This discovery is the basis of the Cyanamid "Atmospheric Nitrogen" industry or the making of fertilizer from the nitrogen in the air.   After the discovery was made and tested on the laboratory scale it took several years to put it on a practical basis, as can well be imagined when it is understood what the problems involved were.   Besides air this process required as raw materials limestone and coke.   The limestone must be burned to quicklime and the quicklime and coke must be fused together to form calcium carbide.   Only the most powerful electric furnaces are capable of performing this work.   Any other means of heating is far from adequate. For instance, the hottest flame that can be produced by the burning of gas, namely, the oxy-hydrogen blow-pipe flame, can be directed against a stick of burnt lime without doing anything beyond making the lime glow brilliantly, thus producing the calcium or lime-light formerly much used in theaters as a spot-light.   In the electric furnaces, however, the lime is heated so powerfully that it actually melts to a liquid, and in this condition it dissolves the coke with which it is mixed and the compound resulting is calcium carbide which can be run off from the interior of the furnace in liquid form.

At the cyanamid plant at Niagara Falls, in Canada, there are seven of these great carbide furnaces, each about fifteen feet long and half as wide and one-third as deep. We all have some idea of how much heat is generated in the ordinary electric arc light such as is used for street lighting. In the carbide furnace the carbon pencil, instead of being six or eight inches long and as large around as your finger, is six feet long and two feet in diameter. There are three of these in each furnace, and when the furnace is in full action it can be imagined that there is a terrific heat generated; in fact, when the fused lime and coke come out of the furnace in the form of molten carbide the brightness of the molten material is so dazzling that one cannot look at it with the naked eyes without injury.

Two of the Carbide Furnaces and Electrode Regulators

Then there is the problem of producing pure nitrogen gas, that is, separating the eighty per cent of nitrogen in the air from the twenty per cent of oxygen. The latter is the element that we breathe and which passes into the body, there to combine with the impurities resulting from the various life activities. If the nitrogen and the oxygen were both allowed to act upon calcium carbide the oxygen would burn up the carbide before the nitrogen could be fixed in it, hence these two elements must be separated and all other impurities removed so that only chemically pure nitrogen is brought to the calcium carbide for fixation. The separation is accomplished by means of liquid air machines. This industry, therefore, not only utilizes the greatest heat obtainable on a practical scale, but it also utilizes the greatest cold.

One of the Carbide Mills

While the electric furnaces produce a temperature of over 4000° F., or about twice as hot as molten cast-iron, the liquid air machines work at a temperature of 372° F. below zero. The air must first be purified and dried. It is then compressed, cooled while under pressure, and then expanded. The expansion lowers its temperature considerably. If this extra cool air is used for cooling another batch of air under pressure, the latter upon expansion becomes still colder than the first batch expanded. By repeating this operation the final temperature of 372° below zero is reached, at which the air liquifies.

How cold this is can be seen from some simple experiments. For instance, if a dipper full of the liquid air is drawn, in an instant the outside of the dipper is covered with a coating of frost deposited upon it from the surrounding atmosphere. The surrounding air is so much hotter than the liquid air that the liquid boils violently. If a piece of rubber hose is held in the liquid air for eight or ten seconds and then struck with a hammer the rubber flies into pieces just like glass. To dip one's finger into this liquid air would freeze it solid in a second and would be as disastrous as dipping it in red-hot iron.

When the liquid air is allowed to warm up a little, the nitrogen gas evaporates, while the oxygen remains behind in the liquid. The pure nitrogen then can be pumped into the fixation ovens.

To fix the nitrogen in the carbide it is necessary to cool the latter after it comes from the electric furnaces and grind it to a very fine powder. This powder is then placed in furnaces that look like steel barrels but are three or four times larger than an ordinary barrel. The oven filled with calcium carbide is then electrically heated with a carbon rod running through the center. When the temperature is about

LIQUID AIR PLANT

as hot as that of molten iron the pure nitrogen gas from the liquid air plant is pumped in and allowed to act on the calcium carbide for about a day and a half. When the carbide has absorbed all it will absorb the crude cyanamid formed is removed from the oven as a single large cake which is run through pulverizing drums and then put through an elaborate process of refinement and finally bagged for shipment in carload lots to fertilizer factories throughout the country.

The fertilizer manufacturers mix the cyanamid with other ingredients to make a balanced plant food and so ship it to farmers for feeding their crops. In 1914 7,500,000 tons of fertilizer worth $175,000,000 were consumed in this country. This seems like a large quantity, but it allows only a scanty application per acre cultivated. Germany, on one-fourth of our cultivated acreage, uses almost twice as much fertilizer as the entire United States. As a consequence she raises 30 bushels of wheat where we average 14 bushels per acre; 52 bushels of oats where we average 30; and 196 bushels of potatoes per acre where we raise 97 bushels per acre. The explanation is simple, German farmers pay only about one-half as much for their plant food as American farmers pay. Where the German farmer gains $2.00 to $3.00 increase in crop from fertilizer that costs him $1.00 the American farmer pays $2.00 for the same fertilizer, which leaves him less profit and less incentive to use fertilizer.

The air-nitrogen industry in the United States is said to be considerably handicapped because the large quantities of electricity required are not available at a low enough price. There are excellent water-power sites in the United States sufficient

A Carbide Cooling Shed

Cyanamid Oven Room

Photo by William H. Rau

FOREVER RUSHING AND FOREVER WONDERFUL

Niagara Falls from Prospect Point on the American side, looking southwest, across and up the stream. The American Falls may be seen in the foreground rushing past to make their plunge of 165 feet to the rocks below.

to furnish many times the required power, but the existing water-power laws are so burdensome that investors will not put their money into power development except on such high terms that the power is much dearer than it can be bought for

SUGAR BEET CROP FERTILIZED WITH CYANAMID MIXTURES. GROWN IN CARO, MICHIGAN

in other countries. Practically every civilized country in the world, except the United States, had one or more cyanamid factories in 1916. These include Germany, Austria-Hungary, Great Britain, France, Italy, Switzerland, Norway, Sweden, Japan and Canada. Their combined output is about 1,000,000 tons per annum. The cyanamid plant at Niagara Falls, Ontario, which was established in 1909, with a capacity of 10,000 tons, had a capacity of 64,000 tons per annum in 1916. It utilizes about 30,000 electrical horse-power twenty-four hours a day, and three hundred and sixty-five days a year. Germany, at the beginning of the war, produced about 30,000 tons of cyanamid; in 1916 she was making 600,000 tons a year. She is using it both to grow crops and to make explosives for her guns.

At the time the war broke out, in August, 1914, Germany was importing nearly one million tons of nitrate of soda per annum from Chile, South America. This supply was immediately cut off by enemy fleets. Not only was her agriculture thereby threatened with a great decrease in crop production but her supply of military explosives was also threatened. Professor Dr. Lemmermann, a famous German scientist, advised his government that unless the nitrogen shortage were made good the resulting crop shortage would amount to 3,300,000 tons of grain. But if people require food, guns require powder, and no powder can be made without nitric acid.

COTTON CROP FERTILIZED WITH CYANAMID MIXTURES. GROWN IN SUMTER, S. C.

It has been reported on good authority that Germany consumed one and one-third million pounds of powder a day during the war. To make one pound of powder requires one and one-half pounds of nitric acid, so that Germany required for military purposes 2,000,000 pounds of nitric acid per day. From her coke ovens

TURBINE GENERATORS, NIAGARA FALLS POWER HOUSE

Eleven turbine generators in the Niagara Falls Power House, each set developing 5,000 horse-power.

she indeed could derive some nitrogen, but this actually furnished only about one-fifth of her total requirements. For the other four-fifths she turned to atmospheric nitrogen. For it is also true that this remarkable compound, cyanamid, which is a food for plants, can be decomposed by high-steam pressure into the purest ammonia gas. The ammonia can in turn be oxidized to nitric acid, which is the basis of all explosives. Without the fixation of atmospheric nitrogen on a tremendous scale there is no doubt that Germany would have become helpless before her enemies within a year after the war began, for no nation can fight unless it has sufficient food for its people and powder for its guns.

The preservation of food is also dependent on ammonia, which produces the refrigerating effect in the numerous cold storage houses and artificial ice plants in this country. In the cold storage plants alone the cold produced by means of ammonia is equal to 750,000 tons of ice consumed per day, while 25,000,000 tons of artificial ice are produced and sold as such per annum. Cyanamid ammonia gas is especially valuable for this purpose on account of its high degree of purity.

Then, too, the ammonia gas can be fixed in any acid desired, for instance, in phosphoric acid, making ammonium phosphate, a fertilizer of unusual merit, or ammonium sulphate, another fertilizer, or ammonium nitrate, an explosive. So, for peace or war, the fixation of atmospheric nitrogen has become a tremendous factor in the life of nations.

If the United States should be forced into war with a foreign power it would be a simple matter for an enemy fleet to cut off our large importations of nitrate of soda from Chile. These amount to about 700,000 tons per annum in normal times and at present about 900,000 tons per annum. In other words, we would be short just this quantity of nitrogen in addition to the quantity that would be required by the government for the manufacture of military explosives. It has been suggested that our coke-oven industry could be expanded to furnish a large part of this requirement, but even with the largest expansion considered practical by the coke-oven people within the next several years, the coke ovens would not be able to supply even one-third of our requirements, thus leaving a large balance which could be furnished only by the establishment of a large nitrogen industry in this country.

The expression "The King can do no wrong" has been widely used since it first caught people's fancy at the time of the explanation, made in England, that the Ministers, and not the King, were responsible for mistakes of government.

What is a Drawbridge Like Today?

We have all read of the castles in olden days into which the owner could retire and raise a drawbridge across a ditch, thus putting a barrier in the way of his enemies.

That old style drawbridge, with, of course, many improvements, has been adopted in these modern times to use in permitting navigable rivers and channels to be crossed by railroads and other kinds of transportation, without preventing the passage of vessels up and down the rivers.

Modern drawbridges across rivers, canals, the entrances of docks, etc., are generally made to open vertically, and the movable portion is called a bascule, balance or lifting bridge; a turning, swivel or swing bridge; or a rolling bridge, in accordance with the mode in which it is made to open.

Swing bridges are usually divided into two parts meeting in the middle, and each moved on pivots on the opposite sides of the channel, or they may move as a whole on a pivot in the middle of the channel.

Rolling bridges are suspended from a structure high above the water, and are propelled backwards and forwards by means of rollers.

Bascule Bridge Open*

Bascule Bridge Closed*

The advantages of this type of bridge are that the entire width of the channel is available for navigation, and the draw may be opened and closed more readily than the swing type. *Courtesy of The Strauss Bascule Bridge Co.

The Story of a Deep Sea Monster*

The early day was blue and silver; one of those colorful mornings peculiar to southern Florida. Sandwiched between the earth and the turquoise sky, the Atlantic lay gleaming like a huge silver wafer in the sunlight. Not the faintest suggestion of a ripple marred its shining surface.

Suddenly out of the stillness of the silver water a huge black fin was lifted, and a little group of men lounging on the deck of an idle fishing craft drew near the rail and used their glasses.

"Shark," remarked the captain pleasantly after a moment's scrutiny. "Who wants to go out with me for a little fun?"

The hastily lowered lifeboat pointed a slim nose toward the large black shape thrashing about in the shallow water. Three men were in the boat—Captain Charles H. Thompson of the yacht "Samoa," one of the yacht's crew, and a winter visitor to southern Florida. As they drew near, the sailor took one look at the gigantic creature and yelled to the captain:

"For heaven's sake, man, don't harpoon that thing; we will be crushed like an egg shell!"

Poised in the bow of the boat, harpoon in hand, stood the captain, and as they drew alongside there was a flash; the steel glittered for a moment in the sunlight, then sank into the huge black bulk. Simultaneously the little boat spun around and shot out toward the Gulf Stream like an agitated and very erratic rocket, flinging great sheets of spray high into the air as it sped.

Thus began a thirty-nine hours' ride filled with wildest thrills, during which time Captain Thompson battled with the fish, the sailor bailed the boat unceasingly, lest they be swamped, and the tourist raised an anxious and eloquent voice to high heaven. The men were without food the entire time, sharing only a small bottle of water among them.

The news of the struggle spread rapidly, and soon hundreds of interested spectators gathered on the trestle of the East Coast sea-extension railway. Scores of times the men in the boat escaped death only by a miracle, as the wildly thrashing black tail missed them but by a hair's breadth. Finally, after two days and one night, the monster was worn out, and the triumphant captor managed to fasten it to the trestle work on Knight's Key, where, after a few hours' rest, it wigwagged a festive tail, smashing the large pilings as though they were toothpicks. After another battle the fish was firmly tied up once more, this time to the yacht "Samoa;" and again it waved a wicked tail, disabling the thirty-ton yacht by smashing her propeller and breaking the cables. A tug was then summoned, and the big fellow was towed one hundred and ten miles to Miami, Florida, where it was viewed by thousands of people.

Five harpoons and one hundred and fifty-one bullets were used in subduing the monster, and it took five days to finally kill it.

It was thought at first the creature was a whale, but later it was classified as a fish, for it breathed through gills of which there were five in number. Upon careful examination it seemed probable that it was a baby of its species, as the backbone was of a cartilaginous nature, a condition found only in a young creature; in a full-grown one this develops into true bone. That it was a deep-sea fish was indicated by the small eye, which was about the size of a silver dollar. The pressure of the water is so great at the bottom of the ocean that were the eyes large they would

* Courtesy of The American Magazine

Photograph by Capt. Chas. H. Thompson

DEEP SEA MONSTER CAPTURED OFF FLORIDA

So far as the scientific world is concerned, this is the only fish of its kind ever captured. Length, 45 feet; weight, 30,000 pounds; circumference, 23 feet 9 inches; diameter 8 feet 3 inches; mouth (open) 31 inches; mouth, 38 inches wide; mouth, 43 inches deep; tongue, 40 inches long; several thousand teeth; hide, three inches thick, no scales; had swallowed an animal weighing 1,500 pounds; tail measures 10 feet from tip to tip; pectoral fin, 5 feet long, 3 feet wide; dorsal fin, 3 feet long, 2 feet 9 inches wide; gills, 4 feet; the liver weighed 1,700 pounds.

be ruptured. That the pupil did not dilate and contract seems additional proof that the fish must have lived at a depth of probably fifteen hundred or two thousand feet, where there is little light.

It is generally believed that some volcanic eruption drove the fish to the surface where, owing to the difference in water pressure, the swim-bladders burst, making it impossible for him to return to his level.

What is an Armored Railway Car Like?

The armored car shown in this picture is the first of a new type of armored car to be constructed by the United States. It was designed under the direction of the Board of Engineers of the U. S. Army, and was constructed by the Standard Steel

THE RAPID FIRE-GUN HERE SHOWN IS A MODEL OF A THREE-INCH FIELD GUN MOUNTED UPON A SPECIAL CARRIAGE. THE WELL IN WHICH THE GUN IS LOCATED MAY ALSO BE USED AS A FIGHTING TOP FOR TROOPS ARMED WITH RIFLES OR MACHINE GUNS.

Courtesy of the Railway Age Gazette and Standard Steel Car Co.

Car Company, Pittsburgh, Pa., at their Hammond, Ind., plant. The car was designed and built within twenty-seven days.

The car consists of heavy steel plate structure, erected upon a flat car of standard type. The interior is divided into three compartments. The end compartments are for use of troops operating machine guns and rifles through the port-holes shown on side of car. The center compartment, which is not the full height of the car, is used for ammunition storage, and is capable of holding a large quantity of ammunition, either for small arms or for the rapid-fire gun which is mounted on top of the car The rapid-fire gun here shown is a model of a three-inch field gun mounted upon a special carriage. The well in which the gun is located may also be used as a fighting top for troops armed with rifles or machine guns.

This car is know as a light-armored car. It is armed with a three-inch rapid-fire gun, two machine guns and any number of rifles which the troops occupying it may gun, two machine guns and any number of rifles which the troops occupying it may carry. The service for which this car is intended is primarily to guard railroads and depots adjacent to railroads. It is not ordinarily to be employed in aggressive move-

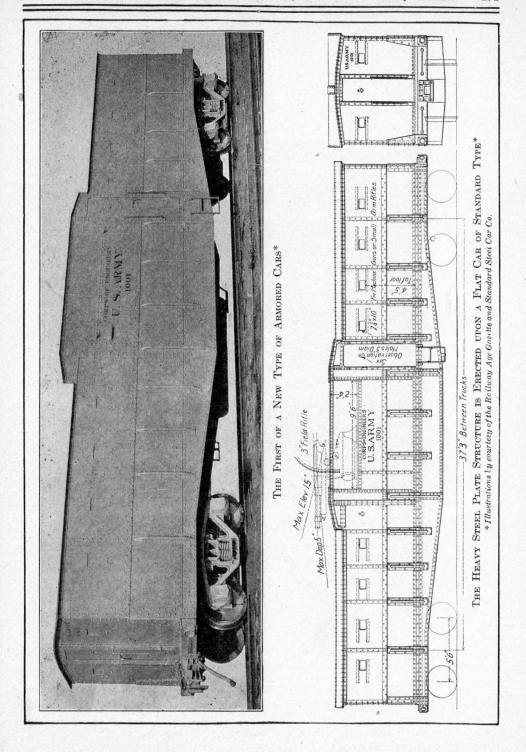

THE FIRST OF A NEW TYPE OF ARMORED CARS*

THE HEAVY STEEL PLATE STRUCTURE IS ERECTED UPON A FLAT CAR OF STANDARD TYPE*

* Illustrations by courtesy of the Railway Age Gazette and Standard Steel Car Co.

ments. In effect, it is a movable block-house which may be used at any point along the line, or it may be used as a retreat for troops when necessary. It may also be used for transporting troops past danger points, and for transporting explosives or other perishable material which might be damaged by fire from the ends. The car as constructed weighs 86,200 pounds. It is 47 feet long, 9 feet 3 inches wide, and 7 feet high at the ends. When used for transportation of troops, it will accommodate a company of infantry seated on camp stools or benches. When used for patrol pur-

THE INTERIOR IS DIVIDED INTO THREE COMPARTMENTS
Courtesy of the Railway Age Gazette and Standard Steel Car Co.

poses, there would not be more than twelve men in the car, to operate the rapid-fire gun and machine guns.

The car was shipped to the Sandy Hook proving grounds to be equipped with rapid-fire guns and ammunition and thoroughly tested and inspected by the Engineer and Ordnance Officer of the U. S. Army.

What is an "Electric Eel"?

This is an eel abundant in the fresh waters of Brazil and the Guianas, which possesses organs capable of developing a strong electric current and thus of giving a violent shock to any one touching the eels. These organs replace the lower muscles along the sides of the tail. The eels can be taken by driving horses into the water to be shocked and seizing them when thus weakened.

The Story of Salt*

Salt is a chemical compound composed of two elements, sodium and chlorine. Chemically it is known as sodium chloride.

It is one of the things which comes into our lives daily, perhaps more than any

A SALT WELL

other, with the exception of water. Probably no other thing than water is used more by all civilized people than salt.

Nature provides salt for us in three different forms. First, in sea water in solution; second, in salt springs; and third, in the form of salt rock.

From time immemorial man has obtained salt from sea water. This is still being done on our sea coasts, but the salt obtained by evaporating the water is very crude and usually contains many impurities.

It has been possible to obtain a large supply of salt from what are known as salt springs. These springs are usually the result of water flowing over a deposit of

* Illustrations by courtesy of Diamond Crystal Salt Co.

salt rock. The amount of salt obtained from evaporating this spring water is, however, so small that salt springs are an impractical source of supply when it comes to making salt for commercial purposes.

Rock salt forms the most common and practical source of supply. It is found in all parts of the world and reasonably near the surface. The deposit is said to be what is left of ancient salt seas. In the United States the largest deposits of salt are found in the states of Michigan, New York, Ohio, Utah, Louisiana, Kansas,

SALT HEATERS AND FILTERS

Texas and California. The above-mentioned states are the largest producers of salt in this country.

One of the largest sources of salt supply in Europe is at Wielizka in Poland. This deposit of salt is said to be the largest in the world, the bed of salt rock being 500 miles long, 20 miles wide and 1,200 feet thick. Some of the salt mines in Poland are so extensive that it is said some of the miners spend all of their lives in them, never coming to the surface of the earth.

Most of the deposits of salt rock contain impurities which need to be removed before the salt is fit for use commercially; however, some deposits show a very pure salt rock and when ground up this rock salt is suitable for table use. In general, however, the salt made from crude salt rock is only fit for the crudest commercial uses. The most common impurity is gypsum and it is necessary to remove this gypsum before the salt can be considered pure.

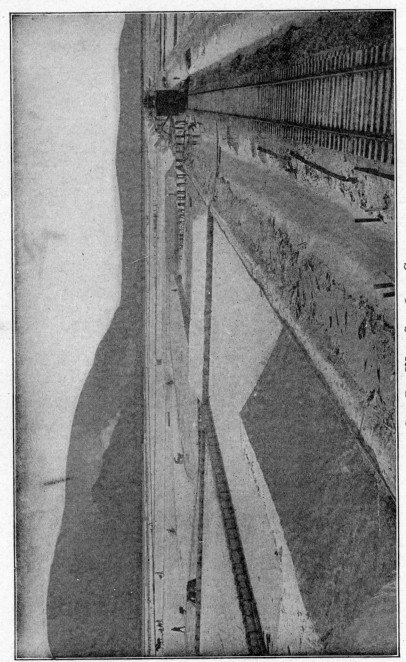

Photo by Brown Bros.

SALT BEDS NEAR SALT LAKE CITY

These extensive salt beds about eighteen miles from Salt Lake City are part of the deposit left when Lake Bonneville dwindled to Great Salt Lake.

The general way of obtaining salt from the earth is by means of salt wells. These wells are drilled in the same way that wells are bored for oil and gas. A pipe about six inches in diameter is lowered to the surface of the salt rock and then an inside pipe is put down, water is forced down between the two pipes and the pressure exerted brings up the dissolved rock or salt brine through the inside pipe.

As the salt brine reaches the surface the salt is extracted from it in various ways. At present the crude open-pan system, where the brine was poured into open pans and fires were built below the pans, is almost obsolete. The most practical methods of refining salt today are known as the Grainer, Vacuum Pan and Alberger systems.

The Grainer system is similar in its operation to the old open-pan system. The brine is run through long, shallow tanks and the heat is applied through steam pipes

BOLTERS FOR SIFTING SALT

inside of the pan. The salt settles to the bottom of the pan and large rakes operated either by hand or machinery collect the salt.

In the Vacuum Pan process tiny cubes of salt are formed and settle to the bottom of the pan in which a vacuum has been created. The salt is then drained out and is ready for drying.

Variations of the two above processes make possible the production of certain grades of table salt. Oftentimes the brine is relieved of impurities through the action of certain chemicals. In some instances a chemical known as "barium chloride" is used, but the wisdom of this process has been much questioned, owing to the fact that barium chloride is a deadly poison.

The Alberger system of salt manufacture is a mechanical process which subjects the salt brine to a much higher temperature and removes the impurities by means of mechanical filters. This process is known to make a very pure salt and has been

Filling Salt Packages

Filling Salt Bags

used for some time as a practical method for manufacturing high-grade dairy and table salt. Unlike the other two common methods of making salt, it forms tiny salt flakes instead of the usual cubes or lumps.

After manufacturers obtain the salt from the brine they usually put it through drying processes. After drying, the salt is sifted and the fine table salt is separated from the coarser products. When salt is sifted it is ready for packing in bags or packages suitable for shipment to the consumer.

According to recent government reports, it is estimated that the average consumption of salt per capita for all purposes is about 100 pounds per year. The salt industry is now said to have reached a very stable basis and the demand for salt in the United States is practically all supplied by American manufacturers. Salt can be put to a great many uses in addition to the usual requirements for table and cooking. It is used by food manufacturers and performs highly important functions in certain commercial fields.

Why do We Call it " Denatured Alcohol "?

Under a law passed by the United States Congress in 1907, on alcohol intended for use as fuel or for illuminating purposes, or other mechanical employment, the internal tax need not be paid. But to avoid taxation it must be rendered unfit for drinking by the addition of such unpalatable substances as wood alcohol, pyridin, benzola, sulphuric ether or animal oil. Thus treated, it is spoken of as denatured.

What is the Difference Between a Cruiser and a Battleship?

A cruiser is a vessel built to secure speed and fuel capacity at the expense of armor and battery strength.

The modern cruiser may be regarded as the offspring of the frigate of the eighteenth and nineteenth centuries. The later construction has been designed for a minimum speed of twenty-five knots an hour, with a possible attainment of thirty knots or over, under favorable conditions.

The battleship and one form of cruiser were evolved from the conflicting opinions of two opposite schools of design. The battleship is the expression of the thoughts of those who stood for extremely developed battery power, great thickness of armor plate, and moderate speed. The cruiser is the result of the triumph of those who contended for high speed at the sacrifice of heavy armor protection and excessive battery strength.

The armored cruiser was the particular development of the antagonistic views prevailing among naval architects. The type of this class in the United States navy was the "Brooklyn," which figured prominently in the war with Spain in 1898.

Recently the armored cruiser has been superseded by the battle cruiser. The armor protection in this type of ship is much lower than that of the battleship, while the ordnance, on the other hand, is practically the same. High speed, wide radius of action and great battery strength are the characteristics of this type; and to meet these requirements the battle cruiser is planned of a size considerably larger than the battleship.

The protected cruiser is a later development of naval construction. Its distinguishing features are certain modifications in the distribution of the mass of protective armor of the ship.

Light cruisers are vessels of from 1,500 to 7,500 tons, used in scouting, as commerce destroyers, etc. They are outside the armored class.

SINKING OF THE GERMAN CRUISER "BLUECHER"

This most dramatic photograph of the Great North Sea Battle, in which the British fleet was victor, January 24, 1915, shows the death agony of the German cruiser "Bluecher" just as she turned turtle and sank. The ship is shown lying on her side with her machinery and armament shot into masses of twisted iron and steel, great fires raging forward, amidship and aft.

Copyright by the International News Service.

THE MOST POWERFUL BATTLESHIP IN THE WORLD

The "Colorado" is 624 feet long, displaces 32,600 tons, and has a speed of 21 knots. She burns oil and her two 18,000 horsepower steam turbines supply electric current to four 8,000 (total, 32,000) horsepower Westinghouse motors, which drive her propellers. She cost $27,000,000.

The Story of the Growth of the Motor Truck*

While exact dates are not easily obtainable, it is thought to be quite within the bounds of reasonable accuracy to say that the motor truck only began to be recognized as a practical vehicle for commercial purposes in 1905.

Today motor vehicles, both pleasure and commercial, are such a common sight in every city and town, and even throughout the rural districts, that one can scarcely believe that they were a novelty such a little time ago.

The statistics show, however, that in 1906 the total registrations of both pleasure

ONE OF THE EARLIEST GASOLINE TRUCKS

and commercial vehicles, as reported by the various states, was 48,000—about one month's production today of one well-known pleasure-car maker.

In 1915 the registrations totaled nearly 2,500,000, and every day has added to the number.

It can be truthfully said that the pleasure car is the father of the truck or commercial car.

The application of the internal combustion engine to the use of propelling vehicles was the beginning of a new era in that world. The idea, born, one might say, with the new century, has already done more to revolutionize transportation than all of the inventions of all the centuries that have gone before.

The automobile, first looked upon as a freak, then a "rich man's plaything,"

*Illustrations by courtesy of the General Motors Truck Co.

has in a few years come to be recognized as a necessity, and literally millions of people are employed in its production and dependent on the industry for support.

To trace the ramifications of the industry back through the mills, mines and factories that produce the iron, steel, copper, brass, zinc, aluminum, lead, leather, lumber, glass, celluloid, etc., would make a long and interesting story, but this chapter deals with the motor vehicle as a commercial car or truck and the part it is playing in transportation of the world's goods.

While the first commercial vehicles to come into use were electrically propelled, and while the electric truck has become a factor in the large cities, the gasoline power vehicles are, as yet, the dominant factor.

At the first, business men were slow to take up the use of trucks for delivery and hauling purposes and one of the specialties of early factories was the making of

A 1907 Model Sight-seeing Car

"sight-seeing" cars which were sold to enterprising individuals in cities and summer resorts for the purpose of showing visitors the sights. These wagons became popular throughout the country and are still being used in many places.

Little by little, however, progressive business men saw the advantages to be gained by motor delivery and the motor truck began to gain favor. Several of the pleasure-car manufacturers took advantage of the awakening interest and added a commercial vehicle section to their plants.

Others began to see visions of the day when horses would no longer be used for other than strictly farm work, and motor-truck factories sprang up here and there, even faster than pleasure-car plants.

Like the seed mentioned in the parable of the sower, some fell on good ground and grew to produce a bountiful harvest, but many withered by the wayside.

In the early days of the motor-truck industry men bought the finished vehicle, but later on the practice of selling chasses only became popular, and while today some manufacturers cater to the body trade, a large percentage of trucks are sold

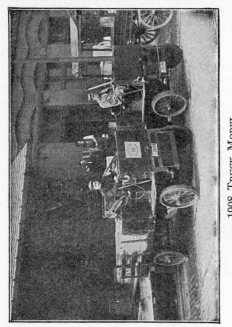

1908 TRUCK MODEL

1909 TRUCK MODEL

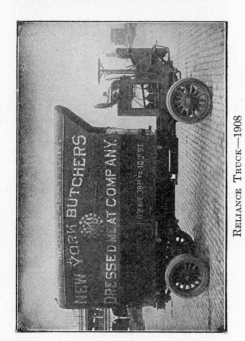

RELIANCE TRUCK—1908

RELIANCE TRUCK—1909

to the purchaser without the body, this being built by a local builder, the truck manufacturer furnishing a body builder's blue-print.

As in everything else, it has taken time to overcome the faults of the early trucks. Most all trucks above 1,500 pounds capacity are equipped with solid rubber tires, and while the solid rubber tires and the springs on the trucks give a great deal of resiliency, it was discovered that the steady pounding over all kinds of pavements soon racked a truck to pieces and that pleasure-car practice could not be followed successfully in building motor trucks.

5-TON TRUCK—1913–14

In the earlier days truck buyers made many mistakes in selecting the size or capacity of trucks. Some made the mistake of buying trucks too light for their work. Others selected trucks large enough to provide for exceptional or emergency loads, and would, for example, buy a truck of 3½-tons capacity when 90 per cent of their hauling was loads not exceeding 1½ or 2 tons. Thus they not only had a greater investment than necessary in the truck itself, but were paying an exclusive charge in the way of operating costs and depreciation.

But the experimental days have passed, both in the manufacture of motor trucks

LATEST ¾-TON MODEL

SOME ¾-TON TRUCKS OF THE LATEST MODEL

A 1½-Ton Truck of the Latest Model Dumping

A 1½-Ton Truck of the Latest Model Loading

REAR END CONSTRUCTION OF A MODERN 5-TON TRUCK

A 3½-TON TRUCK OF THE LATEST MODEL IN ACTIVE SERVICE

The Latest 3½-Ton Truck Doing Duty

and in their adaption to various lines of work. If the buyer has not determined by experience and investigation the kind and capacity of truck he should use, the older manufacturers are able to step in and analyze the work to be done and to intelligently recommend to the buyer what he should have.

That motor trucks not only furnish cheaper transportation than horse-drawn vehicles, but greatly extend the radius of operation, is quite generally conceded. This is shown by the enormous increase in the demand for motor trucks in all lines of business where goods of any kind are to be moved over any considerable distance.

CHASSIS OF THE LATEST MODEL 3½-TON TRUCK

With motor trucks, merchants have extended their deliveries to reach territory they could not touch under the horse-delivery system.

Market gardeners, who must have their product in the city markets early and have it fresh, can now sell their high-priced land adjoining the cities and go miles back in the country where as good ground can be bought for from one-tenth to one-fourth the price their suburban property will bring—and still be closer to market with their motor trucks than they were before with their horses.

Contractors can transport material long distances and save both time and money. Dairymen collect milk over a radius of thirty or forty miles and get it to market fresh. Freight and passenger lines are possible with motor trucks where a steam railroad or trolley system would not be practicable.

In short, the motor truck is revolutionizing transportation. As made today by the leading manufacturers, it is simple, durable and easy to operate and care for.

What is a Diving Bell?

Diving, aside from the pleasure afforded to good swimmers, is important in many different industries, particularly in fishing for pearls, corals, sponges, etc.

Without the aid of artificial appliances a skilful diver may remain under water for two, or even three minutes; accounts of longer periods are doubtful or absurd.

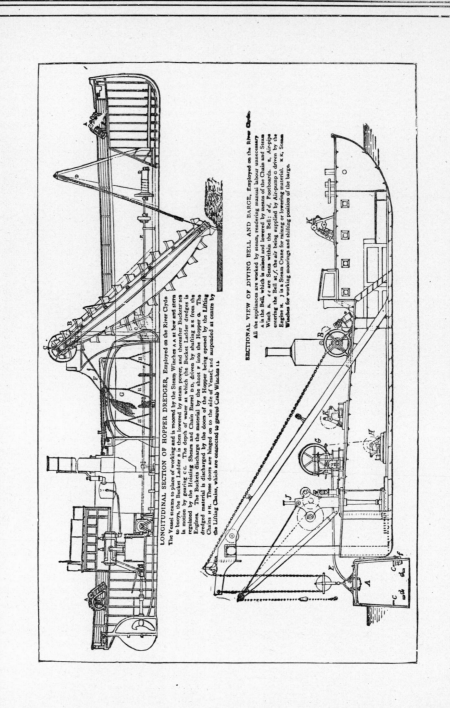

LONGITUDINAL SECTION OF HOPPER DREDGER, Employed on the River Clyde.

The Vessel steams to place of working and is moored by the Steam Winches A A at bow and stern to buoys, the Bucket Ladder B is then lowered by steam power, and thereafter Buckets c c are in motion by gearing c c. The depth of water at which the Bucket Ladder dredges is regulated by the Hoisting Steam and Chain Barrel D D, driven by shafting E E from the Engines. The Buckets discharge the dredged material by the shoot F into the Hopper G. The dredged material is discharged by the doors of the Hopper, being opened by the Lifting Chains H H. These doors are hinged on to the side of Vessel, and suspended at centre by the Lifting Chains, which are connected to geared Crab Winches I I.

SECTIONAL VIEW OF DIVING BELL AND BARGE, Employed on the River Clyde.

All the appliances are worked by steam, rendering manual labour unnecessary A is the Bell, which is raised and lowered by means of the Chain and Steam Winch B. c c are Seats within the Bell; d d, Footboards. x, Air-pipe supplying the Bell; f f, chair of the Bell, the air being supplied by the Air-pump z driven by the Engine H. J I is a Steam Crane for raising or lowering material. K K, Steam Winches for working moorings and shifting position of the barge.

Various methods have been proposed and engines contrived to render diving more safe and easy. The great object in all these is to furnish the diver with fresh air, without which he must either make but a short stay under water or perish.

Diving bells have been used very effectively. A diving bell is a contrivance for the purpose of enabling persons to descend, and to remain, below the surface of water for a length of time, to perform various operations, such as examining the foundations of bridges, blasting rocks, recovering treasure from sunken vessels, etc.

Diving bells have been made of various forms, more especially in that of a bell or hollow truncated cone, with the smaller end closed, and the larger one, which is placed lowermost, open.

The air contained within these vessels prevents them from being filled with water on submersion, so that the diver may descend in them and breathe freely for a long time provided he can be furnished with a new supply of fresh air when the contained air becomes vitiated by respiration. This is done by means of a flexible tube, through which air is forced into the bell.

A form, called the "nautilus," has been invented which enables the occupants, and not the attendants above, to raise or sink the bell, move it about at pleasure, or raise great weights with it and deposit them in any desired spot.

How are Harbors Dredged Out?

There are several forms of mechanical, power-operated dredges. One of the most common is the "clam-shell" dredge, consisting of a pair of large, heavy iron jaws, hinged at the back, in general form resembling a pair of huge clam shells. This with its attachments is called the grapple. In operation it is lowered with open jaws, and by its own weight digs into the ground that is to be excavated. Traction is then made on the chains controlling the jaws, which close; the grapple is hoisted to the surface and its contents discharged into scows alongside the dredge.

The dipper dredge, an exclusively American type, has a bucket rigidly attached to a projecting timber arm. In operation the bucket is lowered and made to take a curving upward cut, thus dipping up the bottom material, which is discharged through the hinged bottom of the bucket. The pump or suction dredge operates by means of a flexible pipe connected with a powerful centrifugal pump. The pipe is lowered into contact with the bottom to be excavated and the material is pumped into hopper barges or into a hopper-well in the dredge itself.

The center ladder bucket dredge operates by means of an endless chain of buckets moving over an inclined plane, which in structure is a strong iron ladder, one end of which is lowered to the sea bottom. The steel buckets scoop up the material at the bottom of the ladder, which they then ascend, and are discharged by becoming inverted at the upper end of the ladder. This dredge is the only one found satisfactory in excavating rock.

How is a Razor Blade Made?

The best scissors, penknives, razors and lancets are made of cast steel. Table knives, plane irons and chisels of a very superior kind are made of shear steel, while common steel is wrought up into ordinary cutlery.

In making razors, the workman, being furnished with a bar of cast steel, forges his blade from it. After being brought into true shape by filing, the blade is exposed to a cherry-red heat and instantly quenched in cold water. The blade is then tempered by first brightening one side and then heating it over a fire free from flame and smoke, until the bright surface acquires a straw color (or it may be tempered differently). It is again quenched, and is then ready for being ground and polished.

The Story of the Tunnels Under the Hudson River*

The building of the Hudson River tunnels was probably one of the most daring engineering feats ever accomplished. As is well known, the Hudson River, for the length of Manhattan Island, is approximately a mile wide, reducing in width at the Palisades north of Hoboken. In consequence of the unusual geographical situation, all trunk lines and other transit facilities in New Jersey terminate on the westerly shore of the Hudson, and passengers were of necessity compelled to use ferries to reach New York. A conservative estimate, which was confirmed by various counts, indicates that, prior to the construction of the tubes, the annual passenger traffic between New Jersey and New York was 125,000,000, and to handle this great volume of traffic the transportation companies assembled in the Hudson River a fleet of rapid ferry boats and maintained them up to the highest and most modern standards. But this very expeditious ferry service was not enough, and for many years there was a demand for facilities for more rapid transportation of the tremendous population residing in the suburban district of New Jersey tributary to New York City. As far back as 1873, a company had been organized to construct a tunnel under the river, but had met with numerous and most discouraging difficulties and obstacles, so that it was finally compelled to abandon the work, although it succeeded in building a considerable length of structure. Efforts were made at various times after that date to revive the work, with little or no results. In 1902 it was resumed, however, and a few years later was pushed to a successful end.

During the undertaking, more than 40,000 men were engaged in air-pressure work and there were many thousand more who did not work under air pressure. This vast army of men consisted of all nationalities and all grades and conditions of labor. The skilled tunnel workmen are men of character and ability, usually young, of good intelligence and sound of body, without a streak of fear or cowardice in their makeup. All of those characteristics are essential to under-water air-pressure work.

As is quite generally known, air pressure and tunnel shields were used in all of the under-water work. It might be well to here correct the misconception which exists in the minds of many, that the use of air pressure for such purposes is something comparatively new. This is not the case. The use of air pressure was a very early invention, and it is a matter of record that in 1830, Admiral Cochrane, afterwards Lord Dundonald, was granted letters patent for the use of air pressure in tunnel construction. The modern engineer has merely developed the art to a high degree.

The method of construction used in the Hudson River tunnels has been designated the "shield method." In this type of construction, the primary part of the tunnel structure consists of an iron shell, formed of segmental rings, bolted together through inside flanges, and forming a large articulated pipe or tube, circular in section. This iron shell is put in place segmentally by means of a shield, an ingenious mechanism which both protects the work under construction and assists in the building of the iron shell.

A tunneling shield consists essentially of a tube or cylinder slightly larger in diameter than the tunnel it is intended to build, which slides over the exterior of the finished lining like the tubes of a telescope. The front end of this cylindrical shield is provided with a diaphragm or bulkhead in which are apertures which may be opened

* Illustrations by courtesy of Jacobs & Davies, Engineers.

THE NEW SHORT CUT TO NEW YORK
Hudson River Tubes of the Hudson & Manhattan R. R. Co.

or closed at will.   Behind this diaphragm are placed a number of hydraulic jacks, so arranged that by thrusting against the last erected iron ring the entire shield is pushed forward.   The hind end of the shield is simply a continuation of the cylinder which forms the front end, and this hind end, or tail, always overlaps the last few feet of the built-up iron-shell tunnel.

When the openings in the bulkhead are closed, the tunnel is protected from the inrush of water or soft ground, and the openings may be so regulated that control is maintained over the material passed through.   After a ring of iron lining has been erected within the tail of the shield, excavation is carried out ahead.   When

ONE OF THE SIXTY-SEVEN-TON TUNNEL SHIELDS

sufficient excavation has been taken out, the jacks are again extended, thus pushing the shield ahead, and another ring of iron is erected as before.

For the erection of these heavy plates, a hydraulic swinging arm, called the "Erector," is mounted, either on the shield itself or on an independent erector platform, according to conditions.   This erector approaches closely the faculties of the human arm.   It is hydraulically operated and can be moved in any desired direction.   This method of construction can be followed in almost every kind of ground that can be met with, and it is especially valuable in dealing with soft, wet grounds.   In passing through materials saturated with water, the shield is assisted by using compressed air in the working chamber.

The employment of compressed air under such conditions is really a rather simple thing in itself, and means merely that the pressure of air in the chamber where men are working is maintained at a point sufficient to offset the pressure of the hydrostatic head of water and thereby prevent its inflow.   A crude comparison may be

CUTTING SHIELD HEAD

made by saying that if the ceiling of a room was weak and threatening to fall—if we filled the room with sufficient pressure of air, it would support the ceiling and prevent it falling in.   In tunnel work, air is supplied under compression from the mechanical construction plant located on the surface, and the pressure of air maintained in the working chamber is determined by the depth of the work below tide level, as the hydrostatic head increases with the depth.

Control of air pressure is never entrusted to any but the most reliable, competent and experienced man, as it is of the utmost importance that air pressure be maintained properly.   The first impulse of an inexperienced man, should he notice an

APRON IN FRONT OF SHIELD, FIVE MINUTES BEFORE SHOVING

inrush of water, would be to increase the air pressure, which might be a very dangerous thing to do.   An experienced man, however, would very likely first lower his pressure in such an emergency, and then put up with the nuisance and difficulty of having a good deal of water in his working chamber.   By doing this, he would permit the greater external pressure to squeeze the soil into the leaking pockets and thereby choke the leak.

To improperly or inopportunely raise the air pressure would be quite likely to result in the air blowing a hole through the roof of the tunnel heading, allowing all air pressure to escape, and permitting an uncontrollable volume of water to rush in and flood the work.

The outer shell of the tunnel shield is composed of two- or three-ply boiler plates, and the interior is braced with a system of steel girders.   The shields used weighed approximately sixty-seven tons each.   Sixteen or eighteen were used.   To move the shield forward, each shield was equipped with sixteen hydraulic jacks, arranged around the shield circumferentially. These jacks were controlled by a series of valves, which were so designed that any one jack or any set of jacks desired could be operated. This was necessary as the direction of the shield was, as it were, guided by the pressure of the jacks. When it was desired to alter the direction of the shield, either upwards or downwards, or to the right or left, the jacks on the opposite side to which the shield was to point, were operated. The hydraulic pressure operating these jacks was 5,000 pounds per square inch, and the total energy, when all jacks

CUTTING EDGE OF SHIELD IN NORTH TUNNEL

were employed at the same time, was equivalent to 2,500 tons, which was equal to eleven tons per square foot of heading.

Air pressure used to prevent the inflow of water and soft dirt varied from nothing up to forty-two pounds, although a fair average throughout was thirty-two pounds. It varied, of course, according to the condition encountered.

The working chamber is the space between the tunnel heading where work is in progress and the air-lock. The air-lock is a device used for the purpose of enabling workmen and materials to pass from the portion of the tunnel where the atmospheric pressure is normal into the portion where the air pressure is greater than normal; that is, the working chamber. The air-lock is a cylinder, usually about six feet in diameter and twenty feet in length, with a heavily constructed iron door at each end. This lock is placed horizontally in the tunnel at such a level as the conditions of the work necessitate, but usually near the bottom, and around this cylinder, and completely filling the cross-section of the tunnel, a concrete bulkhead is built and is known as the lock bulkhead. The two doors open in the same direction; the one at the normal pressure end opening into the cylinder, and the one at the heading end opening away from the cylinder. One door is always closed, and both doors are closed during the operation of entering or leaving the air-pressure section.

Going into the air pressure, the door at the heading end is held closed by the pressure of air against it while one is entering the lock, after which the outer door is also closed. A valve is then opened which permits the air to flow from the working chamber into the lock, until the lock becomes filled with air of the same pressure as exists in the heading. As soon as the pressure is thus equalized, the door at the heading end can be opened and the workmen pass into the heading. Going out, the operations are simply reversed. After the heading door is closed, with the workmen in the air-lock, a valve is opened which permits the air in the lock to

SHIELD CUTTING EDGE BREAKING THROUGH WALL AT SIXTH AVENUE AND TWELFTH
STREET, LOOKING SOUTH, OCTOBER 23, 1907

exhaust into the normal air, until the pressure within the lock reduces to the same as that outside, when the outer door can be opened and persons inside the lock pass out. Both operations must be gradual, as a sudden change from normal to high pressure, or *vice versa*, would be very dangerous to anyone.

In tunneling under the river, nearly every conceivable combination of rocks and soils were met, but for the most part the material was silt. In such material, with a pressure of 5,000 pounds per square inch on the shield jacks, the shield was pushed through the ground as though one pushed a stick into a heap of snow, pushing aside the silt, and thus obviating the necessity of removing any excavated material. Sand or gravel, or any material which would not flow or become displaced by the shield, of course, had to be excavated ahead of the shield, and removed from the heading prior to pushing it forward. In the silt the most satisfactory and economic progress was attained, and a record was made of seventy-two feet of finished tunnel, completely lined with iron, in one day of twenty-four hours.

The most difficult combination that had to be dealt with under the river was when the bottom consisted of rock and the top of silt and wet sand. In such cases, and there were many of them, the upper section of soft ground was first excavated and the exposed face securely supported with timbers ahead of the shield, and the rock underlying then drilled and blasted.   This was very tedious and expensive work.   Exceedingly small charges of dynamite had to be used and the procedure conducted with the utmost caution.

In the course of their progress, the shields were subjected to the most intense strains and hard usage, as may well be imagined.   One of the shields is illustrated. It was used to construct the south tunnel of the up-town pair of tubes, and passed from under the Hudson River, through Morton, Greenwich and Christopher Streets, into Sixth Avenue, and north to Twelfth Street, a total distance of 4,525 feet, of which

NORTH TUNNEL, SHOWING COMMENCEMENT OF NEW WORK

2,075 feet was through rock overlaid with wet sand.   During the progress of this shield, 26,000 sticks of dynamite were exploded in front of the cutting edge, causing great damage to the structure of the shield, so that when it arrived at its destination at Sixth Avenue and Twelfth Street, it was in such a condition of distortion that it was with difficulty that the tunnel lining could be erected behind it.

In pushing a shield forward with the battery of powerful hydraulic jacks, each advance is of two feet, and must be followed immediately by installation of the permanent lining in the rear.   In the early days, brick work was used for lining, and in recent years it has also been used to some extent, but even with the use of quick-setting Portland cement, neither brick work nor concrete has proved successful for subaqueous work, as the cement cannot reach the required strength within the time it is feasible to leave the shield standing before advancing it again.

During the early work on the north tube of the uptown tunnels, a point was reached where the rock was sixteen feet above the bottom of the tunnel, and the overlying silt was in a semi-fluid state.   Five barges of clay had been dumped in the

HOLE BROKEN THROUGH THE SOUTH TUBE OF THE NEW YORK AND JERSEY TUNNEL LOOKING WEST

river over this point to make a roof for the tunnel, but the fluid clay could not be controlled, and crept through the doors of the shield. After trying all known methods to get through, it was decided to bake this wet clay by means of intense heat. Two large barges of kerosene were sent into the tunnel, and an air pipe connected to them. Fine blow-pipes were also attached, and the fire from the blow-pipes was impinged on the exposed clay until it became caked sufficiently dry and hard to overcome slipping. It required eight hours of this baking to dry the clay hard, and, during this period, water had to be played continuously on the shield to avoid damage due to the high temperature. It is believed that this was the first time that soft material

NEW YORK AND NEW JERSEY TUNNEL SHOWING SIGNAL AND CAR

met with in tunneling under a river has been solidified by means of fire. Seven days after passing this troublesome point, the rock suddenly disappeared and the work proceeded without further trouble.

Another unusual situation occurred in the south tunnel of the uptown tubes. When the shield had advanced 115 feet from the Jersey side, the night superintendent in charge of the tunnel work, in his anxiety to push the work, disobeyed instructions, and the tunnel got away from him and was flooded, and his men had a narrow escape with their lives. In order to regain the tunnel, several schemes were considered, including that of sending a dredge through to dredge out the bed of the river just in advance of the shield, a sufficient depth to enable a diver to go down and timber up the exterior opening of the doorway, where the silt and mud had come through and filled the tunnel. This plan had to be abandoned, as the river above was almost entirely occupied by shipping that could not be interrupted.

Finally the difficult situation was met by obtaining two large and heavy mainsails, which made a double canvas cover measuring about sixty by forty feet. This

AN X-RAY VIEW OF A BUSY HALF-MILE UNDER THE GROUND ON THE JERSEY SIDE OF THE HUDSON RIVER

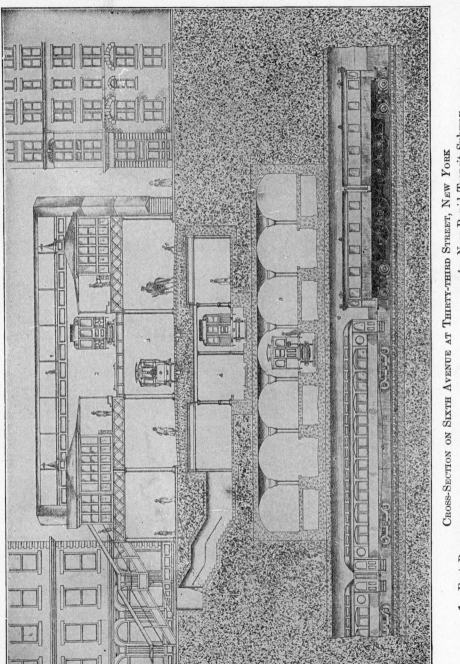

CROSS-SECTION ON SIXTH AVENUE AT THIRTY-THIRD STREET, NEW YORK

1. Foot Passage
2. Manhattan Elevated Railroad
3. Street Surface and Metropolitan Street Railway
4. New Rapid Transit Subway
5. Hudson and Manhattan Railroad Station
6. Pennsylvania Railroad Tunnel

canvas cover was then spread on a flat barge, small sections of pig iron being attached around the edges of it. Ropes were carried to fixed points to hold it in exact position. The barge was then withdrawn, and the canvas cover cropped to the bed of the river, and, most fortunately, it settled over the point where the leak had occurred, and a large number of bags of dirt were then deposited on it. An opening was then made in the bulkhead of the tunnel below, and for eight days material, under hydro-static pressure, forced its way into the tunnel, where it was loaded on cars, and finally the canvas was drawn into the hole, stopping it up. Additional material was then deposited into the river to fill the cavity, and finally the tunnel was recovered, pumped out and work resumed. This event is of somewhat historical interest, in that the two mainsails which were used were procured from the owner of the famous American cup defender, the well-remembered "Reliance."

Probably the most unique and interesting pieces of construction are the three junctions on the Jersey side of the river, where the uptown tunnels from New York diverge, north to Hoboken and south to Jersey City and New York downtown. For safe and expeditious operation of trains, where the schedule is only one and one-half minutes, it was imperative that grade crossings should be avoided. By grade crossings is meant the tracks of one service crossing the tracks of another service at the same grade. At the point in question, this was a knotty problem to solve, owing to the unusual operating conditions which had to be met, there being six separate and distinct operating classes of trains to be handled around this triangle.

To meet this situation, three massive reinforced concrete caissons were built on the surface. They are practically large two-story houses, each being over one hundred feet in length, about fifty feet in height, and about forty-five feet in width at their widest point. The bottom edges were sharp, and, with the use of air pres-sure and great weights, the three structures were sunk in the ground to the same grade as the intercepting tunnels, and the tunnels were then driven into them.

Particular attention should be given to the Jersey City to Hoboken tube, in the lower part of the caisson in the foreground, in the accompanying illustration, which curls around the Hoboken to Jersey City tube, and rises to the elevation of, and connects into, the New York to Hoboken tube, at the caisson in the background, at the left of the illustration. Very few of the people who travel through the tube are probably aware of such manipulation. At the same time, the arrangement absolutely avoids any grade crossing whatever, and without such an arrangement of tracks the road could not be operated with trains run so closely together as under the prevailing system.

In constructing the river tunnels the work was carried on simultaneously from opposite sides of the river, the tunnels meeting under the river, and it is interesting, if not remarkable, when one considers the difficulties under which the engineering work had to be carried on, to note that the tunnels met with practically absolute accuracy.

What Causes Floating Islands?

A floating island consists generally of a mass of earth held together by inter-lacing roots.

They occur on the Mississippi and other rivers, being portions of the banks detached by the force of the current and carried down the stream, often bearing trees. Sometimes such islands are large enough to serve as pasture grounds.

Artificial floating islands have been formed by placing lake mud on rafts of wicker-work covered with reeds. They were formerly used in the waters around Mexico, and may be seen in Persia, India, and on the borders of Tibet. On these the natives raise melons, cucumbers and other vegetables which need much water.

© U. & U.

THE GIANT DIRIGIBLE "LOS ANGELES"

Eighty-one hours after her start from Friedrichshafen, Germany, the Z R-3 arrived at the U. S. Naval Air Station at Lakehurst, N. J., on October 15, 1924. She is seen flying over the great hangar, which later was to house both the Z R-3 (rechristened the "Los Angeles") and the "Shenandoah," another giant of the air. Her length over all is 656 feet, and the diameter amidships is 90 feet. She is 24 feet shorter than the "Shenandoah," but larger in diameter by 11¼ feet. On September 2, 1925, the "Shenandoah," on a mid-western trip was caught in a line squall while attempting to ride out a severe storm, the giant ship's massive framework broke in three pieces, more than half a mile up in the air, and plunged in separate parts to the ground.

THE FIRST AIRPLANE TO REACH THE POLE

To Lieut.-Com. Richard E. Byrd, U. S. N., and Pilot Floyd G. Bennett belong the credit for being the first to fly to the North Pole. The feat was accomplished on May 9, 1926, the flight being made in 15½ hours, leaving Spitzbergen at 1.50 A. M., and returning in the afternoon of the same day. The 1200-mile flight was made in the Josephine Ford, an all metal, three-engined monoplane of 600 horsepower.

Copyright by Underwood & Underwood, N. Y.   THE FIRST PLANE TO CROSS THE ATLANTIC

The honor of being first to make the journey from America to Europe by airship fell to Lieut.-Commander A. C. Read, who piloted the U.S. seaplane, NC-4, from Newfoundland to Lisbon, Portugal, with a stop at the Azores. The photo shows Lieut.-Commander Read and the seaplane, NC-4, in readiness for their long trip, which begun May 16, and ended May 27th.

© U. & U   Home Again After Their Round-the-World Flight

Another brilliant chapter in the Conquest of the Air was written when the U. S. Army aviators returned to San Diego, Calif., Sept. 22, 1924, after their world-girdling flight of 30,000 miles.

© U. & U.   The First Men to Circumnavigate the World By Air

Neither heat nor cold, nor snow nor rain, nor fog nor tempest, frozen lands nor ocean wastes, could daunt these couriers of the air in their epoch-making flight. The aviators who guided the three planes are Lieutenants Wade, Arnold, Smith, Ogden, Nelson, and Harding.

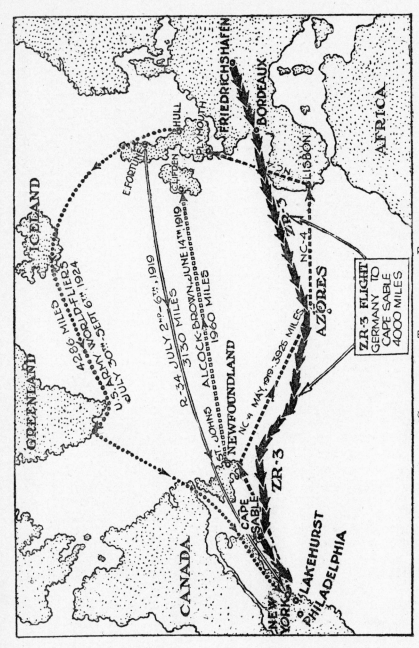

CHART OF THE TRANSATLANTIC FLIERS

This shows graphically the course of the first airplanes and airships which crossed the Atlantic. The U. S. Navy seaplane, N C-4 (Read), was first to make the flight, May 16–27, 1919, making a stop at the Azores (actual flying time 26 hours, 4 minutes). A British biplane (Alcock and Brown) made a non-stop flight, June 14–15, 1919, in 16 hours, 12 minutes. The British dirigible R-34 made a round trip from Great Britain to America and back, in July, 1919. The Z R-3, (now the "Los Angeles"), built in Germany, flew from there to Lakehurst, N. J., in October, 1924. The American round-the-world fliers crossed the North Atlantic by way of Iceland, Greenland, and Canada, in 1924.

The Wright Brothers and their Famous Aeroplane
The machine is shown in action and resting on the ground. The pictures were taken during the army test flights at Fort Myer, Virginia.

© *Underwood & Underwood, N.Y.*

Over the Pole from Spitzbergen to Alaska

Two days after Commander Byrd's historic airplane flight' to the Pole and back, the first transpolar flight', from Kings Bay, Spitzbergen to Teller, near Nome, Alaska, was made by Roald Amundsen (Norwegian), Lincoln Ellsworth (American), and Col. Umberto Nobile (Italian) and crew, in the dirigible airship *Norge*, May 11-15, 1926. On reaching the Pole, May 12, the flags of the three nations were dropped. The airship flew from Rome to Kings Bay, by way of Pulham (England), Oslo (Norway), and Leningrad (Russia). The photograph shows her arrival at Pulham.

COAST TO COAST, DAY AND NIGHT AIR MAIL SERVICE.

Twenty-eight hour transcontinental air mail delivery—an epochal innovation in postal service—has now become a reality. Giant mail planes, each loaded with 400 pounds of mail, leave New York and San Francisco daily. The service embraces delivery-stops at six stations, and besides those, there will be numerous relay stations. As the new service requires night-flying between Chicago and Omaha, great beacons, formed by powerful searchlights pointed into the sky, guide the fliers.

BEACON LIGHT FOR NIGHT MAIL PILOTS

NAVY RACING PLANE

This record breaking machine developed a speed of over 250 miles per hour. It is designed as a pursuit or fighting plane and is driven by a 500 horse-power motor.

© *Underwood & Underwood.*

AFTER A 4500-FOOT LEAP THROUGH THE AIR

Parachute jumping supplies a thrill for aviators that is unparalleled. The photograph shows Stephen Boudreau making a safe landing at Selfridge Field after jumping from an airplane at an altitude of 4500 feet. The 'chute did not open till he was 1000 feet from the ground. When he jumped, head first from his airplane, he dropped 3500 feet before his parachute opened.

ONE OF THE ARMY GIANT BOMBING PLANES

This Martin bomber is powered with two 400 horse-power Liberty motors which give it a maximum speed of $97\frac{1}{2}$ miles per hour. The great size of this plane (74 feet wide by 42 feet long) is necessary to carry the crew of four men together with its armament of machine guns and bombs.

New York Sky Line from an Airship

The Story of an Automobile Factory*

In visiting the factory where a half million automobiles are made each year, the visitor first comes to the power house.

In the construction of this building 5,200 tons of structural steel were used, the equivalent necessary to build a modern twenty-story sky-scraper.

Six engines of a combination gas-steam type, housed in this building, develop 36,000 combined horse-power. They are said to be the first gas-steam engines to be

CRANK SHAFT GRINDING DEPARTMENT

put to practical use. Another engine, using steam only, develops 2,000 horse-power, while several pumping engines increase the total horse-power of the plant to 45,000, probably the largest individual unit of any power-plant in the world, and said to be the only one of its kind in actual operation.

Some idea of the size of the engines is gained from the fact that the stroke is 72 inches, while the gas cylinders are 42 inches in diameter and the steam cylinders are 36 and 68 inches in diameter.

*Illustrations by courtesy of Ford Motor Co.

The Power House Equipment Includes the Largest Direct Current Control Board in the World

In producing the gas and steam for these engines only twenty-two tons of coal **per** hour are consumed, which speaks well for the efficiency of the engines. In addition **to** the steam, the daily consumption of producer gas for power purpose only is 28,512,000 cubic feet. Added to this figure for power gas, is another item of gas used in the factory for various purposes, which averages nearly 1,000,000 cubic feet per day, bringing **the** per diem consumption of gas by the company up to 29,512,000 cubic feet.

The main factory buildings are 900 feet long and 800 feet wide, four stories **in** height and of fire-proof construction. They are so designed that every part of **the** interior receives a full share of daylight.

The heating and ventilating of the factory building is accomplished in a modern, scientific manner. In the winter, warm washed air is forced through long ducts in the

OVERHEAD MONORAIL SYSTEM

floor up into the room. In the summer, cool washed air is handled in the same **way,** thus providing a clean, healthful atmosphere the year around. By this system the **air** in the factory is completely changed five times per hour.

At the right as the visitor enters the factory, is seen the tool construction department. Here are employed approximately 1,000 expert tool makers, machinists and die sinkers. These men are engaged in making new machinery (designed in the company shops), tools, jigs, fixtures and other machine shop accessories, and repairing those in use.

Overhead are traveling cranes which have a capacity of forty tons each. These cranes facilitate the work of the tool construction department by carrying cumbersome parts of machinery to and from it for alterations and repairs.

Here the visitor is standing upon the roof of a great tunnel, in which are all the heating, water and steam pipes, and the power cables running from the power house **to** various parts of the shop. This tunnel is large enough to permit the easy passage of a touring car.

Standing in front of the factory office, the visitor is doubly impressed with the magnitude of the view before him. In one continuous room, containing approximately 700,000 square feet of floor space, there are, in round numbers, 8,000 machines in actual operation, representing an outlay of about $5,000,000. These machines use some 2,500 gallons of lubricating oils and 11,000 gallons of cutting fluids each day. For driving the many machines, about fifty miles of leather belting are used, giving the room the appearance of a dense forest.

The visitor who is familiar with machine shop practice will notice at once the peculiar location and setting of machinery in this shop. The machines of a class, or

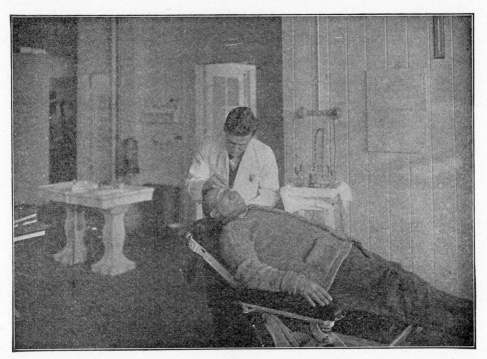

A CORNER OF THE MAIN HOSPITAL

type, are not all located in a single group or unit. Each department contains all of the necessary machinery to complete every operation on each part or piece it produces. To illustrate, a rough forging or casting is started in a department at one point, and after passing through the machines doing the required operations, it leaves this department in a finished condition, ready to be assembled into the car.

Such a system necessitates the grouping together of many different kinds of machines, as well as including brazing furnaces, cyanide furnaces and other special units (most generally found in separate buildings). Chutes run from one machine to another, so that a workman can transport a part from his operation to the next one by gravity. The results of this transportation system are remarkable, making a big saving in trucking expense, loss of material and the absence of usual delays.

As the visitor passes down through the machine shop, he particularly notices the sanitary conditions of the plant. There is a department, enrolling about 500 men,

PISTON MACHINING DEPARTMENT

whose duties are to keep the floors swept clean, the windows washed, in fact to keep the sanitary conditions surrounding the workmen as nearly perfect as possible. The floors of the entire plant are scrubbed at least once a week, with hot water and a strong solution of alkali, which removes the grease. Another department of about twenty-five men does nothing but paint the walls and ceilings of the factory, keeping everything fresh and clean.

To facilitate the inter-departmental transportation of materials in the factory, there is an overhead monorail system, comprising over 1½ miles of I-beam track. On this system are nine monorail cars, each car having two 2-ton hoists, by means of which great boxes and trays of material can be picked up and carried overhead from point to point in the shop.

Near the pay office is the main first-aid department. Here the chief surgeon has on his staff eight regular doctors and several first-aid nurses. The surgical equipment, which includes an X-ray machine, pulmotor, operating table and electrical appliances, as well as improved surgical instruments, enables the surgeon to cope with any accident.

The factory service office houses a department which is responsible for the well-being of factory employees. Of the 200 men in the division the majority are employed in the capacities of watchmen, to take care of the many entrances and exits of the plant and also to inspect the fire-fighting equipment which is distributed over the entire plant.

REAR AXLE ASSEMBLY

This fire-fighting equipment is being continually added to as the plant expands and now embraces more than a mile and a half of large hose, 10,000 feet of smaller hose, and 2,900 feet of hose attached to chemical tanks. There are 1,421 three-gallon chemical extinguishers and fifty-eight 40-gallon chemical tanks, mounted on wheels. Surrounding the plant are twenty-seven water hydrants equipped to handle two and three lines of hose, while inside the plant are eight hose-houses fully equipped. Pyrenes to the number of 175 are distributed about the departments for combatting electrical fires.

A new alarm system, said to be the most modern in the country, is being installed throughout the factory. Back of all other preparation is the sprinkler system, composed of water pipes hung next to the ceiling in all buildings and so designed that there is a sprinkler head every ten feet. Should the temperature in a room, for any reason, reach 160 degrees, the sprinkler heads in the immediate vicinity will open automatically, spraying out water which is piped from two tanks having a combined capacity of 600,000 gallons.

In addition to its other duties the factory service department has charge of the lost and found articles. Since this work was included, almost every sort of personal property, from key-rings to motor-cycles has been found and restored to the rightful owners.

Proceeding from the factory service office, the visitor finds himself in the main crane-way, devoted exclusively to the storage of parts in the rough, or semi-finished condition. This crane-way contains over 67,000 square feet of floor space. Overhead are two 5-ton electric cranes, so arranged that they can unload material from railway cars at one end of the crane-way and deposit it in a position to be picked up by the monorail cars, or placed in bins or barrels for storage. An interesting item in regard to these cranes is that the load can be moved in three directions at one time, this being accomplished by means of the small car hoist. While the crane proper is moving

CYLINDER MACHINING DEPARTMENT

through the crane-way, this car travels across the crane, and at the same time raises or lowers whatever may be suspended from it.

Passing by the crane-way one comes to the rear axle unit assembly. The manufacturing policy of the company is to make unit assemblies in different departments and deliver them to the final assembly.

In the unit assembly departments are received the finished parts from the machine shop. These parts are assembled on progressive traveling tracks. By this system each assembler, or operator, performs one operation only, and repeats this operation on every unit passing through the department. As a result, every operator soon becomes a specialist, and specialization is the fundamental principle of the entire organization.

The economic results from this system have been wonderful, as will be shown in some of the departments yet to be described. It saves floor space, and eliminates congestion due to trucking, as large quantities of material are piled along each side of the conveyor, and the unit in process of assembling is moved to the stock, rather than each individual piece of the assembly being distributed at different places.

After the rear axle has been completely assembled, it is immersed in a tank containing enamel, and is hung on a special trolley which runs by gravity along an I-beam track. This trolley carries the axle to an elevator, which lifts it to a conveyor baking oven, located in a section of the roof. The axles are continually moving through this oven, and at the expiration of about forty-five minutes emerge from the far end com-

MOTOR ASSEMBLY

pletely baked. They are automatically dropped onto another elevator which lowers them to the point near where they are used in the final assembly. All material and unit assemblies move in one direction—that is, toward the final assembly.

Beyond the rear axle section is the department that makes the magnets for the magneto, and also that in which the transmission is assembled on a conveyor track, ending in an automatic elevator which transports the completed transmission to the motor assembly line.

In the rear of the transmission department is the motor assembly. This assembly begins at the point where the cylinder machine shop ends, so that the movement of the cylinder from the time it arrives in the machine shop until it goes into the finished motor, is continuous. In the machining of the cylinder castings, and the operation of assembling the motor, close inspection of the work is noticeable. By the use of the assembling line, better inspection is possible, than where one or two men

assemble the entire motor.   In addition to the inspection in the assembly, there are
three points of trial, or working or testing, which show up any defects in the motor.

The final operation in the motor assembly line is the block test, where the motor
is inspected and tested before being assembled into the chassis.   On the block test, the
motor is driven by an electric motor for the final O. K. and tryout before being installed
in this chassis.

At the end of this testing period, if no defect has developed, the motor is approved,
placed upon a special truck and wheeled to the final assembling line.

The motor department just described furnishes an interesting illustration of the
economy of the moving assembling system.   Before the present system was installed
about 1,100 employees were required in this department, working a nine-hour day to
build 1,000 motors.   Today, as a direct result of the new methods of assembling, and
the efficiency gained through the profit-sharing with employees, about 1,000 men are assembling more than 2,000 motors in an eight-hour day.

The assembling of the front axle, dash and radiator are fully as interesting as the unit just described, but space will not permit a detailed explanation of them.

Perhaps the most interesting department in the whole factory, to the visitor, is the final assembly.   In this division, all the assembled units meet the assembly conveyor at the point where they are needed.   At the start of the track a front axle

Transmission Cover Department

unit, a rear axle unit and a frame unit are assembled.   This assembly is then started
in motion by means of a chain conveyor, and as it moves down the room at a constant
speed of eight feet per minute, each man adds one part to the growing chassis or does
one operation, which is assigned to him, so that when the chassis reaches the end of
the line, it is ready to run on its own power.

In following the final assembly line from the point where the chain conveyor
engages the frame and axles, the visitor is impressed with the dispatch with which
every movement is executed.   The gasoline tank, for example, comes down from the
fourth floor on a conveyor outside of the building, and drops through a chute onto a
bridge over the assembly line.   On this bridge is located a gasoline pump, from which
each tank receives one gallon of gasoline before it is installed in the car.

After the gasoline tank is assembled, a number of small units are added, such as
the hand brake control lever, gasoline feed pipe, and fender irons, until the point is
reached at which the motor is placed in the frame.

Ordinarily the setting of a motor in the frame is a long operation, but in this
assembly the motor is elevated by a hoist, and lowered into place while the chassis is
moving along the conveyor track.   From this point, other small parts are added, and
bolts tightened, until the growing chassis reaches the bridge on which the dash unit is
deposited by a chute from the second floor, where it is assembled.   The dash unit
includes the dash, complete steering gear, coil, horn, and all wiring ready to be attached
to the motor, so that its installation is rapid.

Further along, such parts as the exhaust pipe, muffler, and side pans for the motor are quickly fastened in place, and the wheels are brought into the assembly.

There will be noticed the vertical chutes, extending through the ceiling. Down through these, from the third floor, come the wheels, with the tires mounted and inflated to the proper pressure. From this point the chassis moves under the bridge upon which are stored the radiators, which have been delivered by a belt conveyor.

At the end of the assembly line, the rear wheels on the finished chassis drop into a set of revolving grooved wheels, sunk into the concrete floor, and driven by an over-

INSPECTION OF FRONT AXLE AFTER MACHINING

head motor. Two ends are accomplished by this operation. First, when the wheels of the car revolve with the grooved wheels, this motion is transmitted to the differential, through the drive shaft to the motor, limbering up all these parts. The second is that while the parts are being limbered up, the switch is turned on and the motor started.

At the end of the line the complete chassis is driven out into the yard under its own power. Guided by practiced hands it moves swiftly out into the yard, turns sharply and enters the final inspection line. A corps of inspectors at this point takes charge of the chassis, and the responsibility for each part is assigned to some one man.

From the final testing line the chassis is driven to the body chutes, which extend into the factory yard from the third floor of the new six-story building, and are so constructed that the chassis may be driven under them. The bodies are let down the chutes on belt conveyors, picked up by small derricks and swung over onto the chassis. The bodies are at this time placed on the chassis merely as a means of a rapid transportation to the freight cars, for in ordinary transportation the bodies are packed in the cars separate from the chassis.

In the rear of the main plant are two six-story buildings each 60 feet wide by 845 feet long, built parallel to each other and connected by a crane-way 40 feet wide the full length and height of the buildings.

The boiler house, which furnishes the steam for heating the entire plant, is located in the rear of these buildings.   The method of heating is worthy of particular interest,

INSTALLING MOTOR ON FINAL ASSEMBLY LINE

as the air is forced over coils of steam pipes located in pent houses on the roofs, and from this point is driven down into the various rooms through the hollow columns which support the floors.   In the summer, cool washed air is forced down through these same columns, maintaining a normal, even temperature, compatible with the state of the weather.

Various unit assemblies, small machine departments, and store rooms are located here in addition to all the body work.

Practically the entire first floors are used as a receiving department, where all the material consigned to the company is checked and inspected.   Railway tracks run the full length of both crane-ways, facilitating the unloading and loading of supplies and parts.

The body department occupies the greatest amount of space, requiring, with the upholstering department, most of the three upper floors. In addition to this work the construction of tops, curtains and radiators is carried on, and a large space is used for the storage of equipment and parts, such as lamps, horns, tires, etc. A part of the second floor is devoted to the storage and the shipping of parts to branches and agents.

Having seen the body placed upon the chassis, the visitor passes along toward the north. In succession are the chutes on which the crates of fenders are sent down from the fourth floor of the main factory building to the shipping platform. Here is also a chain elevator, which raises the wheels out of the freight cars to a runway on which

MECHANICAL STARTER—END OF FINAL ASSEMBLY

they travel by gravity to the third floor of the main factory. With this device it is possible for three or four men to unload about 6,000 wheels each day.

One passes the loading docks, where crews of six to eight men each, working as a unit, remove the bodies and wheels from the chassis, and load them into freight cars. So proficient are these loaders that a freight car is loaded in twenty minutes. Approximately 150 loaded freight cars are sent out every day. Besides these factory shipments there are more than 300 loaded freight cars in transit each day from branch factories.

The bodies are shipped separate from the chassis, being stood on end in one-half of the car and protected from dust by coverings.

The chassis are put in the other end of the car, the first one being carried in, minus the wheels, and placed in a diagonal position. Brackets of cast iron, for holding the axle to the floor, are made in the foundry. The front axle rests on the floor, and the rear axle rests against the opposite wall near the top of the car. A block, with a hole which just fits the axle, holds it against the wall.

The next chassis is brought in and placed with its front axle opposite the first one.

The Body Chute, where Bodies are Placed on Each Chassis

In this way the chassis alternate until the car is full. The space in the center of the car contains the fenders, and other removable parts of the equipment.

Just beyond the loading docks is the foundry.

The foundry is one of the most interesting divisions of the entire plant, and ranks, perhaps, as one of the most unique in the country, as far as practice and equipment are concerned. As a general rule, foundry practice has not shown the changes in an increase of production that machine departments have, but in this foundry, due to standardization of parts and specialization on the one car, it has been possible to

CRANEWAY, SHOWING LOADING PLATFORMS

devise and install the unique equipment now used, which brings this department down to the plane of expense and up in the labor-saving efficiency prevailing throughout the entire plant.

This department works twenty-four hours a day, in three shifts of eight hours each; iron is being melted and poured continuously during the day and first night shifts. An average of over 400 tons of iron is poured daily, and 426 tons of gray iron have been poured in a single day. This tonnage is especially interesting, as it is produced on a floor space of only 36,324 square feet.

All this iron is poured on overhead power-driven mold carriers, which travel about twelve feet per minute. These mold carriers have suspended from them pendulum-like arms, on the lower end of which is a shelf. The molders who make the molds for the castings are stationed alongside of these conveyors; the molding sand with which they fill the flasks is stored overhead in a hopper, the gate of which discharges directly onto the molding machine.   There are two molders for each part, one making the "drag," or lower part of the mold, the other making the "cope," or the upper half.

When these two halves of the mold are finished they are put together, or "closed" on the shelf of the conveyor, which carries the finished mold to the man who pours the molten metal. The molten metal is brought to this man's station by means of large ladles, suspended on a trolley on an I-beam track, running from the cupola through the entire length of the foundry. This does away with the necessity of carrying the ladle of iron a long distance, thus saving much time and lessening the liability to accidents.

CONTINUOUS CORE-OVEN

While the mold is being poured it is in constant motion, and continues so from the pouring station to the end of the conveyor, where the casting is shaken out of the sand.   The casting is thrown to one side to cool, the flasks are hung upon hooks on the

QUENCHING STEEL FORGINGS IN HEAT-TREATMENT OPERATION

arm of the conveyor, to be returned to the molder, and the sand drops through a grating in the floor onto a belt conveyor; on this conveyor it is dropped on an elevator, raised overhead and "cut," or mixed with new sand, and passed on to another conveyor, which deposits it in the hoppers above referred to, ready for the molder's use. In all this journey the sand is never shoveled.

In casting cylinders, on account of their size and the care needed in setting the cores, a different style conveyor is used. The molder, instead of putting the mold on a pendulum conveyor, places it upon a track, where it is moved by means of a chain.

During this travel the various cores are set, and the molds closed, moving to the point where the men with large ladles pour the mold. From this point it is transferred to another track. As it travels down this track, the casting is given an opportunity to "set," or cool. At the end of this line it is shaken out over a grating, and the sand handled in the same manner as on the smaller conveyors.

As soon as the castings have cooled sufficiently they are put into great horizontal cylinders, called tumblers. Small metal stars are placed in these tumblers with the castings, and when the tumbler is full it is started revolving. This shakes all the sand from the castings and they come out clean and bright. This process continues for some time, depending on the size of the castings. Near the tumblers are the grinding wheels, upon which are ground off the rough edges and the castings put into shape for the machine shop. They are sorted, inspected and counted before removing from the foundry.

STRAIGHTENING CRANK SHAFTS ON STEAM HAMMERS

Another interesting feature is the handling of sand in the core room. The sand is handled entirely in a gallery built above the room, equipped with storage bins and sand mixers. Over each core-maker's bench is a hopper, connected with the floor of the gallery. When the sand is mixed it is dropped through holes in the floor into the hoppers, which deposit the sand on the bench convenient for the core-maker.

This core room contains perhaps the only endless chain core oven in this country in which are two endless chain conveyors. These have hanging upon them large sets of shelves, upon which the cores are placed for baking. It is impossible to over-bake or under-bake a core, as the rate of travel of the conveyor is fixed at a speed which leaves the core in the oven the correct length of time.

All the aluminum parts as well as a large proportion of the brass, are also cast in this foundry.

The process of heat-treating steel forgings before they are machined is one of the most scientific and accurate features in the manufacture of this car. Vanadium steel is used throughout the construction of the car. It has been found from long and deep experimental work by engineers, that the structural condition of steel may be changed by the application of heat, and with certain conditions ascertained, by bringing a piece of steel to a certain temperature, and then setting the molecular condition in the steel by sudden cooling, or quenching, that the steel of a crank shaft can be made to stand impact, and that the steel of a front axle can be made a most efficient agent to withstand vibration.   Practically every forging in the car is made of a special steel, for which a special formula of heat-treating has been worked out, in accordance with the work, or strain, the part must stand in the finished car.

It is by the use of this high-grade, scientifically heat-treated vanadium steel that it is possible for the company to manufacture a light-weight car, which has the ability to stand up under severe usage, and to sell at the low price at which it is sold today.

The heat-treating department contains about seventy-five large furnaces, which consume from 5,000 to 6,000 gallons of fuel oil per day.   It is into these furnaces that

PYROMETERS BY WHICH THE TEMPERATURE OF THE FURNACES IS REGULATED

the various forgings are placed for heat-treating.   In each one is introduced a pyrometer, connected electrically with a switchboard located in a separate building.   This switchboard is very similar to those used in telephone exchanges.   The operator takes the temperature reading of every furnace on his board about every minute.   The furnace foreman is notified by the operator as to the temperature by means of small colored electric lights, located above the furnace.   The lighting of all the colors at the same time is the signal to pull the heat or, in other words, extinguish the fires and empty the furnace.   After the required heat has been reached, the forgings are allowed to either cool in the air, be covered with pulverized mica, or quenched in a special solution, as the case may require.

In this department are also located many grinding wheels and tumbling barrels, similar to those used in the foundry, so that the various forgings may be put in first-class condition before they are laid down in the machine shop.

The operations in the manufacture of the crank case, or engine pan of the motor

This Belt Carries the Finished Parts and Scraps from the Punch Presses

is of interest for several reasons, and the visitor has the opportunity of viewing these processes.

The crank case in itself is interesting because it is made from drawn sheet steel, instead of cast aluminum, as was once thought necessary.

The presses on which these crank cases are drawn are especially worthy of note,

TAKING INDUSTRIAL MOTION PICTURES
Operator suspended from traveling crane.

for they weigh about fifty tons each, and exert a downward pressure of about 900 tons. It is necessary that this drawing be made in four operations; the first and second are particularly interesting, on account of their depths, which are $5\frac{1}{2}$ and $9\frac{3}{16}$ inches, respectively. After each drawing operation it has been found necessary that the case be annealed, to restore the strained or calloused surface produced at certain points by contact with the dies. to a soft, ductile condition, to conform to the balance of the case, or, in other words, to produce a homogeneous condition of the surface.

This annealing is accomplished by a furnace through which the cases are moved by a chain conveyor onto an elevator which raises them up through the roof, and down again, depositing them near the press which is to perform the next drawing operation. While moving on this elevator the cases are cooled so that they can be handled as soon as they are lowered.

After the drawing operations have been completed, the case is trimmed; the side

ASSEMBLING INDUSTRIAL MOTION PICTURE FILMS

arms, front end supports, and radius rod support, are riveted and brazed to it, making a case as strong and solid, and yet as light, as it is possible to make.

Near these crank case presses are located several hundred punch and drawing presses of various sizes. These presses blank out and draw from sheet steel of special analysis, a large number of parts (which in ordinary practice are made from castings or forgings), carrying the same strength, but also very much lighter in weight.

The interesting feature of this department is the arrangement of the presses, which enables all finished parts, as well as the scrap steel, to be deposited upon a traveling belt conveyor, at the end of which are stationed men who sort the various parts, and place them in proper receptacles. By this arrangement it is possible to place the presses closer together than could be done if it were necessary to leave aisles large enough for trucking the material to and from the presses, effecting a great saving in floor space.

The pictures with which this story is illustrated were all made by the photographic department of the company, and are but a few of the thousands on file, portraying

A THOUSAND ASSEMBLED CHASSIS

At last accounts the production was 2,768 cars in a single day.

details of every operation in the manufacture of a car. The department is completely equipped to take and produce motion picture films of the highest quality.

The growth of this department, in its own peculiar field, has kept pace with the growth of the company as an industrial factor. But a few years ago, this department was an incident only. The quarters were small, the staff was composed of two men, and the entire work was confined to making photographs of the cars and parts for advertising literature.

A modern studio is now maintained on the fourth floor of the factory—the staff of skilled operators numbering twenty.

The moving picture portion of the company's work is, in volume, the largest conducted by any industrial concern. As a matter of interest, it is estimated that the operations of this department in the "movie" field are equal in magnitude to the efforts of many of the better known film-producing studios which specialize in such work. And, large as the scope of operations already is, it is still growing, in response to an increasing demand for pictures of the factory as well as of events of general interest.

The expression "The tune that the old cow died of" has been used to express the giving of advice instead of material help, because of an old song which told of a man who had nothing to feed his cow upon and so played her this tune: "Consider, good cow, consider. This isn't the time for grass to grow."

How do Big Buildings Get their Granite?

Stones suitable for important building purposes are usually found at a good distance below the surface. In the case of unstratified rocks, such as granite, the stone is most frequently detached from the mass by blasting, a process by which much valuable stone is wasted, and a different method is employed whenever it is found possible. In the case of stratified rocks, blocks are separated by hand tools alone. Small holes a few inches apart are cut along a certain length of rock, into which steel wedges are inserted. These are driven in by heavy hammers until the stratum is cut through. The large blocks necessary for monumental purposes are generally obtained in this way, and before they leave the quarry they are usually reduced as nearly as possible to a rectangular form.

Granite is a fire-formed rock which has been exposed to great heat and pressure deep down in the earth. It is one of the most abundant of that species of rocks seen at or near the surface of the earth, and was formerly considered as the foundation rock of the globe, or that upon which all sedimentary rocks repose. Granite supplies the most durable materials for building, as many of the ancient Egyptian monuments testify. It varies a great deal in hardness as well as in color and for that reason must be selected with care when desired for building purposes.

Granite abounds in crystallized earthy materials, and these occur for the most part in veins traversing the mass of the rock. Of these minerals, beryl, garnet and tourmaline are the most abundant. The decomposed felspar of some varieties of granite yields the kaolin used in porcelain manufacture. Granite is not rich in mineral ores.

It is abundant in America and is largely quarried in the United States for building purposes, especially in New England. The best known quarries are those of New England. There is a great deal of granite found in South Carolina and Georgia, but much of this, as well as that of some parts of California, is in a singular state of decomposition, in many places being easily penetrated by a pick. Granite quarried anywhere in which felspar predominates is not well adapted for buildings, as it cracks and crumbles down in a few years.

GRANITE QUARRY

A large quarry near Barre, Vermont. The rock occurs in what is known as "sheet formation."

THE PENNSYLVANIA RAILROAD COMPANY'S "BROADWAY LIMITED," A TWENTY-HOUR TRAIN BETWEEN NEW YORK AND CHICAGO*

ALL-STEEL PASSENGER TRAIN, DRAWN BY ELECTRIC LOCOMOTIVE, AS USED IN THE NEW YORK TUNNELS OF THE PENNSYLVANIA RAILROAD*

* Courtesy of the Pennsylvania Railroad Co.

Electric Train on the Main Line of the Pennsylvania Railroad*

Locomotive Equipped with Fire-Fighting Apparatus*

* Courtesy of the Pennsylvania Railroad Co.

TRAIN OF 120 LOADED COAL CARS DRAWN BY A SINGLE LOCOMOTIVE*

EXPRESS TRAIN READY TO LEAVE THE BROAD STREET STATION OF THE PENNSYLVANIA
RAILROAD AT PHILADELPHIA*

* Courtesy of the Pennsylvania Railroad Co.

Courtesy of the Pennsylvania Railroad Co.   ABOARD THE "BROADWAY LIMITED"
The observation car is provided with book-cases, a writing desk and stenographer.

A String of All-Steel Freight Cars Just Turned Out of the Shops*

Electric Baggage Truck Hauling Trailers*

* Courtesy of the Pennsylvania Railroad Co.

35

BIRD'S-EYE VIEW OF THE PENNSYLVANIA STATION, NEW YORK CITY*

THE "UNION STATION" AT WASHINGTON, D. C.*

* Courtesy of the Pennsylvania Railroad Co.

FREIGHT TRAIN, EASTBOUND, ON THE HORSESHOE CURVE*

OVEN FOR DRYING PAINT ON PASSENGER CARS AT THE ALTOONA, PA., SHOPS OF THE PENN-
SYLVANIA RAILROAD COMPANY*

* Courtesy of the Pennsylvania Railroad Co.

LOCOMOTIVE BUILDING

View in the erecting shop where the locomotives are assembled. The traveling crane in the foreground is capable of transporting a locomotive to any part of the shop.

Courtesy of the Baldwin Locomotive Works.

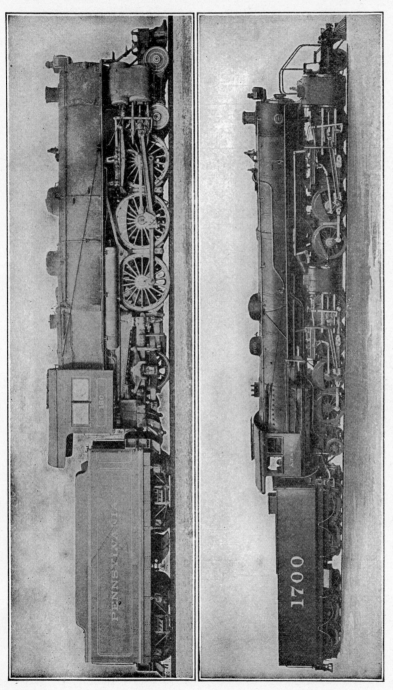

MODERN LOCOMOTIVES

The upper view shows a passenger locomotive used on the fastest heavy express trains. It weighs 272,000 pounds, is 70 feet long with tender, and has a drawbar pull of 30,700 pounds. The lower view shows a Mallet Articulated Type freight locomotive, one of the largest ever built. It consists of two units, linked together to give flexibility to the wheel base. The locomotive is 108 feet 10 inches long, weighs 700,000 pounds, and has a drawbar pull of 96,000 pounds. Oil is used for fuel.

Courtesy of the Pennsylvania Railroad and the Baldwin Locomotive Works.

TYPE FREIGHT LOCOMOTIVE—THE DELAWARE & HUDSON Co.
Built by American Locomotive Company.

FOUNDRY
Schenectady, N. Y., Works, American Locomotive Company

PACIFIC TYPE PASSENGER LOCOMOTIVE—NEW YORK CENTRAL R. R.
Built by American Locomotive Company.

4-8-2 TYPE PASSENGER LOCOMOTIVE—CHICAGO, ROCK ISLAND & PACIFIC R. R.
Built by American Locomotive Company.

MACHINE SHOP
Schenectady, N. Y., Works, American Locomotive Company.

MIKADO TYPE FREIGHT LOCOMOTIVE—DELAWARE, LACKAWANNA & WESTERN R. R.
Built by American Locomotive Company.

ROD SHOP
Schenectady, N. Y., Works, American Locomotive Company.

MALLET TYPE FREIGHT LOCOMOTIVE—BALTIMORE & OHIO R. R.
Built by American Locomotive Company.

CYLINDER SHOP
Schenectady, N. Y., Works, American Locomotive Company.

NEW ENGINE BREAKS TRANSIT RECORDS

Two world records were smashed on November 4, 1925, when a new oil-electric car of the Canadian National Railways completed a run from Montreal, Que., to Vancouver, B. C., a distance of 2,937 miles, in 67 hours. This is the fastest run on record and in addition the motor of the car was not stopped during the entire trip. The average speed was 43½ miles an hour. The car is designed to meet bus competition and seats 57 persons, with ample space for baggage. It can be operated from either end. A fuel oil engine, the lightest of its kind ever developed except for aviation purposes, operates an electric generator, which in turn supplies the motive power for the car.

Courtesy of the Westinghouse Electric and Manufacturing Company.

THE WORLD'S LARGEST LOCOMOTIVES

The world's most powerful locomotives are in operation on the Virginian Railway. These locomotives are electrically operated. They are so large that they had to be built in three sections for ease in turning curves. Each weighs 637 tons, is 152 feet long, and has a normal rating of 7125 horsepower. They are used in hauling heavy coal trains over the steep grades where the railroad climbs the western slope of the Allegheny Mountains. Two of these huge engines are coupled to either end of a coal train nearly a mile long and weighing 6,000 tons, and run it up a 2 per cent grade without apparent effort at the rate of 14 miles an hour. In marked contrast was the operation of the steam engines formerly used. Under steam operation, three of the largest Mallet compound locomotives had to labor heavily in order to move smaller trains up the grade at less than half the electrics' speed.

The Story of an Up-to-Date Farm*

A man who had been tied in a great city all his life made his first visit the other day to an up-to-date farm. He was so surprised at what he saw that he wrote a letter describing his emotions. Some of it is worth quoting because it shows a picture of the modern farm as it was cast upon the eye of a man who had never seen it before.

"I was whisked from the railway station in a big touring car, through beautiful country. Then we turned up a flower and shrub lined concrete driveway, and stopped

THE WOMAN ON THE FARM AT LAST ENJOYING THE BENEFIT OF LABOR-SAVING MACHINES

This small mounted kerosene engine runs the washing machine, pump, cream separator and churn. It is easily drawn about from place to place by hand where its energy is needed to lighten the housework.

by a home, capacious and modern. Inside I found electric lights, electric iron and bathroom with running water.

"I found that the good man of the house had his own electric light and water plant, run by kerosene engines, that his cows were milked automatically, that he pulled his plows, harrows, drills, manure spreader and binder with a kerosene tractor, that his hired men went about the farm doing everything as they rode on some machine, that he went to church and town in an automobile, and that he delivered the products of his farm to market with a motor truck. Everything was managed like a factory. Things went forward with order and with assurance. Everyone was busy and happy."

This is an optimistic picture of one of our best farms, but compare it with the

Illustrations by courtesy of International Harvester Company of America, unless otherwise indicated.

best that could be found only a few hundred years ago.   The best farmer of those days held all the land for miles around and lived in a castle in the middle of it.   The castle was dark and cold and was made of rough stones fitted together.   The poor farmers were serfs and came two or three days out of a week to their master's house to work.   Those were the great days of their lives, for then they ate of the master's food.

Food—that was the problem of those long tired years which dragged through the ages, when nearly everyone was a farmer, and a farmer with crude tools held in his hands.   Time was when practically the whole world went to bed hungry and rose again in the morning craving food, just as half the millions of India do today because they do with their hands what a machine should do.

THE MOTOR TRUCK MAY BE USED BY THE FARMER EVEN IN HILLY AND MOUNTAINOUS PLACES

This photograph was taken near the summit of Pike's Peak.

People in the hungry, unfed ages grew so used to privation that even the philosophers accepted sorrow and woe as a matter of course and dilated upon their virtues for chastening the human soul.   "It is better to go to the house of mourning than the house of mirth," said one of the prophets, and such words brought comfort to the hungry, miserable millions who had to mourn and go hungry whether it was to their advantage or not.

Today the years glide by like pleasant pictures.   We are fed, busy and happy. We almost let the dead bury their dead today while the living drive forward their tasks, achieving as much in a year as the old ages did in twenty.   We have learned to feed ourselves and the food fills our bodies and brains with energy which must find expression in useful accomplishment.   "Blessed is he who has found his work

THE REAPING HOOK WAS THE FIRST IMPLEMENT USED FOR HARVESTING GRAIN OF WHICH WE HAVE RECORD

This pictures the reaping hook as still used in India.

to do," we say nowadays, "but thrice blessed is he who has found a machine to do it for him."

Thread your way back through history to the time when the slender lives of men expanded into full and useful employment, and you will find that, so far as raising the

THE SCYTHE IS A DEVELOPMENT OF THE REAPING HOOK
The blade was made larger and the handle longer so two hands could be used.

world's food is concerned, it all began with the invention of the reaper in only the last century. It is interesting to know something of the precarious entry of this machine and something of the dark background from which it emerged.

The Reaping Hook or Sickle.

From the first pages of history we find that the reaping hook or sickle is the earliest tool for harvesting grain of which we have record. Pliny, in describing the practice of reaping wheat says, "One method is by means of reaping hooks, by which the straws are cut off in the middle with sickles and the heads detached by a pair of shears." Primitive sickles or reaping hooks made of flint or bronze are found among the remains left by the older nations. Pictures made in 1400 or 1500 B. C. upon the tombs at Thebes in Egypt, which are still legible, show slaves reaping with sickles. This crude tool, brought into use by ancient Egypt, remained almost stationary as to form and method of use until the middle of the last century.

The scythe, which is a development from the sickle, enables the operator to

THE CRADLE WAS DEVELOPED IN AMERICA BETWEEN 1776 AND 1800 AND IS AN OUTGROWTH OF THE SCYTHE. IT IS STILL USED IN SOME PLACES

use both hands instead of one. The scythe is still a familiar tool on our farms, but it serves other purposes than that of being the sole means of harvesting grain.

The Cradle.

Gradually the blade of the scythe was made lighter, the handle was lengthened, and fingers added to collect the grain and carry it to the end of the stroke. With the cradle the cut swath could be laid down neatly for drying preparatory to being bound into bundles. This tool is distinctly an American development. The colonists, when they settled in this country, probably brought with them all the European types of sickles and scythes, and out of them evolved the cradle.

With the cradle in heavy grain an experienced man could cut about two acres a day, and another man could rake and bind it into sheaves, so that two men with the cradle could do the work of six or seven men with sickles.

The American cradle stands at the head of all hand tools devised for the harvesting of grain. When it was once perfected, it soon spread to all countries with very little change in form. Although it has been displaced almost entirely by the modern reaper, yet there are places in this country and abroad where conditions are such that reaping machines are impractical and where the cradle still has work to do.

HARVESTING IN THE WEST

Reproduced by permission of the Philadelphia Museums.

STEAM HARVESTER AND THRESHER

The upper view shows side-hill harvesters drawn by teams of twenty-eight horses each. The machines cut the grain, and tie it up in bundles, which are dropped alongside. The machine in the lower view is self-propelling, cuts and threshes the grain, throwing out the straw, and places the grain in sacks ready for loading on the wagon.

Reproduced by permission of the Philadelphia Museums.

Early Attempts to Harvest with Machines.

The beginning of practical efforts in the direction of harvesting by wholly mechanical means may be said to date from the beginning of the last century, about the year 1800, although very little progress was made from that time up to the year 1831.

It is true that the Gauls made use of an instrument nearly two thousand years before, but this contrivance fell into disuse with the decline of the Gallic fields. Pliny describes this machine which was used early in the first century and which might be termed a stripping header. Palladius, four centuries later, describes the same sort of machine. This device of the Gauls had lance-shaped knives, or teeth

THE MOWING MACHINE HAS REPLACED THE SCYTHE FOR CUTTING HAY, AND THE KEROSENE TRACTOR HAS REPLACED EXPENSIVE HORSE POWER FOR PULLING THE MOWERS

The tractor has a pull of 10 H. P. on the drawbar and is pulling three mowers, laying down a swath of hay 21 feet wide.

with sharpened sides, projecting from a bar, like guard teeth, but set close together to form a sort of comb. As it was pushed forward, the stalks next the heads came between these sharp teeth and were cut or stripped off into a box attached to and behind the cutter bar and carried by two wheels. When the box was filled with heads, the machine was driven in and emptied. This is the way in which it is supposed that it was worked, and the illustration is the generally accepted representation of it as roughly reconstructed from the old Latin description by Pliny.

Near the close of the past century, the subject of grain-reaping machines again began to claim the attention of inventors. In July, 1799, the first English patent was granted to Joseph Boyce. In 1806, Gladstone of England built and patented a machine which not only attempted to cut the grain, but also to deliver it in gavels to be bound. In 1807, Plucknett and Salmon both patented machines. In 1811, Smith and Kerr took out patents. In 1822, Henry Ogle, a schoolmaster of Rennington, assisted by Thomas and Joseph Brown, invented the so-called Ogle reaper. The next, and last, reaper of this period was invented by Patrick Bell of Carmyllie, Scotland, in 1826.

Nearly all of these early reapers relied upon scythes or cutters with a rotary motion or vibrating shears. This method of cutting was essentially wrong, and none of the machines ever appeared to have gained or long retained the favor of the farmers. That these early attempts were all unsuccessful is evidenced by the fact that at the great World's Fair in London in 1851, the United Kingdom could not present a single reaping machine. English journals and writers of that period, without a single exception, spoke of the American reapers which were exhibited as "completely successful." For the real progress towards solving the problem of harvesting grain with machines we must turn to America.

THE McCORMICK REAPER OF 1845

American invention in this line, so far as there is any record, began with the patent issued to Richard French and T. J. Hawkins of New Jersey, May 17, 1803. No reliable description of this machine seems to be extant. Five patents of no importance were issued between that time and 1822, when Bailey took out a patent. Cope and Cooper of Pennsylvania obtained a patent in 1826, and Manning obtained one in 1831.

Up to 1831, no successful and practical reaper had been developed. With all

A CORN BINDER CUTS THE HEAVIEST CORN WITH EASE

A VIEW OF THE FIRST McCORMICK REAPER OF 1831 AS USED IN THE FIELD

the patents taken out in England, and with those taken out in America from 1803 down to 1831, we might say that nothing had been accomplished toward perfecting a reaping machine which actually worked successfully.

The First Successful Reaper.

In 1831 came McCormick's reaper, the first practical machine of its kind ever taken into the field. It was crude at first, but improved from year to year. Although McCormick's reaper was not patented until 1834, one year after the patent granted to Obed Hussey for his reaper, young McCormick gave a public exhibition in Virginia three years before, in 1831. It was in the fall of that year when Cyrus McCormick

THE McCORMICK REAPER OF 1845 IN THE FIELD, WITH A SEAT ADDED FOR THE RAKER
Formerly the raker walked by the side of the machine.

hitched four horses to his machine, which had been built in the old blacksmith shop at Steel's Tavern, and drove into a field of late oats on the farm of John Steele, adjoining his father's. The reproduction of an old lithograph depicting this scene indicates the interest of the neighbors in this event.

McCORMICK REAPER OF 1858

Although the United States had been established more than fifty years past, this was the first grain that had ever been cut by machinery. McCormick's machine continued to operate to the surprise of everyone and in less than half a day had reaped six acres of oats—as much as six men would have done by the old-fashioned method.

This was not the first attempt of a McCormick to solve the problem of harvesting wheat by machinery, for Robert McCormick, the father of Cyrus, had, himself, worked on a machine of this kind as far back as 1816. His father tried it again in 1831 and abandoned it, and in that same year the son Cyrus took up the work and started the world toward cheaper bread.

The first practical reaper taken into the field in 1831 embodied the essential parts of the reaper with which we are familiar. It had a platform for receiving the grain, a knife for cutting it, supported by stationary fingers over the edge, and a reel to gather it. The driver of the machine rode one of the horses, while the man who raked off the grain walked by the side of the machine.

Development of the Reaper.

The ten years following this first instance of a successful reaper were strenuous times indeed for Cyrus McCormick, for it was not until 1840 or 1841 that he was able to make his first sale. Twenty more were sold in 1843 and fifty in 1844.

During all these years

THE PROGRESSIVE FARMER OF TODAY DOES NOT LET HIS CORNSTALKS GO TO WASTE IN THE FIELD, BUT CUTS THEM WITH A CORN BINDER AND EITHER PUTS THEM INTO A SILO OR SHREDS THEM INTO STOVER FOR HIS HAY-LOFT
This picture shows the husker and shredder in operation with kerosene for power.

from 1831 to 1844 Mr. McCormick was diligently at work changing, testing and experimenting. In 1845 he secured a second patent, which embodied many improvements—the principal ones referring to the cutting mechanism.

THE McCORMICK REAPER OF 1858 IN THE FIELD

Note that an automatic raker has been substituted for the man who rode on the machine and raked off the cut grain.

In this year, Mr. McCormick started for the western prairie, and in 1847 built his own factory in Chicago, thus starting the world's greatest reaper works. This factory, known as "McCormick Works," is still in progress. It covers today more than 120 acres in the heart of Chicago, and has an annual capacity of 375,000 machines of all types.

The third step in the development of the reaper was the addition to the machine of a seat for carrying the raker. The machine built in 1831 required that the raker walk by the side of the machine. In 1845 Mr. McCormick added the seat, patent for which was added in 1847. This seat which carried the raker enabled him while

A MARSH HARVESTER AS BUILT BY THE McCORMICK COMPANY IN 1874

Note the two men riding on the platform and binding up the grain as delivered to them by the elevator of the machine.

riding to rake the grain from the platform and deposit it in gavels on the ground. This type of reaper, patented in 1847, is the one taken by Cyrus H. McCormick to the first world's fair held in London, England, in 1851, and about which the records of that exposition state "The McCormick reaper is the most valuable article contributed to this exposition, and for its originality and value and perfect work in the field it is awarded the council medal."

This same reaper received the grand prize in Paris in 1855 and is the reaper which created so much surprise at the world's fair in London that the comments made by the press demonstrated beyond a doubt that England had not as yet built a suc-

A McCormick Header Binder which Elevates the Grain into Wagons which Move Alongside

cessful reaper. In 1858 the machine was further improved by substituting an automatic rake for the raker on the machine.

Many other patents were granted from time to time until 1870, when the foundation features of all reapers had been invented and substantially perfected. The reaper is still used extensively, especially in foreign countries.

The interest in this machine centers not in its development as used today, but in the fact that it led to the invention and perfection of the self-binder.

The prototype of all machines designed to bind the grain before being delivered to the ground is the Marsh harvester. It is the half-way mark, the child of the reaper and the parent of the self-binder. The original patent for this machine was granted August 17, 1858, to two farmer boys of De Kalb, Illinois, the Marsh brothers.

Previous to this time, attempts had been made to build harvesting machines which would bind the grain before delivered to the ground, but not one could be considered a success. At the time the Marsh harvester began seeking a place in the market, about 1860, reapers—hand-rakers, self-rakers, and droppers—held the trade substantially to the exclusion of any other kind of harvesting machine.

The first successful Marsh harvester, built in 1858, was operated through the harvest of that year. It has never been changed materially in principle or form

A COMBINED SWEEP RAKE AND STACKER

This ingenious machine is a great labor saver in the hay field. The hay can be gathered by any number of sweep rakes and dumped near the stacker, which will stack on any side and in any shape.

since.   The theory of the inventors was that two men might bind the grain cut by the five-foot sickle in ordinary motion provided it could be delivered to them in the best possible position and condition for binding and if they could have perfect freedom of action.   They knew that the binders must have a free swing and open chance at the grain to enable them to handle it, so they arranged the elevated delivery, the receptacle, the tables and the platform for the man with these things in view.

The second Marsh harvester was built in Chicago in 1859.   Improvements were made during the years 1861, 1862 and 1863.   The manufacture of the Marsh harvester began in earnest at Plano in the fall of 1863 by Stewart and Marsh, twenty-five machines being put out in 1864.

In 1875 McCormick began putting out harvesters of the Marsh type.   Of

No More Tiresome Hay Pitching on this Farm, where Hay Loaders Elevate the Hay to the Men on the Wagons

The small kerosene tractor has taken the place of horses and is drawing two wagons at a time.

straight Marsh harvesters—carrying a man to bind—there had been made up to and including 1879 over 100,000, of which about two-thirds had been produced by the Marsh combination and the rest by outsiders.

The Self-Binder.

The development of the automatic binder followed quickly after the intro-duction of the Marsh harvester. although attempts were made to perfect this machine as early as 1850.

The self-binding harvester was borne on the shoulders of the Marsh harvester. Carpenter, Locke, Gordon, Appleby and every inventor who succeeded in any measure in binding grain, first did so by placing his binding attachment upon a Marsh harvester, taking the grain from a receptacle where it fell to another receptacle where it was bound.   The first record of these attempts is a patent granted to J. E. Heath, of Warren, Ohio, in 1850.   Watson, Renwick and Watson secured patents in 1851 and 1853, but their machines were very complicated and never more than

A MODERN GRAIN BINDER IN HEAVY OATS

THE WITHINGTON BINDER BUILT BY THE McCORMICKS IN 1876
This machine binds the grain with wire.

experiments. From that time until 1865 many patents were granted, none of which may be considered successful.

In 1865 S. D. Locke of Janesville secured a patent which ultimately developed into the Withington wire binder first put out by McCormick in 1875.

THE DEERING TWINE BINDER OF 1879

This is the perfected Marsh harvester with a perfected Appleby twine binding attachment and was first put out by the Deering Company in 1879.

The Withington machine was an improvement on the binding device patented by Locke in 1865. McCormick built 50,000 of these machines between 1877 and 1885. It was a simple mechanism which consisted mainly of two steel fingers that moved back and forth and twisted a wire band around each sheaf of grain.

Farmers did not take kindly to the wire binder. They said that wire would mix with the straw and kill their horses and cattle.

The Twine Binder.

This was the situation in the harvesting industry about the time that William Deering took an active interest. He looked about for a better machine. He found John F. Appleby, who, in 1878, had perfected a twine binder attachment. When Deering saw the strong steel arms flash a cord around a bundle of grain, tie a knot, cut the cord and fling

THE McCORMICK TWINE BINDER OF 1881 WITH THE APPLEBY BINDING ATTACHMENT, WHICH USED TWINE INSTEAD OF WIRE

A TRACTOR PULLING FIVE HARVESTER BINDERS

These machines cut a swath 40 feet wide in the grain field, gathering the grain into bundles and dropping them alongside to be picked up by the sweep rake.

off the sheaf, he knew he had what the world needed.   Appleby began working on his invention in 1858, but accomplished nothing until 1869 when he took out his first patent on a "wire binder."   In 1874 he began what is known as the Appleby twine binder, operating one in 1875 and 1876 and several in 1877.   In 1879 Deering bought out

THE PROGRESSIVE FARMER NOW USES A MECHANICAL MANURE SPREADER TO INCREASE THE PRODUCTIVENESS OF HIS LAND

The modern spreader is built low and equipped with a special wide spread attachment which throws the manure well beyond the wheels.

Gammon, joined forces with Appleby, moved the factory from Plano to Chicago in 1880, and began putting out twine binders.   In 1881 Mc-Cormick, also, and Champion began building the Appleby binder.

With the development of an attachment to bind with twine, a new problem arose —where to get a cheap serviceable twine.   William Deering again arose to the occasion.   He met Edwin H. Fitler in Philadelphia, one of the three twine makers in the United States, and after a good deal of persuasion induced him to take an order for a single-strand binder twine.   From that time on, all manufacturers have been

A GRAIN DRILL WITH DISK AND CHAIN ATTACHMENTS
This drill is large enough to require the strength of four horses to pull it.

A Small Kerosene Tractor can Pull Two or Three Grain Drills Fastened Together by Special Tractor Hitches

building practically the same machine—the Appleby binding attachment on the Marsh type of harvester which, in turn, was founded on the McCormick cutting mechanism. The self-binder of today is of that type.

Other Machines Follow.

The completion of the reaper set the wheels of farm invention spinning. It was the first great battle successfully won and gave a spirit of confidence and an irresistible spirit of victory to the men who were lifting the burdens off the bodies of men. After the reaper, the mowing machine came naturally. Following the binder in easy sequences came the corn binder, push binder, header and harvester thresher.

Every variety of haying machine, from side-delivery rake and tedder to sweep rake and loader, came eventually to make hay-making easy. The thresher, ensilage cutter, riding plow, disk harrow, cream separator, manure spreader and seeding machines succeeded in making the raising of the world's food a profitable occupation; at the same time, they made it an easy one. Lately, the internal combustion engine, together with its application in the kerosene tractor, promises to make the farmer's emancipation practically complete. If Herbert Casson could say "The United States owes more to the reaper than it does to the factory or the railroad or the Wall Street stock exchange," what can be said of these myriad machines that now do the food-grower's work for him?

Where formerly nearly all the people had to engage in food raising and even then went to bed hungry, now nearly half the people live away from the farm and there is a great abundance of bread and of food.

What Causes an Echo?

An echo is caused by the reflection of sound waves at some moderately even surface, such as the wall of a building. The waves of sound on meeting the surface are turned back in their course, according to the same laws that hold for reflection of light. In order that the echo may return to the place from which the sound proceeds, the reflection must be direct, and not at an angle to the line of transmission, otherwise the echo may be heard by others, but not by the transmitter of the sound. This may be effected either by a reflecting surface at right angles to the line of transmission or by several reflecting surfaces, which end in bringing the sound back to the point of issue.

Sound travels about 1,125 feet in a second; consequently, an observer standing at half that distance from the reflecting object would hear the echo a second later than the sound. Such an echo would repeat as many words and syllables as could be heard in a second. As the distance decreases the echo repeats fewer syllables till it becomes monosyllabic.

The most practiced ear cannot distinguish in a second more than from nine to twelve successive sounds, so that a distance of not less than sixty feet is needed to enable a common ear to distinguish between the echo and the original sounds. At a near distance the echo only clouds the original sounds. This often interferes with the hearing in churches and other large buildings. Woods, rocks and mountains produce natural echoes in every variety, for which particular localities have become famous.

In Greek mythology, Echo was a nymph (one of the Oreads) who fell in love with Narcissus, and because he did not reciprocate her affection she pined away until nothing was left but her voice.

The Story of the Motion-Picture Projecting Machine*

Few businesses have had a more spectacular rise than the motion-picture industry. It may be true that there are other industries of recent growth that are more highly capitalized than the motion-picture business. I shall not make any comparisons nor look up statistics, but will present some facts about an enterprise that, scientifically, industrially and commercially, is one of the great wonders of the world.

It is fair to estimate that more than $375,000,000 is invested in this business in the United States. It looks like an exaggeration or as if the typesetter had slipped in several extra ciphers by mistake, does it not? Nevertheless, the estimate is said to be extremely conservative. In the first place, it concerns every branch of the business, of which there are five. Taken in their natural order there are: 1. The manufacture of motion-picture cameras. 2. The manufacture of films. 3. The taking of the pictures. 4. The manufacture of the projecting machines. 5. The exhibition of the pictures.

The projecting machine is the subject of this story. One sees very little about it in the newspapers and popular magazines, in spite of the fact that it is the keystone, so to speak, of the motion-picture industry. Of the entire business, in all its ramifications, this machine is the most important not only from a technical standpoint, but as regards both the pleasure and safety of the public. Here, again, a great deal of money is invested. Its manufacture involves costly and highly specialized machinery, the most intelligent of mechanics and the constant thought and endeavor of the men at the head of the business.

The advancement in the manufacture of motion-picture projecting machines from the start has been along two avenues—to secure better projection, a sharper, clearer and steadier picture, and to eliminate the danger of fire resultant from the ignition of combustible film. Experts have watched and studied the picture machine through all its stages of development. For seventeen years they have slowly improved the machine and brought it to its present high state of mechanical perfection. The development of the fireproof magazine, the automatic fire-shutter, the loop-setter, flame shields and the famous intermittent movement have all been vital factors in the elimination of fire and also in securing perfect projection. The oldest invention was patented by W. E. Lincoln on April 23, 1867. The contrivance was a mere toy, employing no light and being merely a little machine which, when revolved, gave figures, printed in different positions, the semblance of motion. The second oldest was of an "optical instrument" patented by O. B. Brown on August 10, 1869. This was really the first American motion-picture projection machine. There was a sort of disk or moving-shutter movement which, on revolving, gave projected objects the appearance of animation. Of course, there were no films in those days and the inventor had used translucent glass to obtain the results. Yet here was the germ of our native modern machine.

A well-known moving-picture projecting machine manufacturer tells the following story: "A bet was made in 1871 by the late Senator Leland Stanford, of California, that a running horse at no time had all four feet off the ground. Edward Muybridge

*Illustrations by courtesy of the Nicholas Power Co.

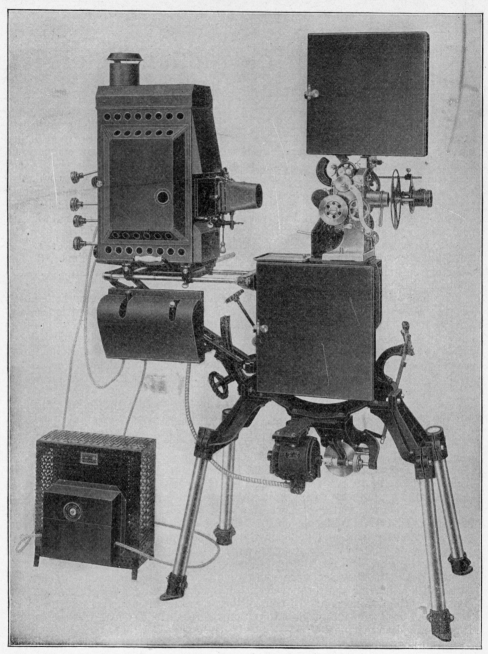

THE LATEST MOTION-PICTURE PROJECTING MACHINE

an Englishman, by way of experiment, placed numerous cameras at regular intervals about the track, which, by electrical contact, were snapped by the horse in passing. It proved that the horse always had, when running, one foot on the ground.   Although this was not the first record of motion pictures, it served to demonstrate their practicability.

"Development had dragged until the Muybridge experiment.   In 1880 Muybridge produced, in San Francisco, the 'Zoopraxiscope,' which projected pictures (on glass positives) on a screen.   Later Muybridge conferred with Edison regarding a combination of his machine with the phonograph, then in its infancy; about 1883 he went abroad and held frequent conferences with M. Marey of the Institute of France.

"Marey first utilized the continuous film, though it was George Eastman who brought it to its present state of high perfection.   A great deal of the tremendous present popularity of motion pictures is due to the invention of the translucent film.   The early kodak film became the great factor in the cinematograph manufacture.

"In 1893 Lumiere produced the 'Cinematograph,' the first machine to project from a film.   Edison in 1896 produced his

THE CONSTRUCTION OF THE LAMPHOUSE AFFORDS EASY ACCESS

'Vitascope.'   These machines became the models of the greatly improved article of today.

"The first real machine was brought to America in 1894.   At least, that is as near as I can recollect the date.   It was a Lumiere cinematograph and was exhibited at the Union Square Theater, New York City. The French manufacturing firm instructed J. B. Cole & Co. to furnish an operator.   The Cole Company was interested in the sale of lanterns and slides and the foreign firm naturally turned to them for assistance.

"They furnished an operator, Edward Hadley.   Although he had never seen a motion-picture machine, Hadley was a man who had been in their employ and was naturally familiar with lanterns and electricity.   To the best of my belief, Hadley was the first motion-picture operator in America. He afterwards became the operator for Lyman H. Howe, the well-known pioneer traveling motion-picture exhibitor, and later became an exhibitor himself,

THE NEW ARC LAMP

"The films then had one perforation on either side of each picture.   That was the French method.   The American method of four perforations on either side of each picture, formulated by Thomas A. Edison, was taken up later.   The Edison perforation method became the standard in America and finally throughout the world.   We find no more single-holed films."

Here, for the benefit of the uninitiated, a little description of the film and the projecting head of a machine is necessary.   A motion-picture film is a thin ribbon of transparent pyroxylin plastic or nitrocellulose, which is highly inflammable. The photographs on the film, one by three-fourths of an inch in size, leave a margin of five thirty-seconds of an inch on each side.   In the margins are the perforations necessary to feed the film through the machine head.   There are sixteen pictures to the foot.

The mechanism of the machine head moves the film over an aperture, so that the rays of light from the lamp will project an enlargement of the film picture upon the screen.   The reels upon which the film is wound are mounted above and below— the upper is the feed reel and the lower is the take-up reel.   Sprocket wheels control the action of the film.   The top feed sprocket pulls the film from the upper feed reel, the middle intermittent sprocket (below the aperture) turns in a way to give

NARROW SHUTTER WINGS AFFORD BRIGHTER ILLUMINATION ON THE SCREEN

each picture a certain time of stop over the projection aperture, and the bottom take-up sprocket assists in winding the film on the take-up reel.

"The early films were in very short lengths," continued the manufacturer. "The average was from twenty to seventy-five feet.   A hundred-foot film was considered extra long.   They were mostly comic and not educational.   The vast possibilities of the film had not yet dawned upon the pioneers.   They aimed only to get a laugh with a crude comic picture.

"But those with more foresight realized that the film had come to stay.   So the advancement began.   Today the public is always looking toward something better.   It has been educated up to an exceedingly high standard.   The average spectator today can see a defect in an exhibited film as quickly as an expert.

"Machines in the early days were very crude, permitting only short films, which were an endless belt.   They were threaded over spools contained in a box at the rear end of the lamphouse, passing over the lamphouse to the head of the machine; thence down through the head, past the projection aperture and back to the spools.   This exposed the film at all times, which was extremely dangerous.   About 1900, longer films came into use, which necessitated a change in handling.   At the machine head, the film was piled on the floor. This being dangerous and destructive, a receptacle was devised and fastened to the frame below the reel, into which the film passed. This soon gave way to a reel known as the take-up reel, which received the film after it had passed from the upper reel through the head and before the aperture, where it was projected on the screen.

"These are a few steps in the march towards improvement. My first machine was called the 'Peerlesscope.' I kept continually improving it, and in 1902 changed the name to 'Cameragraph;' my latest machine, No. 6B, possesses every known device for safety—fire-shutters, which automatically cut off the film from the rays of the lamp while motionless; film-shields, which enclose and protect the film; fire-valves, which prevent entrance of flame into magazines; the loop-setter, which prevents breakage of the film while in motion, etc."

Concerning projection, this manufacturer said: "Pictures cannot succeed without perfect projection, resulting in absolutely clear, flickerless pictures. The longer the period of rest of each picture on the screen, the better the detail and the clearer the picture. This I accomplished by means of an intermittent movement.

"You know that in projecting pictures the motion in the film is not continuous in front of the aperture of the machine head, each picture pausing long enough for proper projection on the screen. Through this intermittent movement I obtain a longer period of rest for each picture, which accomplishes perfect projection of pictures without flicker.

"A very annoying feature until recently has been the losing of the lower film loop, due to poor patching of the film, tearing of the perforations in the films, etc., causing the film to jump the lower sprocket, with the probable tearing and re-adjustment of the film. This I overcame with my loop-setter invention. To explain briefly—

"As the full movement at the upper and lower reel is continuous, while at the aperture it is intermittent, a loop is necessary as a feeder for the take-up or the lower sprocket. If this loop is lost, the film becomes taut, the machine stops and the film may break. The loop-setter instantly readjusts this loop automatically, keeping it always in force."

The taking of pictures is, of course, one of the interesting phases of the business from a popular standpoint. Here we find not only large sums invested but the action, setting, plots—in fact, the entire order of pulsating life and convincing reality that give to motion pictures their remarkable hold upon the public. In vying with each other to make the most attractive films possible, the concerns in this end of the industry engage the most talented players, who are transported on long journeys so that the settings may be realistically satisfactory; while often the company includes not only two-footed actors, but horses, one or two clever dogs and sometimes a trained bear and other animals, besides all of which there is usually an array of "properties" that far exceeds in quantity and variety the list of such appurtenances carried by the average stock theatrical company or theatei of the ordinary kind.

Then, too, there is the presentation of the pictures, where we find another vast outlay of money in land, buildings and equipment. And, remember, the matter of taking and presenting the pictures must not be considered only from the amusement standpoint. Motion pictures are being employed more and more every day for educational and industrial purposes.

The Story of Leather*

We all know that leather is the skins of animals, dressed and prepared for our use by tanning, or some other process, which preserves them from rotting and renders them pliable and tough.

The larger and heavier skins, such as those of buffaloes, bulls, oxen, horses and cows, are called "hides;" while those of the smaller animals, such as calves, sheep, pigs and goats, are called "skins."

The tanning of raw hides taken from animals is an ancient trade. The bark of

SCOURING

trees made into a liquor has been used for centuries in treating practically all kinds of hides.

The oak, fir, hemlock and sumach are the most familiar of the many trees from which "tannin" is obtained for this purpose.

The cow hide is used practically altogether for sole leather and is bark tanned in the majority of cases. After the hide is taken from the animal it is either dry cured, or else salted green, and packed for shipment or storage.

The first process of preparing sole leather is to cut these hides in half or sides. The sides are then run through lime vats for the purpose of loosening the hair. They are then run through the unhairing machine, in which large rollers remove the hair.

From the unhairing machine the hides pass to a fleshing machine, which cuts away all the flesh or fat on the hide. They are then trimmed and scraped by hand, after which the real tanning process begins.

The old method of tanning leather was in large vats, which were filled alternately with tan bark and hides, then filled with water and allowed to soak for a period of eight to nine months before the tanning process was complete. The extract of bark in liquor form is used today by all large tanneries.

---

* Illustrations by courtesy of Endicott, Johnson & Co.

After the hides have been all prepared for tanning they are hung on rockers in the tanning vats, where they are kept in motion both day and night so that all parts

Tanning Vats

of every hide are equally tanned. They are changed from time to time from weaker into stronger liquor until the tanning process is complete.

All sole leather is filled more or less to make it wear the better.

The drying process comes next. The hides are all hung in a dry loft, where artificial heat of different temperatures is used until they are thoroughly dry. The

Rollers

drying of the hide is as important as the tanning. Hides that are dried too quickly become brittle, so that great care must be taken in this drying process. Even the weather conditions play an important part

After the hides are thoroughly dried they are then oiled and ironed by large rollers having several hundred pounds pressure. This gives the grain side of the leather a finished appearance and also serves to press the leather together compactly.

RUBBING

Before this leather can be cut into sole leather it has to be again dried and properly edged to secure the best results.

Bark-tanned leather that is used for upper stock in shoes is tanned practically

BOARDING ROOM

the same way as the bark sole leather, except lighter hides are used and the finishing processes are of a nature to make it softer and smoother.

The above tannage is what is called vegetable tannage. There is also a tannage made from minerals that is called chrome. This is used mostly in tanning soft, glovey upper leather, which when finished makes a very tough yet soft and pliable leather for footwear.

Ninety to one hundred days are required to tan bark leathers, while the chrome tannage is very quick and on the average requires only about three weeks.

The brilliant smooth surface of patent, enameled, lacquered, varnished or japanned leather is due to the mode of finishing by stretching the tanned hides on wooden frames and applying successive coats of varnish, each coat being dried and rubbed smooth with pumice stone. There is also a process called "tawing," which is employed chiefly in the preparation of the skins of sheep, lambs, goats and kids.

MEASURING

In this process the skins are steeped in a bath of alum, salt and other substances, and they are also sometimes soaked in fish-oil. The more delicate leathers are treated in this manner, those especially which are used for wash-leathers, kid gloves, etc.

In currying leather for shoes the leather is first soaked in water until it is thoroughly wet; then the flesh side is shaved to a proper surface with a knife of peculiar construction, rectangular in form with two handles and a double edge. The leather is then thrown into the water again, scoured upon a stone till the white substance called "bloom" is forced out, then rubbed with a greasy substance and hung up to dry. When thoroughly dry it is grained with a toothed instrument on the flesh side and bruised on the grain or hair side for the purpose of softening the leather. A further process of paring and graining makes it ready for waxing or coloring, in which oil and lampblack are used on the flesh side. It is then sized, dried and tallowed. In the process the leather is made smooth, lustrous, supple and waterproof.

What is a " Glass Snake "?

"Glass snake" is the name which has been given to a lizard resembling a serpent in form and reaching a length of three feet.

The joints of the tail are not connected by caudal muscles, hence it is extremely brittle, and one or more of the joints break off when the animal is even slightly irritated.

The Story in Diamond-Cutting*

Diamonds were known and worn as jewels (in the rough) in India 5,000 years ago and used as cutters and gravers 3,000 years ago. India was the source of supply until diamonds were discovered in Brazil about the year 1700, when Brazil became the largest producer and remained so until diamonds were found in South Africa about 1869. The African mines now produce four-fifths of the diamond supply. Previous to the discoveries in Africa, diamonds were known to originally come only from high places in the mountains, because the diamond deposits were found in India and Brazil, on high plateaus, on the sides of mountains, in the beds of mountain streams, and in the plains below, where mountain torrents had rolled them.

In Africa, for the first time, the true original home of the diamond was found at high levels in the mountains, in enormous fissures, open chasms, chimneys or pipes, extending to great and unknown depths. Into these immense chimneys, nature forced from subterranean sources, slow rivers of a peculiar blue clay, a diamondiferous earth termed "serpentine breccia" or "volcanic tuf" and now known by the latter-day name of "Kimberlite." As this soft mixture oozed into the "chimneys" or "pipes" from the bottom, it was gradually forced upwards, filling the whole chasm from wall to wall and to the top, where its progress ended by hardening in a small mound ten to twelve feet higher than the surrounding surface.

In this blue clay or Kimberlite in these chimneys, is found nature's most wonderful creation, the diamond crystallized from pure carbon, in intense heat, and under titanic pressure.

The greatest mines of Africa are the Jagersfontein, Wesselton, Premier and Robert Victor. The Kimberlite of the Jagersfontein mine is free from pyrites, and to that is attributed the remarkable brilliancy and purity of color for which the diamonds of this mine are celebrated. Their color includes the blue, and they command the highest prices of any diamonds.

The Wesselton mine crystals are noted for their octahedra and purity. The color and brilliancy are so superior that nearly all fine white "Rivers" are rated as Wesseltons. The Robert Victor yields a big average of fine white stones, and many of the crystals are very perfect and beautiful. The Dutoitspan diamonds mostly show color, but many are "fancy" and demand a high price. The Bulfontein crystals are usually small white octahedras of very good color, but many are flawed. The De Beers stones are good white, some color, some broken crystals and smoky stones. The Kimberley diamonds are much the same as those from the De Beers mine. The Premier is the largest diamond mine in the world. Of its diamonds some have an oily lustre and are quite blue—many are of the finest quality and color. This mine also produces a large number of "false color" stones which change color in different lights. The Voorspoed and the Koffyfontein produce fair white and some colored diamonds.

Diamonds in small quantities are also found in Borneo, British and Dutch Guiana, Australia, Sumatra, China and the United States.

One of the largest diamonds known (weight 367 carats) was found in Borneo about a century ago, and belongs to the Rajah of Mattan. One of the most celebrated is the Koh-i-noor (Mountain of Light), belonging to the British crown. It weighed originally nearly 800 carats, but by subsequent recuttings has been reduced

*Courtesy of Mr. Charles L. Trout.

to 103¾ carats. The Orloff diamond, belonging to the Emperor of Russia, weighs 195 carats; the Pitt diamond, among the French crown jewels, 136½. The former, which came from India, has been thought to have originally formed part of the Koh-i-noor stone. The largest Brazilian diamond weighed 254½ carats and was cut to a brilliant of 125. Some of the South African diamonds are also very large, one being found in 1893 weighing 971 carats, or nearly half a pound. More recently a much larger one has been found, weighing 3,034 carats. This has been cut into eleven pieces, the largest, a drop brilliant, weighing 516½ carats. This, called the Star of South Africa, has been placed in King George's scepter, and another, of 309$\frac{3}{16}$ carats, in his crown.

A rough diamond is a hard-looking, luminous object, somewhat like a piece of alum, with a dull skin, called the "nyf," over a brilliant body. The ancients wore their diamonds uncut because they could not find a substance that would grind or cut them. About 1,500 years ago, however, it was found that by rubbing or grinding one diamond against another the outer skin could be removed. At Bruges, in 1450, diamonds were first polished with diamond dust. In Holland, in 1700, diamonds were first cut with an idea of bringing out real beauty and brilliance by cutting them square with a large flat table and some small facets, ten in all, sloping to the

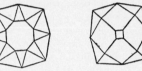

OLD SQUARE CUT DIAMONDS

ENGLISH SQUARE CUT DIAMONDS

edge of the square. From this beginning cutters gradually added additional facets to increase the brilliancy until there were thirty-four in all. Then came the English round-cut brilliants with fifty-eight facets, but the diamond was left thick and lumpy, until about seventy-five years ago, when an American cutter, Henry D. Morse, of Boston, developed the cutting of diamonds to its present perfection by fearlessly sacrificing weight to get proportion. This greatly increased the price of diamonds, but enhanced their brilliancy.

All cutters have been compelled to follow this method, and the perfectly cut brilliant of today has a depth from table to culet of six-tenths of the diameter, of which one-third is above the girdle and two-thirds below. In this form the diamond resembles two cones united at their bases, the upper one cut off a short distance from its base, the lower one having its extreme point cut off. It has fifty-eight facets, of which thirty-three, including the table, are above the girdle and twenty-five, including the culet, below the girdle. Stones which are not scientifically cut in this true proportion, if too deep, are called "lumpy," if too shallow they are called "fish eyes." A slightly spread stone is desirable, provided it has not lost brilliancy, and so become a "fish eye." Looking larger than its weight indicates, it offers a larger appearing diamond for the price of a smaller perfectly cut stone. Most cutters remove as little of the rough stone as possible in cutting so as to retain weight (they sell by weight). This often results in the finished diamond being too thick at the girdle, making a lumpy stone. Many people think deep, lumpy stones are most desirable. This is not true, as they are imperfectly cut.

In preparing to cut a diamond the rough crystal is studied until the grain is found. Along the grain another sharp-pointed diamond is ground until there is a V-shape incision or nick. The blunt end of a flat piece of steel is placed in this nick and a smart blow of a hammer divides the crystal evenly and perfectly. After this "cleavage" has removed the unnecessary portions, or they have been sawed off by the use of rapidly-revolving thin wheels charged with diamond dust, the diamond is set in a turning wheel and ground with another diamond until it takes the shape in which we know it.

The fifty-eight facets are cut and polished one at a time on a rapidly-revolving wheel charged with diamond dust and oil. It takes from two and one-half to four days to properly cut a stone. Knife-edge girdle diamonds are impractical owing to the liability of chipping the thin edge in setting or by blows while being worn.

Polishing the rough edge of the girdle is rarely done and then usually to conceal a girdle which is too thick or lumpy. The principal diamond cutting centers are Amsterdam, Antwerp and New York.

Inherent flaws can be perfectly understood by imagining a pond of water frozen solidly to its center. At the shore, where the ice has been partly forced out along the banks, it will be full of grass, leaves, pebbles and sticks, and presents a broken and frosted appearance. Further out there are only traces of such débris, some bubbles, spots, etc. Out at the center is clear, transparent, unbroken, unflawed,

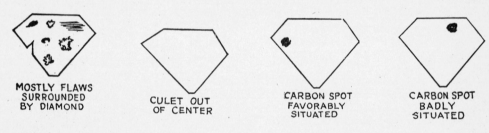

purest blue-white ice, such as you delight to see in your glass on a hot day. So is it with diamonds; some (like the ice along the shore) are full of cracks, carbon specks, bubbles, clouds, splits and cavities; some have all of these; some only a few; others only one, and some are without flaws.

Of all the imperfections (not considering glaring cracks or nicks), carbon spots are the most discernible. They range from mere specks scarcely visible with a powerful magnifying glass, to large black spots or clusters of large or small black specks sometimes quite plain to the naked eye. These are carbon which failed to crystallize with the rest of the diamond, or intrusions of titanic iron. The blackest and often most numerous carbon specks occur in the finest white and blue-white stones. "Capes" and other yellow diamonds are usually perfect, something in the color of these stones seemingly being of a nature which helps clear and perfect crystallization. Blue-white stones of exceptionally fine color are often massed full of shaggy or jet-black carbon spots.

White specks and bubbles are common flaws, which vary in size and which may be best illustrated by looking at a pane of glass in your window. There you will find small knots, white bubbles and whitish specks. These seldom injure the brilliancy, as they are often a glittering silver color, more brilliant than the diamond.

Clouds are dark flat patches in the grain, of a brownish color, and appear as a sprinkling of dust in a small patch in the interior. This seldom injures brilliancy.

Glessen or glasses are flat sectional streaks having an icy appearance. When large or abundant they disturb or cut off the proper reflection of the interior light rays, causing an appearance known as "shivery." When clouds or glessen occur at the surface of a diamond they appear as cracks, and if at or near the girdle are

WHITESPECKS
BUBBLES

CLOUDS

GLESSEN

dangerous, as the stone is liable to split or crack there when being mounted or by any hard blow, which would result in the loss of a sliver or wedged-shaped piece out of the edge.

Surface flaws consist of nicks or cavities in the face of the stone either above or below the girdle. The brilliancy of the diamond hides these flaws when the diamond is clean, but when clouded with soap and dust these cavities fill up and show plainly.

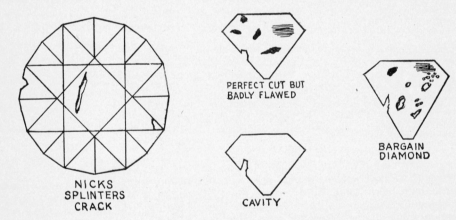

NICKS
SPLINTERS
CRACK

PERFECT CUT BUT
BADLY FLAWED

CAVITY

BARGAIN
DIAMOND

Diamonds are so brilliant, the radiance from the facets so bewildering to the eye, that the flaws cannot be seen by the human eye unless the imperfection is pronounced and at the top surface of the diamond. Each facet of a diamond (by reason of the method of cutting) is a window looking down a clearly defined walled chamber, like a hall-way to the culet. With a one-inch loup or magnifying glass such as watchmakers and diamond dealers use, it is possible to clearly look down through each facet and its hall-way to the culet, and observe throughout each chamber the very slightest imperfection if one exists, thus thoroughly examining and exploring the entire diamond.

Diamond brilliancy is of two kinds: "surface brilliancy" and "internal brilliancy." Light falling vertically on a diamond is reflected back in straight, unbroken rays. This constitutes "surface brilliancy." Light falling in a slanting direction is partly reflected and partly enters the stone; that part which enters is refracted or bent and causes the "internal brilliancy."

In a perfectly cut diamond, the facets are so carefully arranged that entering rays of light jump from wall to wall of this transparent enclosure and emerge again at the very point of entry. Cleverly arranged mirrors sending a ray of light from one to all the others and back again to the first will produce the same effect. Lights entering a diamond are reflected, refracted and dispersed. The dispersion of a ray of white light separates it into its component color rays. These are the spectrum colors often seen radiating from a diamond. Placing a diamond in the sun's rays and holding a sheet of white paper at the proper angle to catch the reflections from the stone clearly shows these colors.

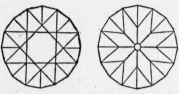

MODERN AMERICAN CUT DIAMONDS

Brilliancy is often said to be the most important quality of a diamond, but that is not true. Yellow diamonds are more flashingly brilliant than white stones that cost much more. In each color grade, greater brilliance determines higher value over stones of the same color grade with less brilliancy. The diamond is the hardest known substance in the world, cutting and grinding all other known hard things, but itself only cut and ground by its mates.

Because of their hardness, diamonds worn by many previous generations remain as brilliant as they were in the beginning and they will continue so to the end of time.

No other thing can scratch or mar the polished facets and sharp corners of the diamond. It is the hardest of all known things. While all diamonds are of practically the same hardness, this is not, however, absolutely true, as stones from wet diggings or rivers are slightly harder than those from dry diggings. All diamonds are infusible and unaffected by acids or alkali. The heat of a burning building will not affect them, they can be raked from the ashes uninjured and can only be burned in oxygen under a scientifically produced intense heat of 4000° F. While the hardest known thing, the diamond is brittle and can be crushed to a powder. It is the only absolutely pure gem, being composed of crystallized carbon—all others are composed of two or more elements

---

The term "Shibboleth" has come to mean a countersign or password of a secret society since the Biblical days, when the Ephraimites, who had been routed by Jephthah, tried to pass the Jordan. They were made to pronounce the word "Shibboleth" and were easily detected as enemies when they pronounced it "Sibboleth."

Why do We Get Hungry?

Hunger is a sensation partly arising in the stomach, since it may be relieved temporarily by the introduction into the stomach of material which is incapable of yielding any nutriment to the body. It may be due to a condition of fulness of the vessels of the stomach, relieved by any stimulus which, acting on the lining membrane, induces a flow of fluid from the glands. But it also arises from a condition of the system, since the introduction of nutriment into the blood, apart altogether from the stomach, will relieve it. This is also evident from the fact that hunger may be experienced even when the stomach is full of food, and when food is supplied in abundance, if some disease prevents the absorption of the nourishment, or quickly drains it from the blood. Hunger may be partially allayed by sleep or by the use of narcotics, tobacco and alcohol, all of which tend to diminish the disintegration of tissues.

The Story in the Modern Lifting Magnet*

Nearly every boy has had among his treasured possessions a small horseshoe magnet, painted red, with bright ends, and has spent many happy hours picking up needles, steel pins or other small objects, and finally tired of it because of its small lifting capacity and dreamed of one which would lift a hammer, or possibly even the family flatiron. Little did he know at that time of the long and interesting history of magnetism, the many stories and superstitions based on its strange power; or of its intimate relation to the wonderful growth of electricity within the last hundred years. His wildest dreams of lifting power would be realized if he could see a modern electric lifting magnet which has only come into use within the last ten

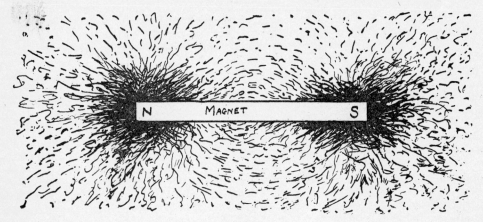

FIG. 1

years and is meeting with instant approval in nearly every industry where iron and steel is handled in any quantity.

There are three primary kinds of magnets: the lodestone or natural magnets, the artificial or permanent steel magnet, and the electric magnet. At present the lodestone is little used. The permanent steel magnet is used for compass needles, as the familiar horseshoe magnet, and in certain types of electric machinery. The electric magnet forms a part of nearly every kind of electrical machinery and is by far the most useful form of the magnet. The modern high-duty lifting magnet is a form of the electric magnet.

The properties of the lodestone and the permanent magnet have been known for thousands of years, while the electric magnet is a comparatively recent discovery.

All magnets, whether natural, permanent or electric, possess the same magnetic properties. Every magnet has two poles commonly called a north pole and a south pole. It has also been found that when a magnet is broken in two each piece becomes a magnet in itself with its own north and south poles.

For practical purposes it has been found convenient to assume that magnetism consists of a series of "lines of force" running through the magnet from one end to the other and back again through the air. Each one of these lines is assumed to

*Illustrations by courtesy of Cutler-Hammer Mfg. Co.

have a certain strength, and the power of any magnet is determined by the number of lines of force flowing through it. These lines are clearly shown in Fig. 1, which was made by sprinkling iron filings on a sheet of paper over a bar magnet, and tapping the paper slightly so that the filings could arrange themselves along the magnetic lines of force.

Since Oersted's first electric magnet in 1820, electric magnets have been made in a variety of forms and for many different purposes. The simplest form of electric

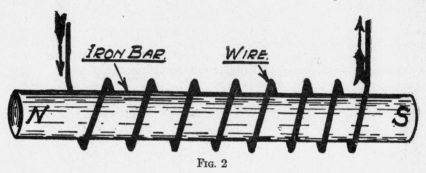

IRON BAR.　　WIRE.

N　　　　　　　　　　　　S

FIG. 2

magnet is shown in Fig. 2. It consists of an iron bar with an insulated electric wire wound around it carrying an electric current.

Another form of the electric magnet is shown in cross-section in Fig. 3. This consists of a short steel cylinder with a groove in its face for the electric coil. The modern lifting magnet is a highly specialized form of this type of electric magnet.

Although the use of a magnet for lifting purposes seems to be a very simple idea and easily adopted, many difficulties had to be overcome and years of experimenting done before the lifting magnet was a commercial success. Nearly all electrical machinery may easily be protected from rough usage and moisture, but the lifting magnet must be so strongly designed that it will withstand the countless blows due to heavy pieces of iron flying against it, and the banging it must get against the sides of cars, ships, etc. All light parts must be placed inside of the magnet or in such a position that they can never be knocked off or broken. To moisture in some form or other nearly all lifting-magnet troubles can be traced. Hence the importance of an absolutely moisture-proof construction. The result of moisture in the interior of a magnet is to weaken the effectiveness of the installation, leading eventually to short circuits and burn-outs. It is necessary not only to guard against moisture in the form of rain, snow or dew, but precaution must also be taken against the entrance into the magnet of moisture-laden air, since moisture so introduced will presently be condensed in the form of drops of water.

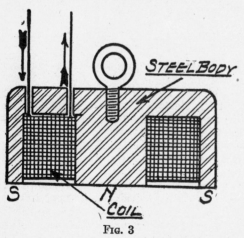

STEEL BODY

S　　　　N　　　　S

COIL

FIG. 3

A very natural question is, how much such a magnet will lift. For a given size of magnet, the lifting capacity varies greatly with the nature of the load handled. With a magnet sixty-two inches in diameter, this may vary from in the neighbor-

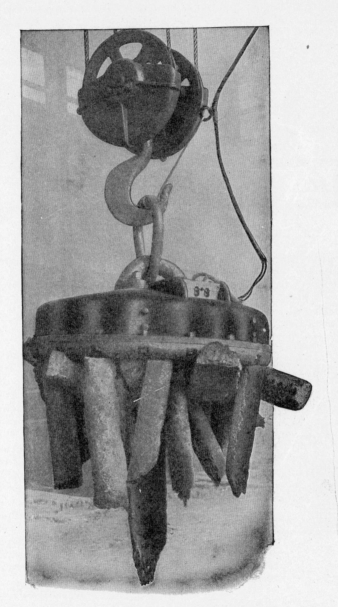

A 43-Inch Magnet Handling Pig Iron

hood of 1,000 pounds for light scrap, to from 4,000 to 5,000 pounds for pig iron, and as high as 60,000 pounds for a solid mass of steel or iron such as, for instance, a skull-cracker ball or a casting affording surface for good magnetic contact.

36-INCH LIFTING MAGNET PICKING UP 3,500-POUND WINDING DRUM

The lifting magnet has been adopted for the handling of materials in all branches of the steel and iron industry. It is used for handling pig iron, scrap, castings, billets, tubes, rails, plates, for loading and unloading cars and vessels, and for handling skull-cracker balls and miscellaneous magnetic material.

Probably one of the best illustrations of the saving accomplished by means of a lifting magnet is its use in unloading pig iron from steamers. By the old hand method it required twenty-eight men, two days and two nights, to unload a cargo of 4,000,000 pounds. When the lifting magnet was introduced, the total time for unloading was reduced to eleven hours, and was done by two men whose labor consisted in manipulating the controllers in the cages of the cranes. Thus two men and two magnets did the work of twenty-eight men in less than one-fourth of the time. Furthermore, the vessels were enabled to double their number of productive trips.

In railroad work, lifting magnets are at the present time used principally in scrap yards and around store-room platforms, where it is necessary to handle iron and steel rapidly and economically. For this class of work magnets are generally used in connection with a locomotive crane, making a self-contained, self-propelled unit which may be operated over the shop-yard tracks as required. The use of this combination has reduced very greatly the cost of handling both new and scrap material, both by reducing the actual expense of handling and by enabling the material to be handled much more rapidly than was before possible.

THREE SKY-WRITING PLANES

AN ADVERTISEMENT AS WRITTEN BY AIRPLANE

The Story of Sky-Writing

A small high-powered fighting plane, of the type known as SE5A in Great Britain, is used in sky-writing. This is a type of biplane which was used very successfully during the latter years of the war, and which has since been fully developed. It is a one-man machine and is adapted to rapid climbing and quick maneuvering, having a speed of about 125 miles per hour. The plane climbs to a height of approximately two miles in eleven or twelve minutes.

The smoke-producing apparatus is built into the fuselage of the plane and is operated by the pilot by means of a series of levers. The apparatus has a smoke producing volume of 250,000 cubic feet per second, and is in such perfect control at all times that the pilot can regulate its production and release it in any volume desired. The smoke is expelled from an outlet at the extreme rear of the plane in such a way that none of it ever comes in contact with the plane or the pilot.

Some idea of the immense volume of smoke used in sky-writing may be gleaned from the fact that it takes from 7,000,000 to 8,000,000 cubic feet to form a single letter. Because of the great height at which sky-writing is done, the letters must be of stupendous size in order to be legible.

While the weather conditions are to some extent a determining factor in the height above the ground at which the writing is done, Major Savage, the inventor, has found that the best results are obtainable at an elevation of about 10,000 feet. The letters themselves vary in height from approximately one-half mile to one mile, the capital letters and loop letters being about one mile from top to bottom. The capital letters which Major Savage's sky-writing pilots form in the air are possibly seven times the height of the Woolworth Building, and the dot over one of the i's might be compared to the size of the Equitable Building.

A word of seven or eight letters stretches across the sky for a distance of about five miles, and at an elevation of about 10,000 feet is visible to the naked eye within a radius of 150 square miles. Frequently the written smoke word will drift three or four miles without losing its formation.

The smoke which is used in sky-writing is formed by the combination of chemicals. It is white in color and stands out clearly against a background of blue sky. Owing to its density, it remains visible, and with very little change of formation, for several minutes after it is expelled from the producing apparatus.

Index

Acknowledgment

The Editor wishes to express his gratitude and appreciation to the following, to whom he is indebted for much valuable assistance in the form of illustrations and special information:

ADDRESSOGRAPH CO.
"THE AMERICAN BOY."
AMERICAN CHICLE CO.
AMERICAN CYANAMID CO.
AMERICAN LAFRANCE FIRE ENGINE CO.
AMERICAN LOCOMOTIVE CO.
"AMERICAN MAGAZINE."
AMERICAN PIN CO.
AMERICAN TELEPHONE AND TELEGRAPH CO.
ARMOUR & CO.
BALDWIN LOCOMOTIVE WORKS.
"BALTIMORE AMERICAN."
BETHLEHEM STEEL CO.
JAMES BOYD & BROTHER, INC.
BRUNSWICK-BALKE-COLLENDER CO.
BURROUGHS ADDING MACHINE CO.
CALIFORNIA FRUIT GROWERS' EXCHANGE.
CALIFORNIA REDWOOD ASSOCIATION.
CHESAPEAKE AND POTOMAC TELEPHONE CO.
COLT'S PATENT FIRE ARMS MANUFACTURING CO.
COLUMBIA GRAPHOPHONE CO.
COLUMBIAN ROPE CO.
COMMON SENSE GUM CO.
CONSOLIDATED FIRE WORKS COMPANY OF AMERICA.
CURTIS AEROPLANE CO.
CURTIS PUBLISHING CO.
CUTLER-HAMMER MANUFACTURING CO.
DIAMOND CRYSTAL SALT CO.
G. M. DODGE CO.
EASTMAN KODAK CO.
ENDICOTT, JOHNSON & CO.
"THE FIELD"
"FIRE AND WATER ENGINEERING."
FORD MOTOR CO.
GATCHEL & MANNING.
GENERAL ELECTRIC CO.
GENERAL MOTORS TRUCK CO.
GLOUCESTER (MASS.) BOARD OF TRADE.
B. F. GOODRICH CO.
HAYNES AUTO CO.
HENDEE MANUFACTURING CO.
R. HOE & CO.

George A. Hormel & Co.
Hotpoint Electric Heating Co.
Hudson and Manhattan Railroad Co.
Indiana Steel Co.
Ingersoll-Rand Co.
International Harvester Company of America.
International Silver Co.
Jacobs & Davies, Engineers.
Lake Torpedo Boat Co.
McClure Co.
Mergenthaler Linotype Co.
Monroe Calculating Machine Co.
New York Central Railroad Co.
New York Edison Co.
Niagara Falls Power Co.
Otis Elevator Co.
The Panama Canal, Washington Office.
Pennsylvania Railroad Co.
The Philadelphia Museums,
Plymouth Cordage Co.
Nicholas Power Co.
Pyrene Manufacturing Co.
"Radio Simplified," by Kendall and Koehler.
"Railway Age Gazette."
Mr. George A. Reading.
Remington Arms-Union Metallic Cartridge Co.
A. I. Root Co.
"Scientific American."
"Scribner's Magazine."
Standard Steel Car Co.
Capt. Charles H. Thompson.
Mr. Charles L. Trout.
Mr. Harold L. Tuers.
United Shoe Machinery Co.
United States Rubber Co.
Waltham Watch Co.
Westinghouse Co.
Winchester Repeating Arms Co.
Wilcox & Harvey Mfg. Co.
"Winston's Cumulative Encyclopedia."

C41/x8
179